HISTORY OF THE BRITISH MEDICAL ASSOCIATION, 1832-1932

SIR CHARLES HASTINGS, M.D.,
Founder of Association, 1832.

HISTORY OF THE BRITISH MEDICAL ASSOCIATION
1832-1932

Compiled by

ERNEST MUIRHEAD LITTLE,

F.R.C.S.

LONDON:

BRITISH MEDICAL ASSOCIATION

Printed by
HARRISON & SONS LTD.,
Printers in Ordinary to His Majesty,
44-47, St. Martin's Lane,
London, W.C.2.

Reprinted by photolithography and bound by
Clark Constable Ltd, Hopetoun Street, Edinburgh EH7 4NF

FOREWORD

No preface seems necessary for a work of this kind, but I cannot let an opportunity slip of recording my thanks to the Medical Secretary, Dr. Alfred Cox, for his advice in general and for the authorship of the Article on the National Insurance Act in particular.

I also here offer my thanks to the Intelligence Officer, Miss A. L. Lawrence, for the Article on Medical Benevolence and for valuable help in the preparation of the Sections of the Great War and on Public Health.

E. MUIRHEAD LITTLE.

CONTENTS

LIST OF ILLUSTRATIONS

" We have no reason to apprehend that our successors will look back to the first proceedings of the Association with any feelings but those of respect ; they will see that our regards, not narrowed to our own little day, were extended forward to their days, and to the hidden days beyond them. Animated by the same pure ambition as the founders, I trust they will carry on medical knowledge beyond the point at which they themselves became engaged in its pursuit, and in their turn will cheerfully transmit it, by them increased, to other generations, by whom, with the permission of Providence, it may be more and more cultivated to the end of time."

Retrospective Address by Dr. John Conolly, at Birmingham, July 18, 1834.

THE PROFESSION IN 1832

THE year 1832 was an eventful one, for besides the foundation of the Provincial Medical and Surgical Association, it saw the passing of the first Reform Bill, and the first epidemic of Asiatic Cholera in Great Britain was raging in that year. Successful trials of the first iron steam vessels were carried out on the Thames, and London Bridge, which had stood for more than six centuries, was demolished, and its successor opened upon a different site. The Anatomy Act, which put an end to Body-snatching and its scandals, became law in August, 1832. Tennyson's first volume of Poems, which included some of his best work, was published this year, and only a few days before the year began Charles Darwin began that 5 years' voyage in the " Beagle," which led to such momentous developments in natural science.

The whole lustrum 1830–1834 was momentous. The country had largely recovered from the economic depression following the long wars with France and her Allies, and the people were full of creative and inventive energy, which manifested itself in many ways.

In 1830, the first passenger railway of any practical value was opened from Liverpool to Manchester, after the Stockton and Darlington line, which was designed for mineral traffic, had proved successful some years earlier.

The Reform agitation had not been entirely peaceful. The mob had burned Nottingham Castle and the Bishop's Palace at Bristol, these riots being accompanied by loss of life. The cholera epidemic had led to the provision of cholera hospitals, some of which were not popular. In *The Annual Register* for 1832 will be found accounts of attacks on such hospitals by the mob. At Manchester the patients were removed and the contents of the building destroyed by the rioters, and at Paisley the windows of the hospital and those of all the surgeons' houses and shops in the town were broken. Some

1

cholera patients were injured by stones and the hearse used for the dead destroyed. Rumours of resurrectionist activity had, however, something to do with this last riot.

In this same year was founded the first of the modern provincial English Universities, that of Durham.

Primitive customs still lingered in England. At Carlisle Market in April, 1832, a small farmer offered his wife for sale, with her own consent, for fifty shillings. Judging from the report of his speech, he and she were by no means uneducated. In *The Annual Register* she is described as a " spruce lively damsel." She was knocked down " for twenty shillings and a Newfoundland dog," and taken away by her purchaser, apparently not ill-pleased.

At this time that great octopus, or " The Wen," as Cobbett called it, London, had not spread its tentacles over the country as it has done since, and it had not yet sucked much of the life blood out of the provincial towns. Such cities as Worcester, Bristol, Exeter, Norwich, Winchester, and many others had a vigorous local life, and supported consultants in medicine and surgery. Many of the landowners in the neighbourhood had their winter residences in these towns, instead of in London, as in later years, and their young folks found entertainment in local assemblies. But the centripetal movement had begun, as is shown by the fact that the town house of the Lechmeres in Worcester became the residence of the founder of the Association.

The medical profession in 1832 found itself face to face with the cholera epidemic, unprepared and unarmed against it. The Committee of one of the great London hospitals, with commendable enterprise and foresight, sent one of its physicians with a prosector to study it on its first appearance at and near Newcastle-on-Tyne. The physician's report revealed the terrible mortality in certain villages, and put on record the symptoms and post-mortem appearances, but was not able to claim any success in treatment. Indeed, *The Annual Register* was not unduly pessimistic when it stated that " The cholera left medical men as it had found them—confirmed in most opposite opinions, or in total ignorance as to its nature, its cure, and the cause of its origin, if endemic

2

—or the mode of transmission, if it were infectious. In Great Britain, as elsewhere, it fixed its residence among the most needy and squalid classes of the community."

The sciences of Epidemiology and Public Health did not, and in the absence of statistical information could not, exist. Until the passing of the Registration Act of 1836, there were no national statistics from which trustworthy conclusions could be drawn, although a beginning had been made with the decennial census of population in 1801.

In the medical profession, as in industry and invention generally, the sap was stirring, but there were no means by which it could make its influence felt as it should be. The profession was not organised and not even defined, for there was no hard-and-fast line drawn between the qualified and unqualified practitioner, nor was there any simple criterion by which the members of the public might distinguish the reputable practitioner from the quack. Twenty-six years were to pass before the Medical Act of 1858, in some measure, removed the abuse and provided a remedy. But, notwithstanding this want of organisation and definite status, it is, we think, a mistake to assume, as more than one writer has done, that there was no body of opinion and feeling which animated practitioners before the passing of the Medical Act of 1858, nor one which inspired a large number of practitioners with a consciousness of professional brother-hood. From the moment in 1823 when *The Lancet* constituted itself the voice of the medical profession, it became evident that there was a body of men who felt that they belonged to a great profession. They were split up into groups, some of which mistrusted or were jealous of others, but ill-defined as its limits might be, the profession of medicine existed.

That this conclusion is sound may, we think, be inferred from the terms of the address delivered by Charles Hastings on the occasion of the first meeting of the Association in 1832. He and his colleagues used the phrase " medical profession " frequently, and he characterised it as a " liberal profession." Evidently the founders of the Association had no doubts as to the profession's existence, and for 26 more years it continued to flourish without any lawful regulation of its members outside the jurisdictions of some of the Corporations. As late as 1709 we find the Churchwardens of Hitchin in Hertfordshire certifying that Robert Taylor of that town was duly qualified to practise Physiche and Surgery. (Hine's " History of Hitchin," Vol. I, p. 329.)

It is not to be wondered at that writers, looking back from a period half a century later, should have doubted the existence of a medical profession in the days of their grandfathers. With characteristic British indifference to definition, regulation and exact order, the nation had allowed a chaotic state of things to exist too long.

The first attempt to regulate surgical practice in the London district since the days of Charles I is represented by an Act of George II, which confirmed the former one. The Royal College of Physicians of London had long had a monopoly of the practice of Physic in London and 7 miles round. In 1815, the London Society of Apothecaries had succeeded in getting an Act of Parliament passed which restricted the practice of pharmacy to its licentiates throughout England, and at the same time entitled it to grant licences to practise physic. In Scotland the Edinburgh colleges enjoyed privileges which restricted practice in certain counties to their members, and the Glasgow Faculty of Physicians and Surgeons had similar rights in counties adjacent to Glasgow. As Mr. Walter Rivington wrote, " Within these bounds no one was to exercise the Art of Medicine without a testimonial of a famous University in which medicine was taught, nor could anyone practise as a surgeon unless he was a member of the Glasgow Faculty." In Ireland, the King's and Queen's College of Physicians enjoyed privileges conferred in 1692, restricting the practice of Physic to their licensees all over Ireland. The College of Surgeons in Ireland does not appear to have had similar jurisdiction.

The ancient English and Scottish Universities stood somewhat aloof from the ordinary practice of medicine and surgery. Their graduates had the right to practise throughout their respective kingdoms, but the Universities exercised no disciplinary control over them and had no powers for the suppression of unqualified practice.

Any attempt to estimate the amount of unqualified practice in England before 1832, or even 1858, is attended with great difficulties. Until the *Medical Directory for England and Wales* appeared in 1846, there had been no list of the great body of general practitioners except for an enterprising publication of which only three issues were made. These referred respectively to the years 1779, 1780 and 1783. This publication was called the *Medical Register*, but, unlike the present *Medical Register*, it was published without authority. Copies of it are now very rare. From the issue for 1783 we learn that sixty years before the foundation of the Association there were 778 members of the Corporation of Surgeons and 301 of the Society of Apothecaries of all ranks, a total of 1,079. At the same time, the College of Physicians had only 114 Fellows, Candidates and Licentiates. The reputed Surgeons and Apothecaries in England and Wales (excluding London) amounted to 1,573, from which it would appear that only about two general practitioners out of three had any qualifications. At the same time there were 337 physicians in the provinces, of whom very few had any connection with the London College of Physicians, most of them holding Scotch or Continental doctors' diplomas. None of them appear to have held Irish degrees. It was stated in the House of Commons in 1841, that out of 1,830 candidates for medical office under the Poor-law, 320 had never been examined in Surgery, 323 never examined in Medicine and 233 had not undergone any professional examination whatever. Yet these persons were all eligible for medical office under the Poor-law !

The 1841 Census gave 33,339 persons as practising one or more branches of medicine. The medical directories in 1853 show that only 11,808 were then qualified, thus leaving 21,531 unqualified practitioners, a proportion of 2 to 1.

The Apothecaries Act of 1815 no doubt wrought a great change, so that by 1832 probably the proportion of unqualified practitioners was much reduced. Nevertheless, in 1853 *The Medical Times and Gazette* estimates the number of unqualified practitioners as double that of the qualified.

From this short survey of the powers of the corporations in 1832, it appears that all over England, except in the environs of the capital, there was no attempt made to regulate the practice of medicine

5

and surgery, but for the Apothecaries Act of 1815, which provided for the sufficient examination of candidates for its Licence, and in the words quoted by Mr. Walter Rivington in 1879, " created a body of qualified general practitioners in England and Wales, who were entirely independent of the Colleges of Physicians and Surgeons, and were entitled to practise medicine not merely by sufferance, but by law." (*Carmichael Prize Essay*, 1879, p. 24.) Thus did a City Company step into the breach and take up a duty which might rightfully long before have been assumed by the Royal College of Physicians of London, which, unfortunately, had preferred to remain aloof in its academic majesty and to take no interest in the rank and file of the profession as long as its monopoly of the practice of physic in the metropolitan area was not infringed. But even its limited power of regulation of practice had fallen into desuetude. The last prosecution undertaken by the College was that of Dr. Edward Harrison in 1828. The practice was found to be surgical, and although the faculty of Physic includes Surgery, the College was non-suited and had to pay costs. (On this subject see the sagacious remarks of Mr. Rivington, *op. cit.*, pp. 16 and 17.)

A hundred years ago the average medical practitioner was a man of little culture or general education. The graduates of Oxford and Cambridge and of the Scottish Universities were probably as well educated as the members of the learned professions of the Church and the Law, at least in those cases in which the degrees had not been granted without due academical training, but the rank and file of the profession had received its training through the system of apprenticeship. Whatever the advantages of this system may have been, it is undeniable that it involved at the best the too early termination of the general education of the lads who, in order to get qualified by the time they reached the age of 21 years, must have left school at the age of 15 or 16. At its worst, if the master neglected his duties, or the pupil was idle and cared little to learn, the period of apprenticeship too often represented so much precious time wasted. The contemporary portraits of the medical students who were " walking the hospitals " after leaving the service of their masters, are not flattering to our

6

professional self-respect. The " Pickwick Papers " began to appear in 1836, and everybody knows what kind of figures were cut by Bob Sawyer and Benjamin Allen. No doubt, these were not meant to be taken as sober portraits, but were painted in a spirit of lighthearted caricature, yet there was a substantial basis of sober truth in their regrettable lineaments. Nor do they stand alone. Thackeray, writing a dozen years later in " Pendennis," in a more serious vein, had made the portrait of Huxter no more attractive than those of Sawyer and Allen. Albert Smith, himself a member of the profession, in his novels did nothing to improve the reputation of the student. In the second volume of *Punch* (February 12th, 1842) one of a set of " Valentines " is addressed to " The Medical Student." The drawing was by John Leech, and the verses by W. H. Wills, and both confirm the descriptions given by Albert Smith.

Even in the pages of a medical journal, which might be expected to avoid fouling its own nest, most unfavourable descriptions are given of the manners and customs of London medical students. These anonymous articles in *The Medical Times* are said to have been written by Albert Smith.

The conclusion seems inevitable that there must have been a large basis of fact behind these writers' attacks on medical students, but there were doubtless many earnest workers who were neither dissipated nor dirty (Dickens and Thackeray both insisted on the lack of personal cleanliness in their medical students), and who became highly respected members of society, but it needed a good many men of the quality of Sir Charles Hastings and a good many years of improved behaviour to live down this scandal.

The best instruction in anatomy, physiology, medicine and surgery had up to this time been provided by the so-called private medical schools, unconnected with the hospitals. Such were the Windmill Street School of the Hunters and Sir Charles Bell, that of Brookes in Blenheim Street, the Webb Street School, Carpue's or the Dean Street School, and Dermott's or the Gerrard Street and Little Windmill Street School. All these once flourishing, if commercial, institutions were gradually squeezed out of existence by the refusal of the College of Surgeons to accept their certificates, and most of them were closed by the year 1832, although one or two lingered on until a good many years later. (See *B.M.J.*, 1895 : " The Rise and Fall of the Private Medical Schools in London.") Their success had in part been due to the better bargains which they were able to make with the " resurrection men " as compared with the official hospital schools. The Anatomy Act of 1832 nullified this advantage.

SIR CHARLES HASTINGS

THE Founder and first Secretary of the Association was born at Ludlow in Shropshire on January 11th, 1794, the sixth son of the Rev. James Hastings, Rector of Bitterley. The rectory being at the time under repair, Mrs. Hastings had been moved into a hotel for her confinement.

The name of Hastings had long been of good repute in and about Worcestershire, and although we cannot now ascertain the exact connection between the Rector and the great Warren Hastings, of Daylesford, they were commonly reputed to be cousins, and the two families were on friendly terms. Not long after the birth of Charles, his father became Rector of Martley, near Worcester, and there Charles was brought up. The school in the village appears to have had a good reputation, attracting boys from a distance, and at that school he received all the general education that he had. But he was evidently one of those who could be trusted to complete his own education.

Of his childhood at Martley there is little recorded, but his god-son, Mr. C. P. Hastings, of Rugby, has communicated an anecdote on the authority of Sir Charles' son, Mr. G. W. Hastings, M.P., which is worth repeating, as it illustrates one of the most valuable qualities that afterwards distinguished the man. His father " met with a riding accident and came in shaken and drenched to the Rectory, and sat for a long time dazed in a chair, resisting all the appeals from his wife and elder daughters to go to bed. Then the little Charles, aged 10, rose, put his hand on his father's shoulder and said, ' Do come up to bed, father.' Whereupon the father got up and went upstairs with the utmost docility."

The history of the adult Charles Hastings exhibits again and again a similar conciliatory and persuasive tactfulness, which was one of his greatest assets in his successful efforts to found the Association, as it was in his relations with his patients and colleagues.

As a boy, Hastings is said to have been devoted to an outdoor life, and not to have been particularly studious, but when his father broke down in mental health the large family found itself in some straits and Charles had to set to work. He was apprenticed to two surgeons, Messrs. Jukes and Watson, at Stourport, Worcs., who were well thought of in that neighbourhood, and who, with a view to his candidature for the House-surgeoncy of the Worcester Infirmary, advised his going to London for further instruction. He accordingly became a pupil at the celebrated Blenheim Street School of Joshua Brookes, and attended lectures at Dr. John Taunton's private school, besides those on medicine of Dr. Robert Hooper in Savile Row. It has been stated that he also received instruction from a Dr. Ager, about whose activities we have been unable to learn anything. In the autumn of 1812 he returned to Worcester, and with the support of Drs. Jukes and Watson and others, he became a candidate for the post of House Surgeon in the Infirmary, although he was only eighteen years old and had no diploma of any kind. The contest was severe, but Hastings was successful by 134 to 133 votes, notwithstanding the fact that his opponent was a much older and a well-qualified man.

He justified his appointment by his care and diligence in taking notes and by his experimental work under Dr. A. P. Wilson Philip on the functions of spinal, ganglionic and cerebral nerves. The results were communicated by Philip to the Royal Society and published in the *Philosophical Transactions*.

After three years of house-surgeoncy, Hastings was advised to go to Edinburgh for a degree. He did so, carrying with him introductions to the leading professors of the University. He soon joined the Royal Medical Society, and took an active part in its discussions. He assisted a friend in experiments on transfusion, the results of which were published in the inaugural thesis of Dr. Leacock, of Barbadoes. In the spring of 1817 he carried out an experimental inquiry into the action of the blood vessels in health and disease, with a view more especially to demonstrate an independent contractile power inherent in the arterial, capillary and venous systems. He was said to have been at that time

10

the only student in the University who used the microscope in physiological and pathological investigation. In
the same year he was elected President of the Royal
Medical Society. In 1818, when he read an account of
his study of the circulation in the frog's foot as seen
under the microscope, some speakers denounced such
methods as useless, and said that " deductions drawn
from experiments on the lower animals were very falla-
cious, and that such investigations were indefensible in
themselves " (see *Lancet*, 1851, Vol. II, pp. 182 *et seq.*).

While in Edinburgh, Hastings attended Professor
Jameson's lectures on Natural History, and the interest
thus aroused in this subject never left him. He graduated in Medicine in 1818, his thesis being *De vi contractili
vasorum*. On the death of Dr. Gordon, it was proposed
that he should succeed him as a teacher of anatomy
and physiology, but the Edinburgh climate did not suit
him, and besides this there was a vacancy on the medical
staff of the Worcester Infirmary. Accordingly, he returned
to the capital of his adoptive county, and was elected
Physician to the Infirmary in 1818, at the age of 24.
This post he held for the following 44 years, resigning it
in 1862. He soon became, and for long remained, the
leading physician in Worcestershire and the surrounding
counties.

From this short account it will be evident that Hastings
was a man of considerable abilities, some originality of
mind and great industry. On his return to Worcester,
young as he was, he seems to have been speedily accepted
as a leader in Medicine and in Natural History. But he
was not content to sink into the position of an ordinary
country physician, enjoying a large practice, and that
otium cum dignitate which he might so easily obtain.
His writings in the years between his establishment in
Worcester and the foundation of the Association show
that he was busy with his pen in setting forth his views
on those topics in Medicine and Natural History which
always interested him. These works will be referred to
more specifically later.

George Eliot was a careful and acute observer : the
picture which she so vividly painted of medical practice,
as she no doubt remembered it in the Midlands about
the 'thirties of the last century, may be taken as

11

substantially true. Middlemarch is made to support two physicians, whose fee was a guinea, besides a number of surgeons and apothecaries. No doubt she had some such man as Hastings in her mind when she put these words into the mouth of Lydgate (" Middlemarch," Book II, Chapter XIII) : " A born provincial man who has a grain of public spirit as well as a few ideas, should do what he can to resist the rush of everything that is a little better than common towards London. Any valid professional aims may often find a freer, if not a richer field, in the provinces."

In 1828, with the view of raising the tone of provincial medical practice and supplying a medium for the interchange of opinion and the diffusion of knowledge, he started a quarterly journal, *The Midland Medical and Surgical Reporter and Topographical and Statistical Journal*, having realised the need of a publication which should make use of the valuable material available in provincial practice and more especially the clinical and pathological knowledge which was running to waste in the county infirmaries. To this Journal, in the four years of its existence, Hastings contributed freely. A more detailed account of the *Reporter* will be found in a subsequent chapter. It may here be noted that in the farewell address in the last number, dated May, 1832, it is stated on behalf of the editors that the great object of their arduous undertaking had from the first been not only the mutual instruction of the members of the profession, but also the foundation of an Association for the diffusion of medical knowledge.

In 1832 Hastings called together a meeting at the Worcester Infirmary, at which the establishment of the Provincial Medical and Surgical Association was decided upon. He delivered an inaugural address at the first meeting, and for many years he was Secretary and the leading spirit of the Association, skilfully guiding it through many difficulties. In 1843 he resigned the Secretaryship owing to its increasing duties, and was appointed permanent President of Council and Treasurer. He was knighted in 1850, on the representations made by certain distinguished and influential persons to Sir George Grey. When the General Medical Council was set up under the Medical Act of that year, Hastings was appointed by the Government a member of that body.

At the meeting in Liverpool in 1839, a portrait in oils, painted by Benjamin Rawlinson Faulkner, was presented to his wife, and now is in the care of the Solicitors to his eldest grandson at Worcester. The engraving of this portrait by S. W. Reynolds, Junior, is fairly well known ; there is a copy of it in Martley Rectory, and, among others, one signed by Hastings in the Association's House in London. From this portrait the obverse of the Hastings Medal and the medallion on the outer cover of *The British Medical Journal* is taken. A later portrait hangs in the Victoria Institute Library and Museum at Worcester. The artist is unknown. Beneath it is the following inscription :—" Presented by Susanna Holyoake to the Worcestershire Natural History Society as a token of her regard for Dr. Hastings, one of the earliest and most zealous of its members, and also as a mark of her respect and esteem for that useful and most honourable institution, 1847."

A full-page engraved portrait of Hastings, taken from a Daguerreotype, appeared in *The Lancet* in 1851. His father died at the age of 100 and his aunt lived to the great age of 104, but he did not share the family longevity, for he died of carcinoma of the duodenum, ending in perforation, on July 30th, 1866, aged 72. He had for many years been lame as the result of some injury to the hip, owing to a carriage accident, but this lameness did not impair his professional activity. His death occurred at Barnard's Green, near Malvern. He was buried at Worcester in what was then the new Cemetery on the summit of Sunrise Hill, and beneath a rustic cross of stone, standing upon a granite pedestal.

The mourners included, besides members of the family of Sir Charles, Dr. Samuel Jeaffreson, President of the British Medical Association, Drs. West and Burnett, and 22 other doctors (*Worcester Herald*, August 10th, 1866).

He had a large private practice, and we have been told by Alderman H. A. Leicester, of Worcester, the author of " A Short History of the Infirmary," that he well remembers as a boy a long line of the carriages of private patients waiting outside Hastings' house in Foregate on certain afternoons.

His interest in Public Health was enduring. When the cholera was epidemic at Worcester, he took a great part, according to his son, Mr. G. W. Hastings, M.P., in removing the stricken poor to camps outside the city. He was President of the Section of Public Health at the meeting of the Social Science Association held at York. His book, " Illustrations of the Natural History of Worcestershire," especially on the Malvern Hills, was published in 1834, and he subsequently published an account of the salt springs of the county, a considerable part of which work was utilised by Sir Roderick Murchison, in his " Silurian System." The prevalence of sedentary occupations such as glove-making —still an important industry in the city—favoured the incidence of phthisis in Worcestershire, and as early as 1820 he published " A Treatise on Inflammation of the Mucous Membrane of the Lungs," to which is prefixed an " Experimental Inquiry respecting the Contractile Power of the Blood Vessels and the Nature of Inflammation."

He was an active member of the Worcester Natural History Society, and took part in founding and supporting the Museum. His bust by Mr. (afterwards Sir) Thomas Brock, R.A., who was himself a native of Worcester, was presented to the City of Worcester by the Association at the Jubilee Meeting in 1882, and placed in the Victoria Institute Public Library. The Sir Charles Hastings Clinical Prize of £50 for General Practitioners was established by the Association in 1924, and has since been awarded annually.

Hastings married in 1825 the eldest daughter of Dr. George Woodyatt, physician to the Worcester Infirmary, whose portrait now hangs on the wall of the Board-room of that Hospital. The issue of this marriage was a daughter and an only son, Mr. G. W. Hastings, who for some years was Member of Parliament for East Worcestershire, and acted as adviser of the Association on matters of medical reform. At the Jubilee Meeting in 1882, Mr. Hastings gave, in a speech at the Worcestershire Hall, an interesting account of his father's career. He and Miss Hastings generously placed the medical library of Sir Charles, with the consent of the trustees, at the disposal of the profession in Worcester. At a meeting held in October, 1866, a cordial vote of thanks was passed by

14

the members of the profession in the city and county, the gift was accepted, and it was determined to form a Medical Society. The books were subsequently transferred to the Library of the Association in London, where they now are. The photograph (reproduced opposite page 23) of the former house of Sir Charles Hastings is taken from a water-colour drawing by Carelli in the possession of Dr. G. W. Crowe, Honorary Local Secretary, when the Association held its Jubilee Meeting at Worcester in 1882.

THE MIDLAND MEDICAL AND SURGICAL REPORTER AND THE FOUNDATION OF THE "PROVINCIAL MEDICAL & SURGICAL ASSOCIATION"

THE first number of this quarterly journal appeared in August, 1828. Hastings and the friends who were associated with him in this enterprise had in view, as he stated again later, when founding the Provincial Medical and Surgical Association, the utilisation of the valuable clinical material which existed in the provincial hospitals and the placing on record of pathological observations made within their walls.

In 1836 Hastings, in a footnote to Vol. IV of the *Transactions*, made the following statement :—" The manner in which the *Medical and Surgical Reporter* was supported by the Provincial Profession was the chief cause which led to the idea of an extensive plan of co-operation being carried on in the Provinces for the advancement of medical science."

The full title of the periodical was *The Midland Medical and Surgical Reporter and Topographical and Statistical Journal*. It bore the following motto, quoted from Bacon's *Novum Organum* : " Homo naturæ minister et interpres, tantum facit et intelligit, quantum de naturæ origine, re vel mente observaverit : nec amplius scit aut potest," which is thus translated by Spedding : " Man, being the servant and interpreter of Nature, can do and understand so much, and so much only, as he has observed in fact, or in thought, of the course of Nature : beyond this he neither knows nor can do anything."—From " Aphorisms Concerning the Interpretation of Nature and the Kingdom of Man."

The assistants of Hastings in the editorship of the *Reporter* were Dr. Malden, James P. Sheppard, Esq., and John Rayment, Esq., all of Worcester ; Dr. Danwall, of Birmingham ; and Dr. Burne, of London. (*See*

16

footnote to Hastings' address in the first number of the Transactions of the Provincial Medical and Surgical Association.)

Of this periodical sixteen numbers appeared from August, 1828, to May, 1832. The immediate cause of its decease was the failure of the printers and publishers in London. Two months later the Provincial Medical and Surgical Association was founded, and its *Transactions* took the place of the *Reporter* to some extent, but its annual volumes were not medical journals in the usual sense of the term, and the *Reporter* had no periodical successor till *The Provincial Medical and Surgical Journal* appeared in 1840. The first volume of the *Transactions* opened with some account of the " Faithful City " (as its inhabitants long loved to call it) of Worcester. There were various articles on medical and pathological subjects, and, under the heading of medical jurisprudence, an account of the appearances in the body of an infant of eleven months, who died from gastritis after swallowing powdered glass. A charge of murder had ended in a verdict of " Not guilty." There were hospital reports from various places by Charles Hastings, and an interesting " Topographical " account of the Worcester General Infirmary, which, as it includes a history of one of the earliest provincial infirmaries, is worthy of note.

The earliest provincial general hospital supported by voluntary contributions was founded at Winchester in 1736.* That at Worcester was only nine years younger. There were three physicians and three surgeons. It is significant that it is stated that " The services of the Physicians and Surgeons are gratuitous, in consideration of which from the commencement of the Infirmary they have been vested with the privileges of Governors. They have votes at all Boards, and each Physician and Surgeon may annually recommend five in-patients and three out-patients." Thus was established at Worcester a system that has since been strenuously objected to by some lay hospital authorities, notwithstanding the fact that some of the best-managed hospitals are and have been governed by mixed lay and medical committees. The details concerning the house and nursing

---

* See *Medical Register*, 1783.

17

staffs are to-day of some interest. In 1827 the House Surgeon (a Surgeon Apothecary) received £80 per annum. A resident apprentice paid £250 premium to the Infirmary and £20 and another £10 at the end of his first and third years to the House Surgeon. The latter officer was not allowed private practice. The matron received £35 per annum. There were five day-nurses and one night-nurse to 97 in-patients.

There were also in the first volume articles on the Malvern Hills and the coal district of Worcestershire, on Atropa Belladonna and on the medical topography and health of Birmingham by Dr. John Malden, who condemned the water supply of that place : a case of " ulcer " of the right hemisphere of the brain by Charles Hastings and reports of the dispensaries at Kidderminster and Cheltenham. Meteorology was not neglected, and there are the Parochial Returns of Births, Marriages and Deaths in the City and suburbs of Worcester. Dr. Walker, of Huddersfield, wrote " Observations on English Hospitals." Some remarkable cases are put on record ; one by a Veterinary Surgeon of a case of Psoas (?) Abscess in a horse, which afterwards recovered and was ridden to hounds, and one of strangulated hernia, in which six inches of gangrenous intestine and some omentum were removed. The consequent fæcal fistula closed in time, and the patient quite recovered. There is also an article on self-supporting dispensaries and a complaint of plagiarism on the part of *The London Medical and Physical Journal*. Thomas Newell, M.D., of Cheltenham, Surgeon Extraordinary to the King (George IV), reported an amazing case of Spontaneous Combustion. Unfortunately, the narrator did not see the body until a few hours after death, when it had been removed from the site of the fatality. This case would have been useful to Charles Dickens in his spirited defence of the account of Krook's death, in the preface to " Bleak House," dated 1853. " Infantile Dyspepsia," " Otorrhœa Purulenta," " Fracture of Os Calcis," " Strangulated Hernia," " A Pot in the Rectum," and " A Singular Case of Ischuria " are the titles of other articles. The last-named was by Hastings. Another article by him in this volume was on the use of the stethoscope, an instrument as yet little used by general

18

practitioners. This was severely criticised in a later number by W. Addison, Surgeon of Malvern, and replied to by Hastings, who also wrote on Medical Jurisprudence, Delirium Tremens, and Testamentary Ability.

This brief *résumé* shows that the *Reporter* was full of interest, and must have been valuable to the practitioners of that day. The other two volumes were of equal merit, and contain articles and reports that are still interesting to the student of the history of medical practice.

The last number of the third volume dated May, 1832, contains a notice of the termination of the work and the proposed formation of a medical association. As this notice and prospectus signalize the crystallization into action of the ideas which Hastings and his friends had so long fostered, it is given here verbatim :—

" The present Number completes the third volume of *The Midland Reporter*, and with it, the Work under the above name will terminate : as the Editors can now congratulate themselves and the Public upon having attained the great object which they contemplated at the commencement of their arduous undertaking. Their appeal to the public spirit, generous feelings, and pure love of Science, which so extensively pervade and dignify our noble profession, has not been made in vain. A wish has, in consequence, been warmly expressed and widely circulated, that the members of the profession residing in the Provinces should unite themselves into an Association *friendly* and *scientific* : that this Association should have for its main object the diffusion and increase of Medical Knowledge in every department of science and practice, and that the valuable communications of its Members should, from time to time, appear in the shape of published Memoirs of the Society. The subjoined Prospectus will afford to our Readers more minute information upon this truly gratifying topic. We here, then, take leave of our numerous friends and correspondents, thanking them most cordially for the valuable aid they have afforded us in the prosecution of our past labours ; congratulating them most sincerely on the means of widely-spread and friendly co-operation which the new Society will open to us all ; and earnestly intreating them to join us with head, and heart, and hand, in the support of so excellent an Association.

Provincial Medical and Surgical Association.

"The diligent collection of facts, accurately observed and faithfully recorded, supplies the foundation of all natural science. From these are deduced general truths, which constitute the principles by which Science is rendered practically available. From their multiplication additional light is continually derived, new truths being elicited, or those which had been inferred from a too hasty or inadequate induction being rendered more accurate and precise. In Medicine the benefits of inductive science have been long felt and acknowledged. But great as is the store of facts accumulated by the labour of ages, and many and various as have been the attempts to generalise them into a consistent and harmonious system of principles, much remains yet to be done for giving to the Science of Medicine the perfection which it is capable of attaining. Nature is perfect in all her works, acting by general laws which are immutable. Man has the power of discovering those laws and of applying them to the uses of life, as is amply exemplified in the history of Physics. The laws of animal life may not admit of being ascertained with the same precision as those to which inanimate matter is obedient—yet by patient observation of facts, and a cautious induction, unbiassed by hypothesis, great accuracy may be attained in determining the inherent powers by which the animal frame lives, moves, and has its being.

"In order that facts should be sufficiently abundant, it is necessary that they be derived from a wide field, and from numerous contributors. But the duties and cares of life prevent many from paying their mite into the general treasury, unless where arrangements are made for inciting to industry, and facilitating communication. Association ministers to these ends more effectually than any other means hitherto devised ; and on this ground it is proposed to associate the Provincial Medical Practitioners of England, or at least as many as can be brought to rally round a common centre, on a comprehensive co-operative Institution, which by collecting the

20

results of individual experience, and bringing the energies of many minds to bear on those unsettled points which have subjected Medicine to the imputation of being a conjectural art, may contribute to redeem its character, and to give to its operations more precision and greater certainty.

"The foregoing views having, through private correspondence, been favoured with very general approval, and with promises of very extensive co-operation, it is now proposed to realise the conception, by founding ' A Provincial Medical and Surgical Association ' for the purpose of collecting useful knowledge, and publishing ' Transactions' at such intervals as the matter furnished may warrant.

PROSPECTUS.

"The objects of the Association, so far as they have yet been canvassed, are recited in the following paragraphs :—

1. Collection of useful information, whether speculative or practical, through original Essays or Reports of Cases occurring in Provincial Hospitals, Infirmaries, or Dispensaries ; or in Private Practice.

2. Increase of knowledge of the Medical Topography of England, through Statistical, Meteorological, Geological, and Botanical Inquiries.

3. Investigation of the Modifications of Endemic and Epidemic Diseases, on different situations, and at various periods, so as to trace so far as the present imperfect state of the art will permit, their connexions with peculiarities of soil or climate, or with the localities, habits, or occupations of the people.

4. Advancement of Medico-legal Science, through succinct Reports of whatever cases may occur in the Provincial Courts of Judicature.

5. Maintenance of the Honour and Respectability of the Profession generally, in the Provinces, by promoting friendly intercourse and free communication of its Members ; and by establishing the harmony and good feeling which ought ever to characterize a liberal profession. For the first year it is proposed to adopt the following Provisional Constitution, to be

21

afterwards modified in whatever way the first Annual General Meeting may decide :—

The Association to be managed by a President, two Secretaries, a Council and Branch Committees. The several officers to be appointed annually, by a General Meeting of Members, convened for that purpose, at whichever of the large Provincial Towns may be appointed ; the Place of such Meeting being prospectively notified each year.

At this Meeting shall be presented a Report, prepared by the Secretaries, of the General State of the Association, its Proceedings and Pecuniary Accounts ; the Report to be afterwards printed and a Copy supplied to every Member.

As one of the objects of this Association is to maintain the Respectability of the Medical Profession in the Provinces, and as this cannot fail to be promoted by doing honour to the Memory of Persons who have distinguished themselves by original Discoveries in Medicine, or who have sustained the character of the Profession by great attainments and moral excellence, it is proposed that one of the Members shall be annually appointed to deliver, before the General Meeting, an Oration on some subject connected with Medical Science, or a Biographical Notice of some eminent Cultivator of Medical Science, who may have resided in the Provinces.

President.

" The office of President to be honorary, and conferred on some senior Physician or Surgeon of eminence, resident in any of the Provincial Towns comprised in the circle of the Association.

Secretaries.

" The two Secretaries to be resident in Worcester, the place of Publication, their duties being to attend to the printing of the *Transactions*, and correct the Press ; to be present at the meetings of the Council, and keep the Minutes thereof ; correspond with the Branch Committees and individual Members, and to receive and submit to the Council all papers

LORD DAWSON OF PENN, P.C., G.C.V.O., K.C.B., M.D., P.R.C.P.,
President of Association, 1932.

Sir Charles Hastings,
m.d., President of
Council and Treasurer,
1833–1866 ;
President of
Association, 1849.

Sir Charles Hastings'
House at Worcester.

transmitted for Publication ; also to keep the Financial Accounts of the Association.

Council.

" The Council to consist of ...... Members, Physicians and Surgeons being in equal proportion as nearly as may be practicable. A greater number must be necessarily derived from Worcester than from any other Town ; but so far as it can be effected, Members to be also incorporated from the principal Provincial Towns.

" The Council, with whom must rest the chief responsibility of Publication, to have full power of deciding on all papers transmitted ; three Members, at least, being required to form a quorum.

" In order to assist the Council, however, in discharging this important duty, Branch Committees shall be formed in all the more considerable Towns, who shall communicate with the Council, and forward such papers as they may approve, for insertion in the *Transactions* ; individual Members, however, being at liberty to send their communications either to the Branch Committees, or to the Council, as they may think fit.

" The Branch Committees to consist of not less than three Members each, and to be appointed by the Members of the Association resident in the respective Towns or Districts.

" Each Member of the Association to pay one guinea on admission, and the same amount annually afterwards ; the Subscription to commence from the first of January each year, and to be considered as due, unless notice of its being withdrawn be given to the Secretary antecedently to the year for which the Subscription would be payable, for which Subscription each Member shall receive a Copy of each part of the *Transactions* published. Each Volume to contain a List of all the Members. All Papers and other Communications to be addressed to the Secretaries, Dr. Hastings or Mr. Sheppard, Worcester, and forwarded carriage free.

" Messrs. Berwick & Co., Old Bank, Worcester, have kindly consented to be the Treasurers of the

Association ; at which Bank the Subscriptions may be paid, or at Messrs. Robarts, Curtis and Co., Bankers, London, on Account of Messrs. Berwick and Co."

The Foundation of the Provincial Medical and Surgical Association.

The subscribers to *The Midland Medical and Surgical Reporter* had had their minds prepared for the movement in favour of the formation of a Medical Association by this notice, and the publication of the Prospectus.

The Prospectus had also been printed as an advertisement in *The Lancet* of July 7th, together with a notice of the meeting to be held at Worcester later in the month. The Editor of *The Lancet* called attention to the advertisement in a note in which its objects were stated and warmly commended (*The Lancet*, Vol. II, 1832, p. 437). Notwithstanding this warm welcome to the project, there appears to be no report of the meeting and no further comment on the Association in this volume of *The Lancet.*

The meeting was duly held in the Board-room of the Worcester Infirmary on Thursday, July 19th, 1832. A full report of it was published in the first volume of the *Transactions* of the Association. More than fifty practitioners were present, including Dr. Edward Johnstone, of Birmingham, who was unanimously called to the Chair, the Regius Professor of Physic at Oxford, Dr. Kidd, and a number of Physicians and Surgeons from Bath, Bristol, Birmingham, Cheltenham, Warwick, Hereford and elsewhere, " including most of the resident Faculty of Worcester and the neighbouring Towns."

Resolutions were passed that a Provincial Medical and Surgical Association be formed and that its management be conducted by a President, Council and two Secretaries to be elected annually, agreeable to the following provisional Constitution :—

The several officers to be appointed annually by a general meeting of Members convened for that purpose ... the place of such meeting being prospectively notified each year. A report was to be presented by the Secretaries and a copy of it supplied to every member.

The two Secretaries were to reside in Worcester, in order that they might superintend the publication of the *Transactions*, but the chief responsibility for publication of papers, etc., was to rest with the Council, a quorum of three being necessary to approve any contribution. Each member was to receive a copy of the annual volume of *Transactions* in return for his subscription of one guinea. Dr. Edward Johnstone, of Birmingham, Physician to the General Hospital in that city, was elected President for the ensuing year, and Dr. Carrick, of Bristol, for the year 1833–1834. Dr. Hastings and Mr. Sheppard to be Secretaries.

A vote of thanks was given to Dr. Hastings " for the indefatigable trouble he has taken in forming a Society which owes its existence to his suggestion and for the able, eloquent and learned discourse with which he has opened the proceedings of this day," and it was resolved that it should be printed and circulated to the members.

The first Council consisted of 70 members, and there were 310 members (including Council). This Council represented a wide area. It included members from as distant places as Swansea, Liverpool, Norwich, Wolverhampton, Leeds, Exeter, Sunderland, Berwick-on-Tweed and many others ; Dr. T. S. Traill, the Professor of Medical Jurisprudence in the University of Edinburgh, being a member.

Although the Provincial Medical and Surgical Association has by some been regarded as a General Practitioners' Society, it is evident from the number of physicians and surgeons to provincial infirmaries and hospitals, such as Carden, of Worcester, that it was representative of the profession in the provinces as a whole, for these local physicians and surgeons were, as has been pointed out previously, as much consultants as those in London.

In the address above referred to Hastings congratulated his colleagues on the large proportion of provincial physicians and surgeons who supported the Association. He spoke of the aid to science rendered by the association of its students, and instanced the recent formation of the British Association for the Advancement of Science. The improved facilities of communication between distant towns, both personally and by letter, were, he said, such that the distance at which members might reside from one another " will oppose but a slight barrier to our undertaking." He was doubtless thinking of the then recent improvement of high-roads as well as of vehicles. In 1832 the coaching system was at its best, before railways had begun seriously to compete with it, but even so the speed of the fastest mail coaches did not exceed eight miles an hour, including stoppages.

In speaking of the numerous charitable medical institutions in the provinces and their possibilities he used the remarkable phrase " if they really were sanctuaries of science, as well as of sorrow." He deplored the spirit of misrule and confusion with which some members of the profession were actuated, and the attempts that had " been made and were making in the metropolis to bring about feelings of hostility between the cultivators of the different branches of medicine." This, he said, was the time in which the friends of peace and harmony should declare themselves. Those who doubted that enough willing labourers would be found he referred to the pages of the sixteen numbers of *The Midland Medical and Surgical Reporter* published in the previous four years, as evidence of the ability of provincial practitioners and of the wealth of available material.

The success of the *Reporter* had encouraged him and his friends to form a society in whose *Transactions* future communications would be published. It is worthy of note that of the five principal objects of the Association specified by Hastings, the first four dealt with scientific matters, and that only in the fifth and last was the maintenance of the honour and respectability of the profession mentioned and an appeal made for that " harmony and good feeling which ought ever to characterize a liberal profession." So far were the founders of the Association from wishing to form anything like a trade union or a society merely interested in the selfish interests of the profession.

He referred with approval to a proposal made by Dr. Conolly, of Warwick, that certain members should be appointed to report upon the state of medicine in foreign countries, and he quoted Professor Whewell, who had advocated the collection of reports to the

26

British Association, pointing out the various ways in which they would be useful, especially in informing inquirers in one branch of science of what was going on in another, and saying that " For want of this information we perpetually find speculations published, which show the greatest ignorance of what has been done and said on the subject to which they refer." Hastings proposed, therefore, that at each annual meeting a report of the progress of the distinct branches of medical sciences during the past year should be presented.

He went on to survey the various branches of medical science, and to point out to the members of the Association the rich mine open to their labours in the department of essays, speculative and practical. In Physiology, Pathology and Therapeutics there were many openings for investigation and progress, which offered subjects for essays which might be of great value. In this field already provincial physicians and surgeons had distinguished themselves, and they might still further do so and make a fuller use than in the past of the experience gained in the provincial infirmaries, hospitals and dispensaries. Medical Topography also was a subject that had long been neglected in this country, although it had lately received attention in *The Midland Medical and Surgical Reporter*. *The London Medical and Physical Journal*, *The London Medical Repository* and *The Edinburgh Medical and Surgical Journal* had all at various times tried to awaken the profession to the necessity of cultivating this branch of knowledge. By the term Medical Topography, Hastings meant the study of population in the various cities and counties, and of the incidence of disease, both endemic and epidemic, and the causes of good and bad health, including climatic conditions ; in short, all those statistical and other facts which are now included under the term of Public Health. He praised the work of Dr. Hawkins on Medical Statistics, and that of Mr. Thackrah, of Leeds, on what are now called " occupational diseases."

The advancement of Medico-legal Science, to which it was proposed that the labours of the Association should be directed, was, he said, of the highest importance. As Dr. Christison had pointed out, there was a great lack of accessible records of medico-legal inquiries in this country, which could not be properly supplied by information collected in different circumstances abroad. Finally he pointed out the need for a code of medical ethics and, after referring in some detail to the proposed organisation of the Association, he wound up with an eloquent peroration, of which the concluding paragraph may fitly be quoted in full, as follows :—

"Gentlemen, you will at any rate admit that the objects I have thus hastily introduced to the notice of the meeting are worthy of deep meditation. The contemplation of them appears to me, indeed, to open to us a vast and unbounded prospect, and to beget high and lofty thoughts of our future proceedings. I may be sanguine in my expectations, but I cannot help indulging the gratifying, the cheering, the delightful thought that if we engage in this undertaking, as we are bound to do by the obligations which our profession imposes upon us, with the zeal and alacrity of men anxious for the good of mankind, the Association must be of some use ; must have a direct tendency to extend the empire of knowledge, and to increase our power over disease.

Valeat quantum valere debet."

It will be noticed that neither in the official programme of the Association nor in the address of Hastings was any mention made of medico-political matters, and the regulation or qualification of medical practitioners, which were so soon to become matters of the greatest moment. It is probable that Hastings and his friends, with that good judgment and moderation which distinguished him, thought that it was better to concentrate on those important but non-contentious subjects which offered so large a field of work, and to leave the contentious political matters to future meetings. That the Association did very soon occupy itself with the advocacy of medical reform will be clearly seen in subsequent pages of this work.

Some space may here be devoted to a note on the place where this momentous meeting, of such importance in the history of British Medicine, was held.

The Worcester Infirmary had been founded, as we learn from the short history of it by Alderman H. A.

28

Leicester, of Worcester, in the year **1745**. It was removed to its present site in **1770**, and was afterwards extended and altered, but in **1832** it must have looked very much as it does now. The Board-room in which the historic meeting took place on July 19th, **1832**, has been added to since, by building out a glass-covered portion ; but the appearance of the unaltered part, in which the meeting took place, is probably very much the same now as that which met the eyes of the venerable Dr. Edward Johnstone and his colleagues on that momentous occasion.

The Association, thus started, rapidly increased in numbers and in influence. At its first Anniversary Meeting, held in Bristol under the Presidency of Dr. Carrick in **1833**, it had **316** members on its roll, of whom **250** attended. Each succeeding year showed a considerable increase of membership.

Although Hastings was the founder and fosterer of the Association, without whom it would not have been begun or have survived its early troubles, it is obvious that he must have had loyal helpers and comrades. Of these, the names of Johnstone, Kidd, John and William Conolly, Hodgson, Sands-Cox, Baron, and in particular Dr. Barlow, of Bath (President, **1838**), should not be forgotten. On the occasion of the death of Dr. Barlow in **1844**, Hastings thus described the part taken by him in the foundation of the Association (*P.M.S.J.*, Vol. VIII, p. 295).

" *The Midland Reporter*, which commenced in **1828**, was the forerunner of this Association, and one of the most gratifying results of the establishment of that periodical was the introduction which it afforded me to my medical brethren, and to it I am indebted for my acquaintance with Dr. Barlow. That acquaintance by degrees ripened into friendship ; and in March, 1832, I consulted him as to the practicability of forming an extensive Association for the advancement of Medical Science in the provinces, having its centre in the Midland district. Dr. Barlow entered enthusiastically into the plan, and he replied to my letter by return of post, saying : ' I have received your prospectus and have no hesitation in expressing my cordial approval of the design, or in tendering you such assistance as I can in

29

any way render.' " There was some discussion on Dr. Barlow's suggestion that a preliminary meeting should be held in Bristol, but Hastings went on to say " from the date of this letter (April 22nd, 1832) until the time of holding the first meeting at the Worcester Infirmary on the 19th of July, I was in frequent communication with Dr. Barlow, and we discussed freely the principles on which the Association should be founded, and especially aimed at simplicity in framing the code of laws. The result was the formation of the Association at Worcester, and the unanimous adoption, with very little alteration, of the code of laws that had been agreed on between us, and which laws have remained almost unchanged to the present time."

Hastings, when he first promulgated the idea of the Provincial Association, was not yet aware of the steps which had already been taken to found the British Association for the Advancement of Science.

OTHER
MEDICAL ASSOCIATIONS

THE Provincial Association thus founded differed from previous medical societies and associations in various parts of the Kingdom, chiefly in the following particulars. In the first place, in its ambitious scope, by which it claimed to include the whole of England and Wales except the capital, and in the second place because, speaking in the name of the whole profession, it plainly stated as one of its objects, " The Maintenance of the Honour and Respectability of the Profession generally in the Provinces." But for this, which was soon to develop into the advocacy of medical reform and the pursuit of a number of medico-political aims, the early volumes of *Transactions* did not greatly differ in the nature of their contents from the annual volumes of *Transactions* of the Medical Society of London or the other societies of a like kind in London or other cities. The Association, however, differed from these societies in meeting only once a year and in not having a fixed place of meeting.

The Association, moreover, in its Prospectus, laid down in no uncertain terms as some of its principal objects, the acquisition of statistical information concerning Public Health and the improvement of means of maintaining it, and the pursuit of knowledge, not for the selfish benefit of the profession alone, but for the good of all classes and callings of the community.

So great was the impetus given by the successful inauguration of the Provincial Medical and Surgical Association to the discussion of those matters which most nearly touched the profession, that numerous local medical associations, with more or less similar aims, were soon started, generally in friendly rivalry. Within nine years of the first meeting at Worcester the delegates of eleven medical associations besides those of the Provincial Association attended a Medical Conference in

London in February, 1841, convened by one of them which had assumed the title of British Medical Association and claimed to represent the medical practitioners of the whole United Kingdom.

As this almost forgotten body made a considerable stir at the time, and appeared likely to be a dangerous rival, and as the name was afterwards assumed by the Provincial Association, some extended notice of it is desirable.

The movement which led to its formation had its origin among practitioners in Camberwell and South-wark. An account of the inaugural meeting of 100 practitioners appeared in *The Lancet* of November 5th, 1836, which also contained a leading article in support of the proposed Association. From this latter it is quite clear that the writer had no liking for the Provincial Association. He referred to " the total failure of the migratory Provincial Medical Club," and alleged this imaginary failure as an excuse for the formation of the new Association, and further alluded to Dr. Conolly and " Green Crosse of Norwich " as puppets. A full account of the foundation and aims of the new Society will be found in the Supplement to W. Farr's *British Medical Almanack* for the year 1838, and a list of officers and council is to be found in the body of the same book, which is now quite rare. Farr—who afterwards was a Gold Medallist of the present British Medical Association, was celebrated as a statistician, and for years was the moving force in the office of the Registrar-General—was himself a member of the Council of the first British Medical Association, of which Dr. George Webster, of Dulwich, was chairman throughout its existence. Dr. Webster's Association seems to have had influential support, and the Annual Oration in 1840 was delivered by no less distinguished a physician and physiologist than Dr. Marshall Hall, whose position, however, in the profession in London was not nearly as high as his great abilities and scientific achievements entitled him to. He was one of the Vice-Presidents, and took an active part in some of the discussions. Among the twenty-three members of the Council, the names of the distinguished Professors of Comparative Anatomy in University College, London, Dr. R. E.

Grant, Robert Liston and Thomas Wakley, stand forth. The Honorary Secretary was in 1838 Mr. M. F. Wagstaffe, of Long Lane, Borough. The address of the Association was Exeter Hall, Strand, where all meetings except the anniversary ones were to be held. This Hall, which was situated where now stands the Strand Palace Hotel, was long celebrated as the scene of Evangelical meetings, and was known to the now middle-aged members of our Association as the scene of a most important meeting in 1900, when the first of the schemes for reformation of the Constitution was debated, but not adopted.

Two General Meetings of Dr. Webster's Association were to be held annually. The subscription was fixed at one guinea a year, a third part of which was to be set apart for a Benevolent Fund. So far as can be ascertained, no transactions were published, but with Mr. Wakley on the Council the pages of *The Lancet* were always open to the Association.

The definitive Public General Meeting of the profession, as announced by public advertisement, was held at Exeter Hall on January 11th, 1837, when Dr. Webster strongly urged the necessity for reform of the medical corporations and the formation of one great Faculty of Medicine for the whole United Kingdom, which should control medical education and practice and put down quackery. He said that they held out the hand of fellowship to other associations whose objects were wholly or partly the same. Petitions to Parliament were adopted at this meeting and signed, asking for the before-mentioned changes and for an inquiry into the Poor Law so far as its provisions affected the medical profession. It was also decided that reports as to patients' state of health should not be given to insurance companies without fees.

This was pretty well for a first meeting, but it soon became apparent that the Association was trying to do too much all at once and that the radical nature of the changes it advocated were likely to arouse an amount of opposition which would be too powerful for it. Hastings and his friends, on the other hand, while as anxious for reform, wished to obtain it by changes from within the corporations and by moderation and reasonableness.

When the delegates from the Provincial and Local Associations attended the Conference in London, they found that Dr. Webster and his friends expected them to endorse their policy and the Bills which they were advocating in Parliament, rather than to discuss what should be done to promote medical or poor-law reform. Some of the delegates from the Provincial Association thereupon resigned with the approval of their Council. *The Lancet* had no patience with Hastings, and went so far as to impute base motives to him. In a leading article of March 31st, 1841, after belittling the Provincial Association as the "Worcester or Central Council in the far-off City of Worcester," the question was asked, apropos of some communications between Hastings and the President of the College of Physicians, "Is it true that Dr. George Burrows has held out any hopes in his correspondence with Dr. Hastings of the possible contingency of a Fellowship in the College of Physicians should the efforts of the numerous sincere reformers in the Provincial Association be rendered abortive?" Wakley even went so far as to advertise this libellous attack on Hastings on the cover of that number of *The Lancet*.*

Like some other concerns in which Thomas Wakley had a hand, the first British Medical Association seems to have led an Ishmælitish existence. In the year 1844 *The Medical Times*, which was always hostile to Wakley and *The Lancet*, published the following report :—"The British Medical Association, suffering a resurrection under the galvanic agency of the new Bill, met in the person of Dr. George Webster on September 28th (1844). The Secretary was absent, and the resolutions appear to have been moved by the President, seconded by the President, put to the vote by the President and carried by the President. He was the whole meeting."

The Association, however, struggled on for a few more years. The latest reference to it that we have found is in *The Provincial Medical and Surgical Journal* for 1846, which reported a meeting of the Council for the discussion of Medical Reform. Those who are curious about these "old, unhappy far-off things" will find much about the defunct Association in the volumes of *The Lancet* and *The Provincial Medical and Surgical Journal* for the years in question.

* "Bribe of the College Fellowship to Dr. Hastings to extinguish Provincial Reform." (See *P.M.S.I.*, March 27th, 1841.)

The local Associations above referred to were : The North of England, Irish, Gloucester, South Devon, Cornwall, East of Scotland and Glasgow, representatives of which attended the Medical Conference in London in 1840. To Conferences held in 1841 two more associations sent delegates, namely, Nottingham and Taunton, besides those from the British Medical and Provincial Medical and Surgical Associations. Besides these there was the Eastern Medical and Surgical Association, which started at Bury St. Edmunds in 1835 with Mr. Crosse, of Norwich, as Secretary, and the 150 members of which unanimously voted to seek an intimate connection with the Provincial Association at the second meeting at Ipswich in 1836. Mr. Crosse, who was a member of both bodies, delivered the retrospective address at the fourth Anniversary Meeting of the Provincial Medical and Surgical Association at Manchester in that year, when the proposal for amalgamation was adopted. Thus, it appears that the Eastern Association formed the first Branch, since owing to distance it was arranged that it should continue to hold local meetings. It is recorded also that there was a Brentford Medical Association formed by the practitioners resident in that " Kingdom " so celebrated in verse ; but how long it existed, or what it did, is unknown to us. The North of England Association, with headquarters at Newcastle-on-Tyne, held its third General Meeting in 1841, and therefore was presumably founded in 1839, but this Association has left but a trace behind it. According to Dr. W. E. Hume, the medical historian of Newcastle-on-Tyne, the North of England Medical Association met in 1840 in the Library of the Society of Physicians and Surgeons, but beyond the record of permission for this having been granted, the Minutes of that Society contain no reference to the Association.

In 1840 the Gloucester and the Cornwall Associations seem to have been specially active in petitioning for reform. There is also mention in the Press of a South of Ireland Association with headquarters at Cork.

The Eastern Medical Association of Scotland, which included the counties of Perth, Fife and Forfar, seems, according to a long quotation from *The Perth Advertiser* in *The Provincial Medical and Surgical Journal* of

January 2nd, 1841, to have been instituted some years before that date. Its objects were practically the same as those of the Provincial and the British Medical Associations, with the latter of which it appears to have been in communication, rather than the former.

There appear to be very few records extant of these early independent associations, and we have no information as to their fates, except in the case of the Eastern Association. Probably, like the early British Medical Association, they gradually died of inanition and the indifference of their members.

Although the first British Medical Association was much more a general practitioners' society than was the Provincial Association, and its President, Dr. Webster, seems to have been in general practice, it repudiated the idea that it was exclusively a general practitioners' association, which, moreover, was negatived by the participation of men like Dr. Marshall Hall and Professor Grant.

There were, however, a number of practitioners who thought it desirable to have a society free from any suspicion of representing all classes of the profession, and some of these founded " The National Association of General Practitioners in Medicine, Surgery and Midwifery." This was in existence in May, 1846, when George Ross was its Secretary and refused to send tickets to Mr. T. Wakley for a Dinner to be given to its President, Mr. R. R. Pennington, because the Editor of *The Lancet* had displayed hostility to that gentleman. In *The Provincial Medical and Surgical Journal* of April 29th, 1846, p. 197, there is a report of a meeting of this society at which 700 persons were present, and it was proposed to establish a National Institute of Medicine as a licensing body. A joint deputation of the General Practitioners' Association and the Society of Apothecaries had an interview with the Home Secretary, which, however, had no result. The proposed institute would apparently have been a rival to Wakley's College of Medicine.

In *The London Medical Directory* for 1845 we have found the following entry :—

PENNINGTON, Robert Rainey, Physician, *Qualifications :*
    M.D., M.R.C.S.E., April 5, 1787 ; F.R.C.S.E., 1844 ;

President of the National Association of General Practitioners in Medicine, Surgery and Midwifery.

from which it appears that the President did not claim to be a general practitioner. In this, the first issue of *The Directory*, general practitioners, surgeons and physicians are described as such.

George Ross, the Secretary, appears as of 2, Leicester Place, Camberwell New Road, and a general practitioner. His qualification, if any, is omitted. The Society was still active in 1848 (see the Chapter on Medical Reform).

THE TRANSACTIONS
OF THE PROVINCIAL MEDICAL AND SURGICAL ASSOCIATION

IT is to the first nine volumes of its *Transactions* that we turn to learn the early history of the Association, for these bridge over the interval between the last issue of *The Midland Medical and Surgical Reporter* and the first issue of *The Provincial Medical and Surgical Journal* in October, 1840. The *Transactions* continued to be the sole *official* mouthpiece of the Association for some years longer, until, as already stated, the *Journal* assumed that part in April, 1844. From this date until 1851 the two publications continued to appear, one weekly or fortnightly, and the other annually. The *Transactions* are well printed in clear type on good paper, and illustrated by lithographs, some of which are coloured, and form excellent specimens of the illustrative art of this country in the 'thirties of the last century. They compare favourably with the illustrations of any medical journal which have appeared in the ensuing half century. The enterprise of the Council is shown by the fact that some seven hundred pounds of the capital of the Association was expended in 1840 in producing the 34 beautiful coloured lithographic plates which illustrate Dr. Ceely's paper on " Cowpox and Vaccination," in Vol. VIII of the *Transactions*. Besides this notable article, the *Transactions* contained others worthy of remark ; such as, a " Report on the English Influenza Epidemic of 1836–37," which was at its height in January, 1837, and was characterized by respiratory troubles and also by gastro-intestinal symptoms. In Vol. VIII will be found, besides Dr. Ceely's paper already mentioned, the report of the Vaccination " Section " (a kind of Sub-committee) of the Association, which was the first of the proposed sections " for the investigation of particular departments of medicine." In the same volume is

SIR CONSTANTINE
HOLMAN, M.D.,
TREASURER, 1888–1891.

EDWARD WATERS, M.D.,
PRESIDENT OF
ASSOCIATION, 1866.

EDMUND OWEN, F.R.C.S.,
CHAIRMAN OF COUNCIL,
1907–1910.

SIR HENRY BUTLIN,
F.R.C.S., TREASURER,
1891–1896 ; PRESIDENT,
1910.

reported the " Retrospective Address in Medicine," by Dr. John Addington Symonds, F.R.C.P., of Bristol, the father of the historian of the Renaissance. Vol. XI contains an important paper, especially considering the date of its appearance (1842), on dislocations of the Astragalus by Thomas Turner, of Manchester, with excellent illustrations.

A few years later (Vol. XVI (1843)), Mr. Thomas Nunneley, of Leeds, read a pioneer paper on " Anæsthesia and Anæsthetic Substances Generally," and in the same volume we find a " Report on the Medicinal Action of Arsenic " by Mr. Thomas Hunt, which is an early specimen of a collective investigation, for it was " collected from the reported experience of the members of the Provincial Medical and Surgical Association and other sources."

To the last volume but one, Joseph Toynbee, F.R.S., F.R.C.S.Eng., communicates a paper on the " Nature and Treatment of Diseases of the Ear."

We cite these communications here as evidence of the general level of quality of the papers and addresses discussed at the early meetings and published in the *Transactions*.

At the same time, the *Transactions* enable us to realise how much surgery has changed in its ways, when we read an account of an operation performed before the assembled members of the Association at Oxford in 1835, when the Regius Professor of Physic, Dr. J. Kidd, was President. The operation was one of lithotrity, by Mr. Costello, and it was performed successfully before a large assembly, by means first of a hammer and afterwards by manual pressure. The scene is described as follows :—

" The Anatomical Theatre having been found incapable of holding all the members of the Association who were anxious to see the operation, application was made to the Mayor, who kindly gave the use of the Town Hall for the purpose. The patient seemed to suffer nothing, and *expressing himself grateful for the relief he experienced, put on his clothes and retired.*"

At this meeting, honorary degrees were conferred on Drs. Pritchard and Abercrombie, an honour which, the Regius Professor stated, the University twenty years before had refused to bestow upon Edward Jenner. (This was a partial truth only. Soon after Jenner's discovery had been made known, a proposal to confer a degree upon him was rejected, but that occurred much more than " 20 years before." In 1813 Convocation unanimously conferred the diploma of M.D. upon Jenner, and Dr. Kidd himself was one of those who presented him with the diploma.)

BRANCHES

THE idea of having Branches of the Provincial Association seems early to have occurred to some of its members. At the third Anniversary Meeting in 1835 it was recommended "that in places where many members of the Association reside, occasional meetings of such members should take place." The question of Rules for such meetings was to be "left to the consideration of the respective parties." We do not, however, know whether this resolution was acted upon, or not. As already stated (*vide* section "Other Medical Associations," page 35), the first Branch was formed by the Eastern Medical Association, which was originally started in September, 1835, in full sympathy with the Provincial Association, and which amalgamated with it a year or two later.

Regulations.—At the Annual Meeting at Cheltenham in 1837 the following regulations for the formation and conduct of Branches were unanimously adopted (*Transactions of Provincial Medical and Surgical Association,* Vol. VI, p. 15) :—

" 1. That in order to fulfil more effectually the several purposes for which the Provincial Association was formed, it is expedient that a still more intimate union of its members be promoted, by the establishment of District Branches.

2. That members of the Association be at liberty to form District Branches whenever it may suit their convenience.

3. That in order to facilitate the formation of such Branches, and maintain uniformity among them, the General Council provide suitable instructions for the guidance of those who may unite in instituting them.

4. That conformity with these instructions be further ensured, by the initiating proceedings, and organisation of each Branch being submitted to the General Council, for their revision and approval.

5. That the District Branches be free to govern themselves as their respective members may think fit ; but

that the by-laws ordaining the special government be submitted to the General Council previously to their taking effect, in order to guard against the possibility of any such by-laws contravening the fundamental laws of the Association.

6. That all members appointed to offices by the District Branches, be forthwith enrolled as members of the General Council, on the appointments being officially notified to the General Council, it being highly expedient that all who engage on the executive management of the District Branches, should be also members of the General Council.

7. That the expenses incurred by the District Secretaries in conducting the proceedings of the District Branches be defrayed out of the general fund, provided such expenses do not in any instance exceed one-seventh part of the guinea subscribed by each member enrolled in the District Branch.

8. That if any circumstances arise in the formation of District Branches, which call for a larger expenditure than what is allowed by the foregoing resolution, such expenses, provided they do not exceed one-fourth of the guinea, may be allowed by a statement of the circumstances being made known to the General Council."

The above were proposed by Dr. Holme, of Manchester, seconded by Mr. Soden, of Bath, and carried unanimously.

One of the earliest Branches to be formed was the South-Western, of the formation of which Mr. Russell Coombe, of Exeter, gives the following account :—

" The attendance by medical men from Exeter at the inaugural meeting at Worcester showed keen interest in medical politics, and so it came to pass that in 1842 the Tenth Annual Meeting of the Association was fixed for Exeter. To prepare a fitting reception the South-Western Branch was founded, chiefly by the efforts of Dr. Thomas Shapter, who became its first Secretary, in that place in 1840, with Dr. Blackall (descendant of a Bishop of Exeter of that name) as its ' Patron,' and Mr. J. H. James as its first President. Its members were at first drawn from Devon and Somerset, but after an annual meeting of the Branch at Plymouth in 1843 it gained many members from Cornwall. In 1877 a

Branch was formed for South Devon and Cornwall, but in 1878 its members returned to the South-Western Branch.

" The Branch was founded chiefly for social intercourse and to promote good fellowship amongst its members.

" Like the Midland Branch (*q.v. infra*), it was intensely anti-homœopathic in feeling and its annoyance at the inaction of the Committee of Council in this matter was so great that in 1882 it passed a resolution calling on its members ' to take such steps as would secure that the Committee of Council will unhesitatingly carry out resolutions that have been adopted by the Association.'

" It will have been noticed that up to this date (1899) four methods of publicly putting forward their views and opinions have been used by members of the Association :—

" Firstly, the introduction and promotion of a Bill in Parliament to give effect to their views. Such Bills have either been attempts to remedy acknowledged public deficiencies or at other times to attempt to reform the status and efficiency of the profession ;

" Secondly, the presentation of petitions to Parliament by the Central Council ;

" Thirdly, the presentation of such petitions by individual Branches, a very undesirable course, since different Branches might present opposing views ;

" Fourthly, the approach by a Branch to those members of Parliament whose constituencies were within the area of such Branch."

By the time of the Anniversary Meeting at Bath in 1848, there were eight Branches, namely :—Southern, Yorkshire, Eastern, Shropshire and North Wales, Newton (Lancashire), South-Western, Taunton and Somerset, and South-Eastern. Of these the Eastern Branch was the most important. It included all members of the Provincial Medical and Surgical Association residing in the Counties of Cambridge, Essex, Huntingdon, Lincoln, Norfolk and Suffolk. It had five local Secretaries, namely, for Suffolk, Essex, Lincoln and West Cambs, Hunts and East Cambs, and Norfolk and Suffolk.

The South-Western Branch founded in 1840 especially prides itself on the fact that one of its Secretaries

(Dr. W. Gordon), who for some years took a very active part in central Association affairs, was the person who in a lengthy interview with the then Secretary of State for War (Lord Lansdowne) finally converted His Lordship to the creation of the Royal Army Medical Corps.

In the report of the next Annual Meeting at Worcester in 1849, a list of eleven Branches is given, somewhat differently named from those of the previous year. These were :—Bath and Bristol, Dorsetshire, Cambridge and Hunts, Yorkshire, Eastern, North Wales, Shropshire, Lancashire and Cheshire, South-Western, West Somerset, South-Eastern. The Regulations of the District Branches are printed in the same report. (*Transactions*, Vol. XVII, 1850.)

In 1852 there were fourteen Branches, according to the *Transactions*, bearing the following titles :—Bath and Bristol, Dorsetshire, Eastern, Lancashire and Cheshire, Metropolitan Counties, Midland, North Wales, Shropshire, South-Eastern, South-Western, South Wales, Suffolk, West Somerset and Yorkshire.

These changes in titles and in the distribution of the Branches no doubt denote a certain amount of fermentation in the new wine of the Association before it settled down into a stable combination of elements, and in 1840 the Council reported " that the formation of District Branches has fully answered the purpose for which they were originally proposed." But in 1846 the name of the East Yorkshire Branch, and in 1847 that of the Bridgewater Branch had disappeared from the list. Their places were apparently filled by means of a more convenient arrangement of districts.

In 1882, the Jubilee year, there appeared in the *Journal* a series of short accounts of all the Branches then existing. These were twenty-five in number. The following list gives their names in order of seniority with the year of the foundation of each. These twenty-five Branches correspond to a remarkable extent, as regards the districts represented, with the twenty-five Groups of Branches, each of which now elects one member of the Council of the Association :—

East Anglian, 1835.

Bath, 1836. (The name was afterwards changed to " Bath and Bristol.")

Lancashire and Cheshire, **1837.**
South-Western (Exeter), 1840.
West Somerset, **1844.**
South-Eastern, **1844.**
Cambs and Hunts, 1850.
Midland, 1851 (Headquarters at Derby).
Monmouthshire, 1852.
Metropolitan Counties, 1853.
Birmingham and Midland Counties, 1854.
Reading, 1856.
South Midland, 1856 (Headquarters at Northampton).
East Yorkshire and North Lincolnshire, 1856.
Thames Valley, 1857.
North of England, **1865.**
Border Counties, **1868.**
Southern, 1874 (Headquarters at Portsmouth. Divided
    into six " Districts ").
Staffordshire, **1874.**
South of Ireland, 1874.
Glasgow and West of Scotland, 1876.
Dublin, 1877.
Jamaica, 1877 (First Overseas Branch).
North of Ireland, **1878.**
Worcestershire and Herefordshire, 1880.

The history of the formation of the East Anglian
Branch has already been given in a previous chapter.

The Bath Branch was founded in 1836, and the
Bristol Branch in 1839. In 1841 they were united as
the Bath and Bristol Branch. Dr. Barlow, who took
a large part in the foundation of the Provincial Medical
and Surgical Association, was the first Secretary, and
Mr. W. Tudor, Sergeant Surgeon to the King, was the
first President.

The flourishing Lancashire and Cheshire Branch was
founded on June 30th, 1837, at Newton, a place
about half way between Liverpool and Manchester, as
the Newton Medical and Surgical Association. This
society proclaimed itself strictly in alliance with the
Provincial Medical and Surgical Association, but refused
any pecuniary assistance from the older body, and did
not require its own members to be enrolled as members
of the Provincial Medical and Surgical Association.
However, six weeks later the Newton Medical and

Surgical Association joined the Provincial Association as its Newton Branch. Except for two meetings at Warrington, it continued to meet at Newton for a number of years. Doubtless it was difficult to give to either Manchester or Liverpool the preference as a place of meeting. In 1849 the name of the Branch was changed to "Lancashire and Cheshire," having 90 members, most of whom were resident in South Lancashire. The meetings thenceforward were held in Liverpool and Manchester, but not till 1857 did the Branch spread northwards to meet at Preston in 1861. Two years later, when it met at Chester, it had 230 members practising in all parts of the two counties. By 1882 it had 805 members, and was the largest Branch with the exception of that of the Metropolitan Counties.

The West Somerset Branch was originally founded as the Taunton and West Somerset Medical Association, which in 1844 became a Branch of the Provincial Medical and Surgical Association. Its name was changed to West Somerset in 1849.

The Branch languished in the 'fifties, till in 1860 it had but 14 members, and had held no meeting during the two preceding years. It revived, however, in the following year.

The South-Eastern Branch was founded by the efforts of Mr. Thomas Martin, of Reigate, in 1844. Its area was large, including the counties of Kent, Surrey and Sussex. The first Anniversary Meeting was held at Tonbridge in 1845 under the Presidency of Mr. W. J. West. Very soon it was found that its size made meetings difficult, and in 1857 the West Kent District of the Branch was formed with its own Honorary Secretary. East Kent followed this example in 1861, East Surrey in 1866, West Surrey in 1867, East Sussex in 1869, and West Sussex in 1870, so that in that year the Branch was divided into six "Districts," which had their local meetings as well as taking part in meetings of the whole Branch. Thus a kind of microcosm of the parent Association was formed within it, foreshadowing in some sort the organisation later adopted of Branches and Divisions. The former South-Eastern Branch is now represented by the Kent, Surrey and Sussex Branches, with their seventeen Divisions. The Cambridge and

46

Huntingdon Branch was formed in 1850 out of the East Anglian Branch.

The Midland Branch was formed at a meeting in the Town Hall, Derby, in 1851, when Sir Charles Hastings was in the Chair. This Branch took a strong line on the subject of Homœopathy, and in 1858 passed a resolution condemning its professors and all medical men who might consult or co-operate with them.

The Monmouthshire Branch was founded in 1852 at Neath, and held its first meeting at Swansea in August of that year. Its vitality seems to have depended largely on the energy of Mr. W. H. Michael, who was appointed its permanent Secretary, for when he left Swansea it fell into abeyance. No proceedings are on record from 1856 until the formation in 1871 of the South Wales and Monmouthshire Branch.

The Metropolitan Counties Branch was formed soon after it had been decided at an Annual Meeting of the Association that the *Journal*, which had hitherto been published in Worcester under the title of *The Provincial Medical and Surgical Journal*, should henceforth be published in London as *The Association Medical Journal*. This step, which was not taken without hesitation, marked the end of the Association's existence as a merely provincial society. As long as the original British Medical Association existed in London the older Provincial Association excluded the metropolis from its scope, but on the former's disappearance the field was clear, and despite the fears of some that the interests of the provinces might be neglected, the Association formed a Metropolitan Counties Branch, and henceforth claimed the whole United Kingdom as its province. "It was not thought desirable to make the promotion of medical knowledge and the reading and discussion of papers an object of the Branch, it being felt that this was already performed to as great an extent as was consistent with the comfort and convenience of the members by the numerous societies already existing" (*B.M.J.*, 1882, Vol. II, p. 45). Occasionally, however, papers on strictly medical subjects were read. In 1878 District Societies on the plan of those of the South-Eastern Branch were formed for North London, East London and South Essex, and for South London.

The Metropolitan Counties Branch was from the first active in its support of the Association's policy of medical reform, poor-law and the teaching of midwifery.

The Birmingham and Midland Counties Branch was only founded in 1854, although Birmingham had so much to do with the foundation of the Provincial Medical and Surgical Association, and provided the first President, Dr. Johnstone. Many of the special general meetings of the Association have been held in Birmingham on account partly of its central position, but no doubt also because of the strong corporate feeling which the local profession has displayed and its activity in Association affairs.

The Reading Branch was formed in 1856, largely owing to the influence of Dr. Charles Cowan, " who was one of the leaders of the movement which at the meeting at Oxford in 1852 changed the whole character of the Association by starting a weekly journal instead of a volume of yearly transactions, and thus gave the movement a professional influence which it could not otherwise have acquired " (*B.M.J.*, 1882, Vol. II, p. 44).

The North of England Branch was started at Newcastle-on-Tyne in 1864, and held its first general meeting in that City in June, 1865. Dr. G. H. Philipson was its Secretary and Honorary Treasurer for the first 14 years of its existence. The comparatively late formation of this important Branch was due to various causes. As already noted, there had been a North of England Association as early as 1839, which met in Newcastle. The City and its neighbourhood had a vigorous local life of its own, and its first Medical Society was founded in 1786. We are indebted to Dr. W. E. Hume, of Newcastle, for the information that, according to the Minutes of the Society of Physicians and Surgeons, " At the monthly meeting held on January 29th, 1839, Dr. Headlam, the President, laid before the Society letters from Dr. Barlow, of Bath, the President for the year, and Dr. Hastings, of Worcester, the Secretary of the Provincial Medical Association, acknowledging the receipt of the report of this Society on the State of the Profession and inviting this Society to unite with that body as a Branch. On February 26th, 1839, a discussion took place as to the expediency of uniting

48

as a Branch of the Provincial Medical Association, and it was resolved that the Society deem it inexpedient at present to form such a Union." Four years after the formation of the Branch—in 1869—proposals were made for the amalgamation with it of the Northumberland and Durham Medical Society (originally called the Newcastle and Gateshead Pathological Society). After an animated discussion by a specially appointed Committee, the proposal was rejected by 13 votes to 7. The matter was brought up again in 1870 with a negative result. There was room in Northumberland and Durham for both the local Society and the Branch, as the continued existence of both has shown.

The Border Counties Branch was started in 1868 at Carlisle as the Cumberland and Westmorland Branch. In 1874 its title was changed to the present one, and its territory enlarged to include " Cumberland, Westmorland, Dumfries, Kirkcudbright, Wigtown, Roxburgh, Selkirk and Peebles." The " Border " character of the Branch is still maintained, for it has its Scottish as well as its English Divisions.

The Southern Branch was founded at Portsmouth in 1874. Its area was so great that it was decided to follow the example set by the South-Eastern Branch, and to divide it into six Districts, each having its own officers and local meetings, but all joining together in an Annual General Meeting of the whole Branch. These districts in 1882 were :—Southampton, Dorset, Isle of Wight, South Wilts, Winchester and South Hants.

Staffordshire Branch. In the last century there were various ephemeral medical societies in Staffordshire, of which the North Staffordshire alone did not deserve that epithet, for it maintained a useful existence for 25 years, but " wishing to extend its influence and usefulness, its members resolved at a meeting held at Stoke-on-Trent in April, 1874, to amalgamate itself with the British Medical Association." It was decided that Annual Meetings should be held in Stoke, Stafford and Wolverhampton in succession, and once in four years in some other town.

South of Ireland. There had been as elsewhere stated an Irish Medical Association, which sent its delegate to the Conference in London in 1840, the further history of which is obscure. The South of Ireland Branch, formed in 1874, is the premier Irish Branch of the Association. It included the Counties of Cork, Waterford, Kerry and Limerick. After its successful organisation, other Branches were formed in Dublin, Belfast and Galway. Professor McNaughton Jones, of Cork, who originated the idea of and organised the Branch, took the position of Honorary Secretary, which he held for three years.

The Glasgow and West of Scotland Branch was founded in January, 1876. It included the Counties of Lanark, Renfrew, Stirling, Dumbarton, Ayr, Argyle and Bute. Professor Allen Thompson was its first President, and in 1879 Professor (afterwards Sir) W. T. Gairdner adorned that office.

Dublin Branch. Until the formation of the South of Ireland Branch in 1874, members of the Association resident in Ireland had no local organisation, and consequently no representation on the Council. The only official of the Association in the country was an Honorary Secretary for Ireland. This official had no seat on the Committee of Council of the Association as a Branch Secretary had, and his chief, if not his sole, duty consisted in the transmission of such subscriptions as he received for the Association to its General Secretary. This office of Honorary Secretary for Ireland was held by Dr. J. W. Moore for $6\frac{1}{2}$ years. Eleven members of the Association met in Dublin in May, 1877, and considered the formation of a Branch, which was formed at a subsequent meeting when the leading men of the profession in Dublin agreed to serve on the Council. The avowed object of the Branch was to support the British Medical Association, but it was clearly understood that the Branch would not run counter to the Irish Medical Association, but would endeavour to work with and aid that Association.

The Worcestershire and Herefordshire Branch was in 1882, as Dr. Henry called it, " the youngest of all the Branches in Great Britain, for it was not established till 1880." Sir Charles Hastings appears never to have contemplated a Branch for Worcester, probably because he was prone to consider it the headquarters of the Association, which, indeed, for many of the first years

50

of its existence it had been. Of late years the Birmingham and Midland Counties Branch stretched its arms over this district, and many residents of the county still belong to that Branch. When, however, the Jubilee Meeting was to be held in Worcester the Branch was organised for the reception of the Annual Meeting of 1882.

OVERSEAS.

AUSTRALIA.

The first Branch established in Australia was the South Australian, with its headquarters at Adelaide.

The following account of the foundation of the South Australian Branch and other Australian Branches is based on information supplied by Dr. W. Lendon, of Adelaide.

In the 43 years between 1836, when the province was proclaimed, until 1879, when the South Australian Branch was founded, there had been various medical societies, culminating in the South Australian Medical Society, which Iwas dissolved in the latter year. The Association at home was then appealed to by Dr. Thomas Cawley for advice as to the procedure in forming a Branch. Before an answer could reach Adelaide a meeting had been held at the house of the leading surgeon of South Australia, Dr. William Gardner, and the formation of the Branch decided upon. The Chairman of the meeting was Dr. William Gosse, the doyen of the local profession, who was elected President. Three members of Council were elected and Dr. W. L. Cleland was appointed Honorary Secretary and Dr. Hawkins Treasurer. There were at this time only 6 members of the profession in the Colony who were already members of the B.M.A. These were called into requisition to provide a kind of apostolic succession by signing the nomination papers of some 30 new members who were duly elected on October 15th, 1879, by the Committee of Council in London, but it was not till July 7th, 1880, that the petition of 22 South Australian members was considered and the formal recognition of the Branch adopted by the Committee of Council, the New South Wales Branch being recognised at the same session and

51

Victoria a month later. It was not till September 4th that the overworked Mr. Fowke was able to find time to notify the Honorary Secretary in Adelaide that the Branch had been duly christened. Probably the business of the Annual Meeting accounted for this delay. The Branch has flourished, and now at the end of 50 years it has some 400 members. One outstanding feature of its activities during its early years, was the inauguration in 1887 of the series of intercolonial medical congresses. The innovation was well received in the other Colonies* of Australia, as well as in New Zealand. The Western Australian Branch was one of the earliest to admit qualified women to full membership. The Branch, like others in Australia, has been largely concerned in establishing and maintaining fair conditions in " Lodges," *i.e.*, club or friendly societies' practice.

The other Australian Branches, in order of seniority, are :—New South Wales, Victoria, Queensland, West Australia and Tasmania.

The Association is now represented in Australia by the Federal Committee of the British Medical Association in Australia.

The Western Australian Branch was formed at a meeting held at the Perth Public Hospital on August 6th, 1898. The population of the whole Colony at that time was only 167,802. It is now nearly half a million. The date of the actual recognition of the Branch in London was March, 1899.

The Branches of the Association in Australia publish through the Australasian Medical Publishing Company, Ltd., *The Medical Journal of Australia*. This Company, which is closely associated with the Association, has its own printing house, and does much publishing work of a medical and general nature.

In 1929 the foundation stone of a fine new House for the New South Wales Branch was laid by Sir Ewen Maclean, then President of the British Medical Association, who was on a visit to Australia as official delegate of the Association. The House was completed in 1930, and is a very imposing structure of 12 stories high, the main room in which is the Robert H. Todd Assembly

* Dr. Lendon's term "Colonies" as they then were.

Hall, being, as the obituary notice of Dr. Todd states, " a lasting monument to the man who did more than any other in Australia for the advancement of the British Medical Association and the medical profession as a whole."

The House was formally opened by the Governor of N.S.W., on the occasion of the Branch's Jubilee. An account of the House will be found in *The Medical Journal of Australia* for October 25th, 1930, p. 571 (see illustration, p. 327).

The British Medical Association in Australia has many outstanding names associated with its history, but it must suffice here to mention three—Dr. R. H. Todd, of Sydney, Sir George Adlington Syme, of Melbourne, and Dr. Wm. T. Hayward, of Adelaide.

Dr. Todd's untiring work for the Association from 1906 to the time of his death in December, 1931, did more to unify the Association and extend its influence in Australia than that of any other man. He was Honorary Secretary of the New South Wales Branch from 1908 to March, 1931, when he was made President-Elect of the Branch. He was made a Vice-President of the Association in 1923, and received the Gold Medal of the Australian Federal Committee in the same year, together with Dr. W. T. Hayward, this being the first occasion of the presentation of this Medal. An obituary notice of Dr. Todd will be found in *The British Medical Journal* of March 12th, 1932.

Sir George Syme, in addition to being one of Australia's most prominent surgeons, occupied for some years the Presidency of the Federal Committee of the British Medical Association in Australia. By his influence with the profession, exercised through a steadfast and impressive personality, he was of the greatest service to it in that country. He was made a Vice-President of the Association in 1923.

Dr. W. T. Hayward, in addition to great work for the South Australian Branch, was the first Chairman of the Federal Committee of the Association in Australia, and was made a Vice-President of the Association in 1914. On the occasion of the Annual Meeting of the Association in 1914, while he was in this country, he was given the honour of the LL.D. by Aberdeen University.

NEW ZEALAND.

The New Zealand Branch, formed in 1896, has had a very prosperous career and now contains 13 Divisions, representing all parts of the Dominion. It publishes its own journal—*The New Zealand Medical Journal.* Among the names of many persons instrumental in the success of this Branch must be singled out that of Dr. H. E. Gibbs, who was, from 1908 to 1923, Honorary Secretary of the Branch, and was created a Vice-President of the Association in the latter year.

The history of the New Zealand Medical Association, which preceded the New Zealand Branch, will be found in *The New Zealand Medical Journal,* Vol. I, 1887–8, and that of the formation of the present New Zealand Branch in *The Australasian Medical Gazette* for 1897.

SOUTH AFRICA.

In the Union of South Africa and the Mandated Territory of South-West Africa there are 12 Branches, now in a very flourishing condition. The first South African Branch—Griqualand West—was formed in 1888, and the Cape of Good Hope Branch followed in 1889. The situation in South Africa is interesting as showing not only the adaptability of the Association to new conditions, but also the similarity of its constitution to that which allows the British Commonwealth of Nations to work so well in spite of its difficulty of definition. During the few years previous to 1925 there had grown up a South African Medical Association which appealed by its name to those South Africans who were jealous of their autonomy and rather resented being " governed from London." The rivalry with the well-established Branches of the B.M.A., while not regarded as very serious, was proving decidedly inconvenient, and was naturally giving a handle to those who had to deal with the profession. and preferred a disunited to a united profession. At the request of the Association in South Africa, the Council in 1925 sent out Dr. Alfred Cox, its Medical Secretary, to take stock of the situation and to endeavour to arrive at some solution which should heal the widening breach. After a visit which extended over 5 months, during which he visited all the Branches, a solution was happily found which satisfied the aspirations of the ardent nationalists while leaving the Association in South Africa intact—nay, much stronger than before. This was done by the simple expedient of giving the whole of the Branches in the Union and in South-West Africa the right to call themselves collectively the Medical Association of South Africa (British Medical Association), the Branches remaining in the same relation to the home body as before, and their members still being ordinary members of the parent body. The Branches have formed a Federal Council on the model of Australia, and publish their own journal, *The Journal of the Medical Association of South Africa* (*British Medical Association*), under the editorship of C. F. L. Leipoldt, who also acts as organising Secretary in South Africa. Since this change in 1926 the Association in South Africa has prospered exceedingly, and the credit for this is largely due to the work of Dr. A. J. Orenstein, C.M.G., of Johannesburg, who has been the President of the Federal Council since its inception, and who was made a Vice-President of the Association in 1932.

EAST AND WEST AFRICA.

Branches of the Association exist in East and West Africa. In 1920, Branches were formed in Uganda, Nyasaland and Kenya. Sierra Leone followed in 1920. The East African Branches, and particularly the Kenya Branch, have exhibited great activity.

CANADA.

The case of Canada is peculiar, as although the Association has many members there, no Canadian Branches exist. The following extracts from the report of Dr. Alfred Cox and the late Sir T. Jenner Verrall, who went as delegates to Canada in 1924, give a clear account of the situation as it then existed :—

" In presenting the report of our mission to the Canadian Medical Association, it will be helpful to recall briefly the facts which led to the sending of the delegation.

" During the past few years, correspondence with many members of our Association in Canada, and visits from some of them, have made it clear that an influential section of the Canadian profession would welcome close

E

and more formal relations with our Association. On our side certain facts had drawn attention to the special nature of our relations with Canada as compared with the other Dominions. The growing strength of the Association in Australia and the happy result of our efforts to satisfy the aspirations of our Branches there as regards their right to hold property ; the great prosperity of the New Zealand Branch ; the interesting situation in South Africa, where the South African Committee is making a determined effort to consolidate and extend the influence of the Association in South Africa ; the establishment of new Branches and the growth of old ones in Colonies and Dependencies all over the world ; all these facts tended to make the position of Canada stand out distinctly as the weak point in the claim of our Association to represent the British medical profession over the whole Empire.

" The Association has held two very successful Annual Meetings in Canada, in 1897 at Montreal, and in 1906 at Toronto, and if these had been energetically followed up, it is possible that the Association might have been in Canada what it is in the other Dominions—the only practicable medical organisation. But the fact is that at the present time, out of a medical population of about 9,000 in Canada, there are only 374 members of the B.M.A., and though there are nominally 5 Branches of the Association, these exist only on paper, have held no meetings for years, and, as we found by personal inquiry, have no chance whatever of functioning as Branches.

" In these circumstances, the suggestion of a possible affiliation led to a warm invitation from the Canadian Medical Association to send delegates to discuss the question."

The result of the visit of Sir Jenner Verrall and Dr. Cox to Canada was the affiliation of the two bodies, which took place in 1925. The bond, which is more sentimental than material, is sufficiently strong to have induced the profession in Winnipeg to invite the Association to hold its Annual Meeting there in 1930, with a Winnipeg doctor as President of the Association (Dr. Harvey Smith)—a meeting which proved triumphantly successful. Another result is that a considerable party of members of the Canadian Medical Association are

56

proposing to pay a return visit to the Centenary Meeting in London this year.

The affiliation arrangements are working well. They include reciprocal rights for members of each to attend sections and functions of the other, reciprocal use of respective headquarters and libraries, and help of the respective central staffs.

INDIA.

Ceylon was the first Branch to be formed, in 1887, and it has always been a very active unit of the Association. The Bombay Branch was formed in 1889, and since then Branches have been established in each of the Provinces. Their history is a somewhat fluctuating one, as they naturally had to depend, in former years at any rate, mainly on the members of the Indian Medical Service, and the activities of the Branches, depending, as they always do, mainly on one or two active spirits, suffered when service exigencies caused the removal of these officers. Latterly, however, the Branches have had the services and membership of more and more Indian medical practitioners. With political conditions so unsettled as they have been for some years now, it is not surprising that the membership and activities of the Indian Branches have suffered, but with more settled conditions it is to be hoped that the example of the self-governing Dominions will lead to a great extension of the membership and influence of the Association in India.

COLONIES AND DEPENDENCIES.

The following list will show how the Association has extended its influence over the world, and especially of course in the British Empire, though not entirely confined to it as the names of the Egyptian, Mesopotamia, and Hong Kong and China Branches testify. Jamaica was the first Branch (1877) outside the British Isles and still flourishes. British Guiana followed in 1883. The Hong Kong and China Branch (founded 1891), and the Malaya Branch (1894) are very prosperous units of the Association, the latter publishing its own Journal, *The Malayan Medical Journal*. The name of J. W. Scharff, of Penang, is specially connected with the growth and success of this Branch.

FORMATION OF BRANCHES—CHRONOLOGICAL LIST.

The following list gives the names of the Branches founded since 1882, in chronological order, and at the same time records change of name or area of Branches, and the names of those bodies discontinued or dissolved since that date :—

Branches formed since 1882.

1883 British Guiana ;
　　　Dorset and West Hants.
1884 South Indian and Madras.
1885 Oxford and Reading (formerly Oxford and District, and Reading and Upper Thames District).
1886 Bermuda.
1887 Ceylon ;
　　　Halifax, Nova Scotia.
1888 Griqualand West ;
　　　Malta ;
　　　Perth.
1889 Barbados ;
　　　Bombay ;
　　　Cape of Good Hope (now Cape Western) ;
　　　Punjab ;
　　　Stirling.
1890 Leeward Isles.
1891 Burma ;
　　　Hong Kong and China ;
　　　Montreal.
1892 Trinidad and Tobago.
1893 Dundee ;
　　　Grahamstown and Eastern Province (now Cape Eastern) ;
　　　Munster ;
　　　South Eastern of Ireland.
1894 British Columbia ;
　　　Gibraltar ;
　　　Malaya ;
　　　Queensland.
1896 Natal, Coastal ⎫ Formerly Natal Branch.
　　　Natal, Inland ⎭
　　　New Zealand ;
　　　Quebec.

1897 Ottawa.
1899 West Australian.
1903 Connaught ;
      Fife ;
      North Lancs. and South Westmorland.
1906 Egyptian ;
      St. John's, New Brunswick.
1907 Border, South Africa.
1908 Assam.
1910 Baluchistan.
1911 Tasmanian.
1912 Mashonaland
      Matabeleland and ⎱ Formerly named
        Northern Rhodesia ⎰ Rhodesian Branch.
1913 Orange Free State and Basutoland ;
      Pretoria ;
      Southern Transvaal (formerly named Witwaters-
        rand Branch).

      Kent   ⎱ Formerly South-Eastern Branch, which
      Surrey ⎰ was originally formed in 1844.
      Sussex
1914 Hyderabad ;
      Wiltshire.
1916 Grenada.
1919 Essex   ⎱ Formerly East Anglian Branch, which
      Norfolk ⎰ was originally formed in 1836.
      Suffolk
1920 Uganda ;
      Nyasaland ;
      Kenya.
1921 Fiji ;
      Mesopotamia ;
      Sierra Leone ;
      Zanzibar.
1922 Northern Bengal.
1923 St. Lucia ;
      Tanganyika.
1925 Cape Midland.
1926 South-West Africa.
1928 Calcutta.
1929 Hertfordshire.

Branches discontinued or dissolved since **1882**.

1897 Channel Islands and Isle of Man.
1900 British Columbia.
1901 Deccan ;
      Quebec.
1902 Thames Valley (merged into Metropolitan Counties Branch).
1903 Ottawa.
1926 Halifax, Nova Scotia ;
      Montreal ;
      St. John's, New Brunswick ;
      Saskatchewan ;
      Toronto

Dissolved on affiliation of British Medical Association with Canadian Medical Association.

There are now (1932) 101 Branches, with 246 Divisions.

THE ASSOCIATION AND MEDICAL REFORM

A LTHOUGH Medical Reform was not one of the specific objects of the Provincial Association, as stated in the Prospectus, it speedily became one of them, as already stated, for at the Fifth Annual Meeting at Cheltenham in 1837 a Medical Reform Committee was appointed " to watch over the interests of the profession at large."

Ever since the meetings in London in 1841, which were attended by delegates from the Provincial Medical and Surgical Association, it had been impossible, even were it desirable, to keep the subject of the reform of medical education and of the status of the practitioner out of the discussions at Branch and Annual Meetings. So closely has this subject been interwoven with the life of the Association that it is very difficult to treat of it apart from other medical affairs. The first important step in the movement was taken in 1839 by the Association, when it presented to Parliament a memorial in which the crying needs of the profession and the public were set forth and the petitioners prayed for the necessary legislation to effect reform. A year later its delegates met those of the first British Medical Association, and discussed the question, and in the same year they had interviews with representatives of the College of Physicians, the College of Surgeons, and the Apothecaries' Society, and met at the House of Commons the M.Ps., Warburton, Hawes and Wakley, who were bringing forward Bills for the regulation of medical education and the restriction of unqualified practice. On this occasion Warburton and Wakley agreed to support the Bill, backed by Hawes, if Wakley satisfied himself that the medical profession would forego restrictive measures against unlicensed practice, should (as seemed likely) the House of Commons object to such measures.

This question of the suppression of unlicensed medical practice was the Scylla upon which many a hopeful Medical Reform Bill suffered shipwreck, even if it escaped the Charybdis of the Medical Corporations. In the end, as will be seen, the reformers had to accept compromises, for Parliament would not give up the right of every individual to be treated by any quack he chose, and the representatives of the Corporations, who were well known and influential members of London Society, had the ear of Royalty and of the members of the governing classes of that day, to the almost complete exclusion of the provincial physicians and other practitioners, who pressed for radical reform. Wakley and his friends had advocated the abrogation of the privileges of the Corporations, and the substitution in their place of a State Examining Board, whose licence should constitute the sole qualification to practise. The Provincial Association, recognising the magnitude of the obstacles in the way, and acting on the principle announced in clause 5 of its Prospectus of "establishing the harmony and good feeling which ought ever to characterize a liberal profession," passed the following resolution in the year 1841 :—

" That in the opinion of this meeting, it is expedient that existing institutions be respected, provided their existence can be rendered compatible with uniformity of qualification, equality of privilege to practise medicine, and a fair system of representative government." (See *P.M.S.J.*, March 13th, 1841, p. 395.)

The Bill introduced by Mr. Hawes, M.P. for Lambeth, came up for second reading on March 17th, 1841, but was counted out when only thirty-three members were present. In supporting it, Mr. Hawes referred to the findings of a Committee on Medical Education which sat in 1834. He stated as evidence of the need of legislation that out of 1,830 candidates for medical office under the Poor Law, 320 had never been examined in surgery, 323 never examined in medicine, and 233 had not undergone any professional examinations whatever.

In 1845 the Secretary of the Association was directed to send a copy of the report of its Medical Reform Committee " at once " to Sir James Graham in reference to the Bill which he was introducing.

62

In the Minutes of the Royal College of Surgeons of England* there is a record of negotiations between that College, the Royal College of Physicians, the Apothecaries' Society, and the National Association of General Practitioners (*vide supra*) at the College of Physicians in February, 1848. At this conference the heads of a measure of medical legislation were agreed upon, including the appointment of a General Council, the registration of practitioners and students, reciprocity of practice, etc. It was resolved :—

" That a Charter of Incorporation should be granted to the Surgeon Apothecaries of this country under the title of ' The Royal College of General Practitioners of England.' "

Under a proposed Clause 8, penalties by summary process were to be imposed on all unqualified persons practising medicine or surgery.

The Council of the Provincial Medical and Surgical Association appealed to the Members of the Royal College of Surgeons of England in general practice for an expression of their opinions on these subjects.

In 1850 Sir George Grey brought forward a Medical Bill. In this year the Report of the Council contained a statement of the proceedings of the year as regarded Medical Reform. On the replies received by the Council to inquiries " taking as a basis the principles of uniform and sufficient qualification, equal right to practise and the representative principle in the formation of the Councils or Governing Bodies," the Council had forwarded a memorial which had been presented by the President of the Association to Sir George Grey.

In 1852 Mr. George Hastings, M.P., the son of the Founder and the Secretary of the Medical Reform Committee, on behalf of the Association, drafted a Medical Bill, which was not passed into law. In 1855, at the Annual Meeting, the Medical Reform Committee recommended the reintroduction of this Bill, which recommendation was adopted and steps taken to organise support of the measure in Parliament. A vote of thanks was passed to Messrs. Headlam, Brady and Craufurd, M.Ps., and to Mr. G. W. Hastings, M.P., for his untiring

---

* For this information I am indebted to the Assistant Secretary of the Royal College of Surgeons.

zeal as Secretary to the Committee. At the Annual Meeting in 1856, Dr. Alexander Henry was associated with Mr. Hastings in the office of Secretary of the Committee. This Bill was read a first time (*pro forma*) in June, 1855, but it did not pass, and at the Annual Meeting at Nottingham in 1857, Sir Charles Hastings announced that the Right Hon. W. Cowper had implied his intention to introduce a Medical Reform Bill in the next session of Parliament, and requested a personal interview with Sir Charles before deciding. The meeting decided to press for reforms, in the main as in Mr. Headlam's Bills of 1856 and 1857 " which have been triumphantly recognised by the House of Commons by a very large majority." Votes of thanks were passed to Mr. Headlam and those 225 members of the House of Commons who formed the majority by which the second reading was passed.

Before the Anniversary Meeting of 1858 the Medical Act of 1858 became law, and thanks were voted to the Right. Hon. W. F. Cowper, M.P., for his exertions. But the Association was by no means disposed to rest on its oars. It was decided that the Medical Reform Committee be thenceforth called the Committee on Medical Legislation, and it was " directed to draw the attention of the Government to the necessity of appointing as the six members of the General Medical Council to be nominated by Her Majesty, persons really representing the bulk of the medical profession." Sir Charles Hastings was appointed by the Crown one of the members of the Council. After nearly twenty years of active agitation and many failures, a great measure of success had been attained, although much disappointment was felt that a more decisive victory had not been won.

The General Council of Medical Education which was thus formed was given the functions of :—

    1. Obtaining from the licensing bodies information with regard to their courses of study and education.

    2. The establishment of a Medical Register.

    3. The preparations of a National Pharmacopœia.

These things were good in their way, but they were not half of what the profession had asked for. The one portal of admission to the profession, by which it was hoped to ensure an equal minimum qualification all

64

over the United Kingdom, was not provided for. The Act did not attempt to suppress unqualified practice, except in the service of the State, and the representative principle in the selection of the members of the Council was practically disregarded, for in the selection of the representatives of the Universities and Medical Corporations the great body of graduates and licensees had no direct and but very little indirect influence. The representatives sent to the Council by the various Colleges were naturally more concerned with the reputations and pecuniary resources of the institutions which they represented, than with the suppression of quackery or the improvement of the culture and status of their licensees.

The Act of 1858 was almost entirely the work of the Association. Short as it fell of the mark set up by the profession twenty years earlier, it was the first really official recognition of the existence of the great body of practitioners and of their importance to the State. As Sir Dawson Williams wrote (" The Middle Age," *Glasgow Medical Journal*, July 1st, 1892) :—" If it had never done anything else the Association would thereby have earned the gratitude of every member of the medical profession in the United Kingdom, and indeed throughout the British Empire, for this Act of 1858 set a standard the Dominions and Dependencies could adopt, and provided a model their legislatures might follow." To this we would add that if it benefited the profession much, it benefited the public even more, by improving the education and acquirements of the practitioners of the future.

The newly-named Committee on Medical Legislation appointed as its Chairman Dr. Edward Waters, of Chester, than whom no better could have been found. During the ensuing twenty-eight years, his energy, *savoir-faire*, eloquence and tenacity led up to the amended Medical Act of 1886.

The Association took up meanwhile the question of the election of members of the Council of the College of Surgeons, which was carried on by personal voting only, so that the choice of members was practically in the hands of those Fellows of the College who lived in and near London. At the Anniversary Meeting, in 1865,

65

a memorial was directed to be sent to the Council in favour of the introduction of voting by ballot-papers through the Post. The Council of the College, however, declined to apply for the new or supplementary charter which such a change would have made necessary, and in 1866 a deputation of the Association sought the Home Secretary on this matter and on the question of amendment of the Medical Act.

The Act of 1858 being only accepted by the Association and the profession at large as a small instalment of what was needed for their protection and that of the public, efforts were made again and again to secure its amendment.

On May 15th, 1870, a Special Meeting of the Association was held for the consideration of the Bill to amend the Medical Act, which had been introduced in the House of Lords by Earl de Grey and Ripon, the President of the Privy Council. On the following day, a numerous deputation of members of the Association waited on him and submitted a clause providing for the introduction of direct representatives of the profession into the General Medical Council. But this Bill became only another abortive measure.

Under the heading of "The Abandonment of the Medical Bill of 1870," *The British Medical Journal* of July 30th, 1870, stated that as the Medical Bill had been withdrawn, its friends and its opponents would be able to look more calmly into its character. As its defeat was partly due to the action of the Association, the writer could not affect to regret its decease. The concluding paragraph of the article, however, contained these passages :—" We trust, however, that there were few who understood the matter who did not on Wednesday morning experience a pang of real regret in reading in the list of ' dropped Bills ' the title of that for the Amendment of the Medical Acts. . . . It would practically have reduced our Examining Boards to one for each Kingdom, and it would have put an end to the disgraceful competition which has for so long existed." Earlier in the article, however, it was stated that the Bill " proposed to confirm the privileges possessed by certain mediæval Corporations to dignify those bodies by the title of ' Medical Authorities,' and seemingly

66

to fasten them about the necks [*sic*] of the profession for ever."

This article only reflected the divided opinion in the profession, which was evident later at the Annual Meeting at Newcastle-on-Tyne in August, when considerable dissatisfaction with the action of the Council was expressed by some distinguished members of the Association, and Dr. Stokes, of Dublin, and Dr. George Paget, of Cambridge, the proposer and seconder of the vote of thanks to the retiring President for his Address, took the unusual course of severely criticising the Council for its action in reference to the dropped Bill, and incidentally reflecting upon the orator, to whom they were ostensibly offering a vote of thanks. An attempt to pass a vote of condemnation of the action of the Council having failed, three Vice-Presidents, Drs. Acland, Paget and Stokes, and two other members, Drs. Embleton and Rumsey, seceded from the Association, all five being members of the General Medical Council.

It seems to have been thought that by opposing this Bill the profession would shortly get a better one, but this expectation was doomed to disappointment, for it was not till the year 1886 that an Amending Act was passed into law.

After the efforts made in connection with the abortive Bill of 1870, the Association made little effort in the promotion of measures in Parliament, but watched hopefully the negotiations which were going on between some of the Corporations to form Conjoint Examining Boards. In its Report for 1873 the Reform Committee drew attention to one advantage which had been gained from the action of the Association in the past, namely, that it showed that no measure of medical reform would be accepted by it or the profession which did not provide for the direct representation of practitioners on the General Medical Council. Satisfaction was also expressed with the steps being taken to form a Conjoint Examining Board for England. For the same reason, the Association and its Reform Committee continued to mark time for some years, noting with regret in 1876 that in filling three vacancies on the General Medical Council neither the Association nor the general body of general practitioners had been recognised, and also that the

67

General Medical Council had not succeeded in the establishment of Conjoint Examining Boards.

In 1881 the Association succeeded in procuring the appointment of a Royal Commission, which in its Report emphatically upheld all the contentions urged before it by the Association's representatives. It favoured :—

1. A one-portal system of entry into the profession ;

2. A reduction in the numbers of the members of the General Medical Council ;

3. A large direct representation of the medical profession on the Council ;

4. The imposition on the Public Prosecutor of the duty of taking action against offenders against the Medical Acts.

Subsequently an Amending Bill was introduced into Parliament, and after many delays we find the following record :—

" At a special meeting of the Council of the Association held in May, 1883, Dr. Edward Waters moved :—

' That the President, the President of the Council, and the General Secretary of the Association, together with the Members of Council, sign the petition to the House of Commons in favour of the Medical Act Amendment Bill presented by the Lord Privy Seal, as providing for the direct representation of the profession on the Medical Council and for the compulsory formation of one Conjoint Board of Examiners in each division of the United Kingdom of Great Britain and Ireland for the examination of all candidates for the medical profession.' "

This resolution was carried and the Petition signed by all present.

It is to be noted that not only had the Council of the Association repeatedly petitioned Parliament in favour of reform, but important Branches such as the Metropolitan Counties and the South-Eastern had done so directly. A sub-committee appointed by the Metropolitan Counties Branch to examine the provision of the Medical Act Amendment Bill of 1883 decided to recommend amendments with the following objects :—

To Clause 9 : To exclude women from sitting on Medical Examining Boards.

To Clause 18 : To prevent compulsion of Medical Schools to admit women students.

To Clause 27 : To secure the absolute prohibition of unregistered persons from [*sic*] practising medicine in any of its branches for gain.

To Clause 34 : To prevent the issue of " bogus " or low-class diplomas or without examination by medical authorities.

At this meeting, Dr. Glover stated that between the years 1870 to 1881 twenty amending medical Bills had been brought into Parliament, besides three Government ones.

In the Editorial Retrospect in *The British Medical Journal* at the end of 1883, the Bill and its fate are spoken of as follows (*B.M.J.*, Vol. II, 1883, p. 1305) :—

" The prospects of a settlement of the long-agitated question of medical reform were for some time during the present year very encouraging. In fulfilment of a promise made by the Lord President of the Privy Council to a deputation representative, as far as possible, of the British Medical Association and of the profession, in November, 1882, his Lordship in March last introduced a Medical Act Amendment Bill into the House of Lords. The Bill embodies, among other matters, three points which had always been regarded as cardinal by the Association, and had been recommended in the Report of the Royal Commissioners on Medical Reform, namely, (i) the introduction of the principle of direct representation into the constitution of the General Medical Council, (ii) the establishment of a minimum uniform qualifying examination for practice, by Conjoint Examining Boards, one being formed in each division of the United Kingdom ; the strengthening of the penal clause of the Medical Act, so as to effect adequate protection against the false assumption of medical titles by unqualified and unexamined persons."

The Medical Reform Committee of the British Medical Association suggested various amendments, some of which were accepted. Numerous petitions were presented in favour of the Bill, which was read a third time in the House of Lords on April 27th. On May 2nd it was read a first time in the House of Commons. The second reading was deferred from time to time, until at the end of the session the Bill was withdrawn.

In this year the Council of the Royal College of Surgeons of England acquired the necessary powers to establish voting by postal ballot by its Fellows in the election of members of Council. The Victoria University of Manchester obtained a supplementary Charter empowering it to grant degrees in Medicine and Surgery.

In 1884 it was still possible for a candidate to be granted a licence to practise without his having been examined in all three subjects of Medicine, Surgery and Midwifery. The General Medical Council in this year adopted the proposal of Mr. G. M. Humphry, of Cambridge, that no person ought to be granted a degree, diploma, or licence to practise until his competency in Medicine, Surgery and Midwifery had been proved by examination before one or more licensing bodies. The Council also decided that the visitation of Examinations should be resumed and approved of the proposals for the institution of Conjoint Examinations in London by the Colleges of Physicians and Surgeons, and in Scotland by the Colleges of Physicians and Surgeons of Edinburgh and the Faculty of Physicians and Surgeons of Glasgow.

The President of the Association announced that rather than risk the loss of the Bill the Association would not insist on the creation of State Examining Boards.

The year 1886 must be ever memorable as that in which the Act amending the Medical Act of 1858 was passed, and which Her Majesty the Queen, in her speech from the Throne, referred to as "effecting important reforms in the medical profession." In the Editorial Retrospect for the year the event was referred to in the following terms (*British Medical Journal*, 1886, Vol. II, p. 1253) :—

"The first Medical Act was passed after twenty-six years, reckoning from the foundation of the Provincial Association. The second, Amending Act, was the result of fifty-four years of struggle. The first act provided reciprocity of practice throughout the Kingdom, a Register of members of the profession, the preparation of a national pharmacopœia and the formation of the General Medical Council."

In summing up these efforts and their results, the Editor of the *Journal* wrote :—

"Strenuous efforts were at that time (1858) made on behalf of the Association to enforce improved general

70

LORD LISTER,

*Chairman, Scientific Grants Committee, 1888–1892 ; President, Surgery
Section, 1870 and 1875, Address in Surgery, 1871.*

ERNEST HART, M.R.C.S.,
Editor of British Medical Journal, 1867–1869 and 1870–1898.

education on the part of all entering on the study of medicine and to make the double qualification in Medicine and Surgery obligatory before registration, but on both points the Association was beaten owing to the strength of the Corporations." The General Medical Council was timid and loath to act.

In 1868 the Association appointed a Committee to secure direct representation on the Council. The Government Bill of 1870, which was carried through the Lords, was lost in the Commons because it did not concede this principle of direct representation.

" Bill after Bill has been introduced by this Committee " (that on Direct Representation appointed in 1870) " on behalf of the Association. Select Committees have taken evidence, a Royal Commission has reported, and the result has been that all the principles in regard to Medical Reform with which the Association started in 1832 have received the sanction of the legislature. Repeated efforts were made by a powerful Government to embody these principles in an Act of Parliament ; the result would have been the diminution of the numbers of the General Medical Council, the indirect representation of the Universities and Corporations, and the direct representation of the profession in it. The attempt failed, and in the last instance a less ambitious measure was framed which is embodied in the Medical Act of 1886. Though the Act is not all that could be desired, it is an unquestionable improvement upon that of 1858, and deserves the commendation bestowed upon it. As regards professional education, the three-fold qualification is compulsory and placed under the supervision and control of the reformed Medical Council ; as regards the composition of the Council, the rising Victoria University embracing the flourishing colleges of Manchester, Liverpool and Leeds, will be represented, whereas the provincial schools previously had no voice in it ; but, above all, the profession will send five direct representatives to take part in its deliberations. The Medical Act of 1886 may well be regarded as a great triumph, virtually achieved by the Association, and will constitute a vantage ground whence further improvements may be accomplished. Twenty-eight years have gone, during which the Association has unceasingly laboured to improve the Medical Act of 1858, and the result is a victory which must exercise a powerful influence over our profession."

The further improvements here alluded to have not yet been obtained, and although in 1895 a Sub-Committee of the Parliamentary Bills Committee considered the question of preparing a Medical Act Amendment Bill, nothing practical came of it.

The representation of the licensing bodies on the Council so far from being diminished, has been increased. Owing to the creation of English and Irish Universities there are now twenty-eight representatives of those bodies, while the number of direct representatives of the profession remains fixed at six, though, owing to the representations of the Association, the Privy Council has consented to the appointment of an additional Direct Representative at the next election in 1933. Those bodies such as the Colleges of Physicians and Surgeons, which only grant their lowest qualifications in conjunction, are still separately represented, although for qualifying purposes the conjunction may be considered as one body. We are farther than ever from the goal of " one portal of entrance " and from direct representation of the diplomates and licentiates of the Universities and Corporations.

THE CONSTITUTION OF THE BRITISH MEDICAL ASSOCIATION

IN compiling this section I have drawn freely on the articles contributed to *The British Medical Journal* by the late Dr. John C. MacVail and published in book form by the Association in June, 1924. Dr. McVail was in an exceptionally favourable position for the authorship of these articles, for he was a member of the Constitution Committee, and his contributions to its work were of solid value. He was firmly convinced of the necessity of reform ; yet at the same time his influence was cast on the side of moderation. It would be impossible to improve upon his account of the evolution of the Constitution, which, however, required condensation for the purpose of the present work.

CHANGES IN THE CONSTITUTION.

An Association of people so independent in outlook and in their daily work as are medical men was bound to have occasional disturbances of its equilibrium, which have happily turned out to be mere growing pains which have passed away and left the society stronger than before. On two occasions at least such disturbances have seemed likely to cause a disruption of the Association, or at best a serious secession, but on each occasion good sense and toleration have prevailed and the organisation has emerged from the struggle stronger and more united than before.

The first of these occasions was when the proposal was made to change the name from " Provincial " to " British." This change involved more than a name, for it connoted an expansion of the Association so as to include the Metropolis and, as the older members foresaw, it also meant the shifting, sooner or later, of the centre of gravity from the provinces to London.

Naturally the founder and his friends wished that Worcester should retain the proud position of cradle of the Association on sentimental grounds, while they feared that the inclusion of London might lead to a change in the character of the society from the inclusion of London physicians and surgeons who might swamp the provincial influence in the counsels of the Association, for it is to be remembered that one of the causes of its foundation had been dissatisfaction with the preponderating influence and pretensions of London medical and surgical institutions, and those concerned in their direction and management. Sir Charles Hastings gracefully yielded to the opinion of the majority as ascertained by a referendum, and the subsequent history of the Association has shown that its scope has been widened and not narrowed since the assumption of the more comprehensive title. At the same time the Council was rendered more truly representative.

The other occasion arose half a century later, when it had become apparent that the votes of the few members who took part in Annual Meetings could not be considered as representative of the whole constituency of the Association, and, in consequence, after considerable time and trouble the present representative system was established. The spirit of the Association has thus shown itself to be not averse from change when change has been seen to be necessary, and we may with confidence foretell that the same spirit will lead to future changes when once again these are shown to be desirable.

In the original prospectus of the Provincial Association, which is given in full in an earlier chapter, it was stated that the Association was " to be managed by a President, two Secretaries, a Council and Branch Committees," but no details were given as to the mode of election of the Council. At the first inaugural meeting in Worcester a Council of 70 members was elected by the meeting, and at each Anniversary Meeting afterwards this number was increased by the election of local members at each place of meeting, so that the Council soon became of an unwieldy size, for no machinery was provided for the retirement of members of the Council. Officials of Branches were *ex-officio* members of Council, and as the number of Branches increased these swelled the numbers of the Council still more, so that by 1853,

74

when there were 1,853 members, the Council had swollen to a membership of 312.

In effect the Association was governed by the members living in and near Worcester, where the President and the two Secretaries lived, and where the *Journal* was published. In 1854, however, the publication of the *Journal* had been transferred to London, and at the meeting in Manchester in that year an attempt was made to regularise the position by passing the following resolution :—

" That the members of the General Council resident in and within twenty miles of Worcester be requested to act as an Executive Council, and to continue their services as hitherto in furtherance of the business of the Association, to which Executive Council the Editor of the *Journal* and the Secretary of the Association shall be responsible."

There had been signs during the previous two or three years that the members of the Association were not quite satisfied with the management of affairs, and that the rather informal arrangements which were adequate for the government of a small local association of a few were unsuited to a much wider spread society of over two thousand members. Accordingly the following resolution was proposed and carried :—

" That, in the opinion of this meeting, the representative principle ought to be fully adopted in the constitution of the governing Council, and that a Committee be appointed to examine, revise, alter and amend the laws of the Association, especially those relating to the members of the Council and the constitution of the Branches."

This Committee was also instructed to ascertain the opinion of each member of the Association on the whole of the changes recommended, and to report at least four weeks before the next Annual Meeting. The report is to be found in the *Journal* of May 5th, 1855. At the Annual Meeting held at York in that year there were animated discussions on the Report and on finance, and a proposal to change the name of the Association was defeated by 50 votes to 31. Sir Charles Hastings was re-elected President of the Council and Treasurer for life, and it was resolved that the Council should consist of the Officers of the Association and of members elected by the Branches, according to their size, those with less than thirty members being represented by their Presidents only, but those with over thirty having also their Secretaries on it, and for every twenty members beyond thirty there was to be an extra member. It was further proposed that the Annual Meeting should elect an additional member of Council for every twenty members not belonging to any Branch. The Council thus to be formed was to elect an Executive Council, to consist of two central officers, ten members of Council chosen by the Council and one Secretary from each Branch. This Executive Council could delegate its powers to any five members.

The proposal of an Executive Council shows that it was recognised that even as reformed the Council would be too unwieldy to be efficient.

A large majority of the members, however, who did not record their votes at York were still unsatisfied with this measure of reform, and also did not accept the vote on the proposed change of name as representing the real opinion of the majority of the 2,188 members. Several Branches sent in requisitions for a special general meeting for the reconsideration of these questions. This was summoned and at the same time the Council issued voting papers on the question of the proposed change of name, thus putting into practice the principle of the Referendum.

The Special Meeting was held at Birmingham in November, 1855, when Sir Charles Hastings announced that the voting papers returned showed a decisive majority in favour of the change of name, which expression of opinion he and the Council accepted frankly. There was some discussion as to whether the name should be British Medical Association or British Medical and Surgical Association. Dr. G. Webster, the former permanent President of the original British Medical Association, who had long been also a member of the Provincial Association, opposed the amendment that the longer title should be adopted, and the present name was decided on with only three or four dissentients. *The Lancet*, in commenting on this decision, stated that the older British Medical Association had "long ceased to exist."

Sir Charles Hastings himself proposed that at the next Annual Meeting the name should be changed, and further proposed that the principle should be adopted that "each member of the general body may have, by his representative, a voice in the management of affairs." Threats of resignation which had been made were thereupon withdrawn, and peace was restored. At the ensuing Annual Meeting in 1856, which also was held at Birmingham, a new code of laws was unanimously adopted, which has been summarised by Dr. John C. McVail as follows :—

1. Name, British Medical Association.

2. Council, excepting as to *ex-officio* members, to be elected solely by the Branches, one for every twenty members besides the Honorary Secretary of each Branch.

3. Every candidate for membership of the Association to be recommended by three members.

4. The Executive Council to be called the Committee of Council, and to have *no* power to delegate its functions to five members.

It is to be noted that the representation of members who did not belong to any Branch, which had been provided for a year before, was now abandoned. Nevertheless, the constitution thus established continued unaltered for twelve years.

During the six years 1868–1873 various alterations were made in the constitution of the Council and in the methods of representation of members unattached to Branches, details of which will be found in the Historical Survey of the Constitution and Government of the Association by Dr. McVail. These changes and proposals of change showed that there was a certain amount of dissatisfaction with the prevailing conditions among members, and in 1873 things seemed ripe for change. A sub-committee was appointed to prepare a complete code of laws and by-laws.

Accordingly, at the Annual Meeting held in London in that year, the Council announced that a proposal to register the Association as a limited company under the Companies' Acts had been under consideration, with a view to which revision of the laws was recommended. The incorporation was carried out in 1874, and at the Annual Meeting held at Norwich a Memorandum and Articles of Association were adopted, and the preparation of by-laws was entrusted to the above-named sub-committee. The members of Council became Directors, and the liability of a member was limited to one guinea should the Company at any time be wound up. Voting by proxy (as in other limited companies) was allowed, the proxy to be a member of the Association.

The weak point in this scheme, which in ensuing years become very obvious, was the fact that this Association, then having a membership of 6,000 and steadily increasing, was placed under the absolute control of the General Meeting, which was held in various parts of the country, in some cases remote, and of which the quorum was only twenty-five. In theory proxy voting might have acted as a counterweight, but in practice this did not occur. The Articles and By-laws may be read in Vol. II, page 121, of the *Journal* for 1874. The Council was to elect annually twenty members of its own body to act as the Committee of Council. Representation of the Branches was provided for, but did not give universal satisfaction, so that at the Jubilee Meeting, held in Worcester in 1882, it was resolved " That the Committee of Council be requested to consider in what way direct representation of Branches can best be secured."

The Committee of Council met quarterly, and was in practice the real governing body, except for the influence of the General Meeting. It appointed a special sub-committee to carry out the inquiry enjoined on it by the above resolution. Its report was considered by the whole Council at Birmingham in 1883. The Council adopted various recommendations as to the representation of Branches, which involved the formation of a new governing and representative body elected " directly " by the representatives—one for each Branch. It also recommended that the travelling expenses of the elected representatives should be paid by the parent Association, but this was negatived by the General Meeting at Liverpool in 1883. A lengthy by-law was adopted detailing the method of election and the powers and duties of the Council, which, it was decreed,

" shall manage the general affairs and business of the Association, except as otherwise provided by the articles or by-laws."

As Mr. Wheelhouse, President of Council, said at Belfast in 1884 : " Instead of having a proportion of members of Committee of Council elected by the Annual Meeting they were electing a larger number of Branch representatives, and the Branch representatives would henceforth take the government of the Association more largely into their own hands."

The constitution remained unchanged until 1896, when once more it became evident to many members that it was not entirely suited to the needs of the day. This feeling of dissatisfaction with the organisation of the profession led to the calling of an Extraordinary General Meeting at Birmingham in 1896, preliminary to the Annual Meeting at Carlisle, when Sir Willoughby Wade and Dr. Ward Cousins brought forward a resolution which led to the appointment of a Constitution Committee, whose Report was submitted to the Annual Meeting in 1897, which (*B.M.J.*, 1897, Vol. II, p. 302) referred it back to the Council for reference to the Branches and to a reformed Constitution Committee. The result of this reference to the Branches was that only eighteen of them replied and only one of these approved of the Committee's first resolution, which proposed that unattached members should have votes for Branch representatives on the Council. This demonstration of lack of interest of the Branches led to the subject being dropped for a time, with the approval of the Annual Meeting at Edinburgh in 1898.

A year later the question of constitutional reform was brought to the front again, by a movement which originated outside the ranks of the Association. In 1899 the Medical Guild of Manchester, largely on the initiative of Dr. Samuel Crawshaw, of Ashton-under-Lyne, called a Conference of delegates from societies and associations of general practitioners throughout the country. The Guild was only one of a considerable number of local medical societies which sprang up in the late 'nineties and early this century, societies which had for their main objects the discussion of medico-ethical and medico-political matters, which it was felt were not receiving from the Association the attention they deserved. The objects of the conference were :—

1. The promotion of greater adhesion and better organisation of general practitioners.

2. The provision of opportunities for meeting and for discussion of all matters concerning their welfare.

3. The exertion of their influence on public opinion.

4. The provision of machinery whereby the advantages of an annual conference might be secured to the profession.

These objects were to a great extent the same as those which Sir Charles Hastings and his friends had in view when they founded the Provincial Association, and it was obvious that there was a grave danger of the proposed conference leading to the formation of a rival society, and all the evils of disunion of the profession and loss of the Association's power to impress its views on the public and the Government. The feeling behind the Guild's action was one of dissatisfaction with the Association's record in the sphere of political and ethical work. The Conference was duly held, at which it was reported that fifty-four delegates representing the same number of medical bodies, including seven Branches of the Association as well as representatives of its Council, were present. The Conference sat for the first three days of May, 1900. The first speaker called upon was Mr. Victor Horsley, who, although he was not nor had he been a general practitioner, held strong views upon medical reform. His reputation as a surgeon and a physiologist does not here concern us, but his character as a man had a strong influence on the development of the Association. Horsley was an enthusiast, and whatever opinions he held, whether on experiments on animals, on total abstinence or medical reform, he held them very strongly, and it was difficult for him to realise that those who differed from him were actuated by as honourable motives as he was himself. His impressive personality, his untiring energy and his radicalism, tempered with a strong belief in constitutional methods, made him the great driving force in the movement, just as Dr. Smith Whitaker was the chief draughtsman who put Horsley's principles into practical form in resolutions. On this occasion Horsley criticised the

British Medical Association and the General Medical Council, and urged amendment of the Medical Acts. Various grievances of the profession and defects in the protection afforded by the Medical Acts to the public, as well as public health questions, were debated on the first two days of the meeting, but the important part of the work of the Conference was done on the third day. The Secretary to the Conference Committee, Dr. Crawshaw, of Ashton-under-Lyne, despaired of the Association as incapable of adequate reform, and proposed three resolutions designed to secure the appointment of local associations whose delegates should meet annually at a conference *at which only medico-ethical and medico-political topics should be discussed and voted upon,* and the election of a Central Executive Committee elected for three years, one-third to retire annually.

Dr. Crawshaw voiced the feelings of a good many who had gone to the Conference more than half prepared to set up a new body. Dr. Smith Whitaker, afterwards so prominent as the first Medical Secretary of the Association, was one of these.

No reference was made to the British Medical Association in these resolutions, and this was pointed out by Dr. Alfred Cox, of Gateshead, who effectively argued the case for reform within the Association. The following resolutions were passed, which embody substantially the proposals of Dr. Cox :—

" That this Conference is of opinion

(1) That the present need in medical organisation is concentration ;

(2) That the multiplication of associations other than those purely local is to be deprecated ;

(3) That the size, position and wealth of the British Medical Association make it the most suitable national medical organisation ; and

(4) That the efforts of all medico-ethical and similar associations and of the Conference should be directed to the conversion of the British Medical Association into an energetic body really representative of the majority of the members of the profession."

Subsequent events have fully justified these resolutions.

Dr. Cox's subsequent services to the profession and the Association as Medical Secretary and in other capacities are well known, but none of these can equal in value and importance that which he rendered when at Manchester in 1900 he introduced proposals and led the movement which prevented the disruption of the Association and the evil results which must have ensued, while at the same time he supported the projects of reform which the advocates of secession desired.

The Council of the Association were no doubt spurred by the discussions at Manchester, as well as their own sense of the dangers and difficulties inherent in a constitution under which twenty-five members at a perhaps remote Annual Meeting could dictate the policy of the whole or change its constitution. They therefore proposed a scheme which would have strengthened their hands, by ensuring that out of one hundred members three-fourths would be elected by the Branches. The new Articles of Association which were proposed would have placed the power of deciding the policy and constitution of the Association in the hands of a Council thus rendered more genuinely representative, instead of in the Annual Meeting. This scheme, however, did not provide for the localisation of meetings of members throughout the country for medico-political purposes, which the Manchester Conference had desired. The local unit was still to be the Branch, and the Branches, generally speaking, covered too much ground for busy practitioners to be able to attend their meetings regularly. Moreover, at a Branch Meeting, as Dr. McVail says, "the subjects discussed were mainly clinical or scientific. . . . Medical politics and medical ethics, questions of contract practice, abuse of hospital charities, the conditions of Poor-Law and other such matters, would not bulk so prominently as in gatherings of a dozen or a score of men working in a single town and its immediate neighbourhood. It is doubtful, indeed, whether the members of Council throughout the United Kingdom realised the strength of feeling behind the Manchester movement, even if they had read in the *Journal* the account of that three days' conference." The Council submitted the new Articles to an Extraordinary General Meeting held in Exeter Hall, London, on July 18th, 1900. The President, Dr. Ward Cousins, of Portsmouth, was in the Chair, and 270 members

82

attended. Much dissatisfaction was caused owing to members not having realised that legally no amendments could be put as the meeting was called to adopt or reject the proposed Articles. Although Dr. Roberts Thomson, of Bournemouth, pointed out that the object of the proposal was to throw the responsibility back upon the Branches, who could advise the Council, and that the new Articles could be rescinded in a year's time, the Meeting would have none of them. Mr. Victor Horsley attacked the President and the Council and the proposed Articles. It was, moreover, pointed out that the unattached members, who amounted to forty per cent. of the Association, would be left disfranchised, except at the Annual Meeting. Drastic reorganisation was clearly needed. On a show of hands the resolution in favour of the proposed Articles was declared to be lost. Thus ended the Council's scheme of reform from within itself.

At the next Annual Meeting at Ipswich soon afterwards Mr. Victor Horsley brought forward the following resolution :—

" That a Committee be appointed to consider and report upon the best means of reorganising the constitution of the British Medical Association, such Committee to furnish a provisional report to the Branches by March 1st, 1901." (*British Medical Journal*, 1900, Vol. II, pp. 224-321.)

This resolution was carried unanimously, and a Committee of 24 was appointed, half of whom were elected by the meeting and the remainder by the Council. It was also resolved :—

" That the Committee be invited to consider and report upon the question of delegation in their deliberations, but that they be not instructed that they must evolve such a principle."

A thoroughly representative Committee was elected, including *ex-officio* the President and President-Elect. At the first meeting of the Committee Mr. Edmund Owen, Surgeon to St. Mary's Hospital, was elected Chairman. At the first meeting Mr. Victor Horsley proposed that the local Medical and Medico-Ethical Societies throughout the Kingdom should be affiliated as Branches of the Association. This not very practical suggestion was put aside in favour of a suggestion by Dr. Smith Whitaker, of Yarmouth, which Mr. Horsley adopted. The first resolution then stood thus :—

" That the primary unit of the Association should be such that every member thereof shall have a reasonable opportunity of attending every important meeting."

This was a fundamental resolution, and its adoption paved the way for the whole scheme of reform. The first decision that the area covered by the unit should correspond to a parliamentary constituency was, however, rescinded in favour of smaller districts—the present Divisions.

Another radical reform was the result of the resolution moved by Dr. Brown Ritchie, of Manchester :—

" That every member of the Association be *ipso facto* a member of the unit in whose area he resides."

These members, unattached to any Branch, took no interest in the local affairs of the Branches, although some of them may have shown interest in the politics of the Association as a whole. They got their money's worth in the form of the *Journal* for their annual subscriptions of one guinea each, and though they may have wanted the paper originally for its scientific contents only, its perusal could not fail in very many cases to arouse interest in medical politics and create a wholesome public spirit.

Formerly subscriptions to Branches had been quite apart from the annual subscription to the Association, and the amount of a Branch subscription was fixed by each Branch. The Constitution Committee, on the motion of Dr. Whitaker, resolved :—

" That the subscription be uniform and inclusive, and the necessary working expenses of Branches and other sub-divisions be defrayed out of the general funds of the Association."

It was further recommended that the primary units should be called Divisions, and the groups of units, Branches.

The crucial question which divided the Committee the most was that of the relative powers to be given to the new form of Annual Meeting, which has now become the Representative Meeting and the Council.

Those who were in sympathy with the views expressed by the Manchester Guild meeting, such as Dr. Cox, Mr. Horsley and Dr. Smith Whitaker, desired to place the direction of policy in the hands of the Representative Meeting, while the older and more conservative members of Council on the Committee wished that the Council should retain the power of direction. Issue was joined over the following resolution, which Dr. Whitaker submitted:—

" *Political and Ethical Work.*—That the work of the Association in maintaining the honour and interests of the medical profession, apart from that carried on in the Branches and Divisions, be conducted by the Council and other executive bodies (if any) in accordance with the competent decisions of an Annual Meeting of representatives of the Divisions."

The important part of this resolution was in its latter part. After much discussion, which included a suggestion of winding up the Company and obtaining a Charter in place of registration under the Acts, this important motion was carried by 10 votes to 5. Thus the Council was no longer to be administratively supreme, but only executively, the Representative Meeting being the governing body in maintaining the honour and interests of the profession. The general and sectional scientific meetings were to remain under the sole charge of the Council.

The composition of the Council was to be fixed not by Articles but by By-laws.

Dr. Roberts Thomson proposed a resolution which, regarded as a constitutional safeguard, reconciled some of those who were apprehensive of the possible results of the new recommendations by providing machinery for a referendum to the members at large. It ran as follows :—

" Provided also that the Council in any case where it is of opinion that any resolution adopted by the Annual General Business Meeting or Delegate (that is, Representative) Meeting does not properly represent the wishes of the Association, shall at any time within four months from the adoption thereof refer such resolution, accompanied by such observations as the Council may think desirable, to the consideration of special meetings of all the Divisions, and that in that case the said resolution shall not be valid and binding except it be approved by a majority of the members of the Association present and voting in the said special meetings of the Divisions."

In the words of Dr. McVail, who was a member of the Constitution Committee, " It is to be observed that in this resolution the question to be considered by the Council in determining to resort to a referendum was not the welfare but the wishes of the Association. Where the Council was the dominant power it needed no referendum. Political and ethical work belonged to the Representative Meeting, and whatever doubts the Council might have as to welfare, it could not intervene, the question being not whether the meeting was right, but whether it represented the wishes of the Association."

The referendum principle had been acted on before with good effect when the question of a change of name had become acute, although there was no provision made for it in the original simple organisation. As now embodied in one of the Articles of Association of a Limited Company, it has only once been called into action, namely, in the year 1907.

The Committee discussed the question as to the minimum membership of a Branch. This was a difficult matter owing to the tremendous differences in density of population in different parts of the Kingdom and Empire. Ultimately, by By-law 21 it was enacted that a Branch or group of Branches should have one Council representative for the first 200 members, another for the next 200, and after that one additional member of Council for every 600. Branches in the United Kingdom with less than 200 members would be grouped, unless in the opinion of the Council there were special conditions justifying separate representation. The quorum of the General Business Meeting was agreed to be 200, subject to Counsel's opinion. Article XXIII provided that the quorum be fixed by By-law, but should not be less than 100. Of the Representative Meeting, one-half of the number appointed to attend was to be a quorum. First-class travelling expenses for attendance at the Annual Representative Meeting were recommended.

Arrangements were made in many areas for meetings of Branches and groups of members to discuss this report

FRANCIS FOWKE,
General Secretary of Association, 1871–1902.

LORD ILKESTON,
M.D., F.R.C.P.,
PRESIDENT OF COUNCIL,
1884–1887 (THEN SIR
WALTER FOSTER, M.P.)

MRS. ELIZABETH GARRETT
ANDERSON, M.D. FIRST
WOMAN TO TAKE A
MEDICAL DIPLOMA IN
ENGLAND. FIRST WOMAN
MEMBER OF THE B.M.A.

of the Constitution Committee, and a considerable number were held, but the aggregate attendance at these meetings was only 2,000, although the membership of the Association in 1901 was 18,402.

The comments and criticisms sent in by these meetings were carefully considered, and some modifications of the details of the scheme were accordingly made.

The change most generally desired was that greater elasticity should be given to the mode of formation of Divisions, the boundaries of parliamentary constituencies being pronounced unsuitable to the local conditions of many districts. To limit the expense of meetings of the Representatives, the Committee recommended that the number of representatives should not exceed 300, and that this restriction should be made feasible by the combination of small divisions for the purpose of representation.

At the Annual Meeting of the Association held at Cheltenham in July, 1901, a resolution approving of the report of the Constitution Committee in general terms was passed. A Committee was appointed to prepare new Articles of Association and By-laws. Under the Companies' Acts the new Articles had to be approved at an Extraordinary General Meeting called for the purpose, by a three-fourths majority, and if so approved the decision must be confirmed by a bare majority at a subsequent meeting. The first of these meetings was held at Exeter Hall on June 18th, 1902. Although by law no amendments could be made, a very free discussion was allowed, at the end of which the resolution in favour of the new Articles was passed by 96 to 28, thus securing the necessary majority, but not with many votes to spare. A minority of 33 would have meant the defeat of the resolution and probable disruption of the Association. At the Confirmatory Meeting on July 9th, when 146 members were present, the necessary majority was secured and the new Articles of Association came into force. The By-laws could be altered at any time by a much simpler procedure.

Since the year 1902 many changes have been made, most of them dealing with matters of detail, but one of them has been of primary importance.

As previously stated, in 1907 the Council had resort to the referendum on two questions, namely, the

G

constitution and mode of election of the Central Council, and the question of the appointment of separate Finance and Journal Standing Committees. The Representative Meeting had resolved on a change in the election of the Council, namely, the appointment of twelve members by itself. The Council objected on the ground that such a change would take the management of affairs out of its hands and place it in that of the Representative Meeting. On referendum, the Council was defeated, so that it is now more than ever an executive instead of a legislative body. As to the two Committees, the separation of functions was agreed upon, and each Committee, as well as all other *Standing* Committees, has representatives elected both by the Council and the Representative Meeting.

The question of applying for a Royal Charter of Incorporation was discussed in the years 1907-1910, but after correspondence with the Privy Council it was decided to form a new company in order to carry out certain new powers, and this was carried through in 1924, without altering the essential Constitution of the Association.

To quote the *Annual Handbook* of the Association— " The Association is practically a federation of Local Medical Societies, called Divisions. Each Division has its own area, local administration and rules, subject only to such limitations as are deemed needful for the co-operation of all. The Divisions are linked together in the Association by the facts (*a*) that every member of a Division is a member of the Association, and conversely every member of the Association is a member of the Division in the area in which he or she resides ; (*b*) The whole Association is subject to the provisions of the Memorandum, Articles and By-laws. The Divisions are grouped together for certain administrative and scientific purposes into Branches."

The Council, therefore, instead of being a Parliament, is practically an executive committee, which carries on its work through sixteen standing committees and others appointed as may be required, meeting at headquarters in London, with the exception of the Scottish and Irish Committees, which meet in Edinburgh and Dublin respectively.

The Annual Representative Meeting in 1912, disquieted by the result of a recent action at law, instructed the Council to report on the desirability of the Association's becoming a registered trade union. The report, made in 1913, was unfavourable to the suggestion. The question was raised again in 1917 by a Local Medical and Panel Committee and again negatived.

After the failure of a large number of members to redeem their pledges in the Insurance dispute, some members thought that better discipline might be kept if the Association were constituted a trade union and the Council was instructed to report on this question.

Its Report appeared in 1913 (Supplement 13, Vol. I, p. 17, Appendix X). The following passages set forth the gist of it.

" . . . Dissatisfaction with the constitution of the Association and the demand for a medical trade union have undoubtedly received a strong impetus from the breakdown of the resistance of the profession in January last. But it may very seriously be questioned whether the form of the organisation of the profession had anything to do with that failure.

" Trade unions, after all, depend mainly on the loyalty of their members, and loyalty is a sentiment which differs greatly in strength in different people. A few will go to the stake for it, but in most people its strength largely depends on social and economic conditions. In a strike workmen often disobey their trade unions when they are either compelled to give in by privation, or are convinced that they have obtained all they are likely to get by the strike. In the same way it is obvious that large numbers of the medical profession in January last came to the conclusion either that the profession could not successfully resist the Government, or that the terms offered by the Government were good enough to be given a trial. It is extremely doubtful whether these practitioners could have been induced to refrain from putting their names on the panel by any imaginable form of organisation. Even if the Association had been a trade union offering financial support to its members who declined to accept service under the Act, it is probable that the non-members, together with those members who were never very strong in

89

their resistance, and those who were convinced that the Act would be beneficial to them, would have been sufficiently numerous to provide a service in many parts of the country.

" 16. It is open to serious doubt whether trade unionism as a form of organisation is suitable for the medical or indeed any profession. The strength of a trade union lies mainly in the following facts :—

(*a*) Its members generally work together in large groups, and it has never been found possible, for example, to form an effective trade union among agricultural labourers or other scattered workers. It is much easier to bring moral suasion to bear on a man who works in a mine or in a workshop, and whose comfort, if not his daily bread, depend on his making common cause with his fellows, than on one whose work must always remain largely an individual affair.

(*b*) Another great source of strength to a trade union lies in the benefits which it gives to its members ; the facts that a member loses all claim to these benefits if he leaves the union, and that he can be expelled from the union for disloyalty, undoubtedly go far to explain the adherence of trade unionists to their union, often in the face of great temptation.

It is doubtful whether this resource is available to the medical profession. The subscription to a medical trade union which professed to give benefits equivalent to those given by a trade union (out-of-work pay, strike pay, accident pay and death benefit) would have to be very considerable, and there is no evidence that members of the medical profession are willing to pay such subscriptions. Investigations into subscriptions paid by several trade unions show that the amounts paid by each member vary from one-fiftieth to one-eighteenth of the workman's total income, and, as was shown in a leading article in *The British Medical Journal* of April 5th, 1913, members of the London Society of Compositors, whose average weekly wage may, perhaps, be stated at 45*s*. per week, recently for a considerable period paid a subscription of 2*s*. 6*d*. per week ; that is to say, one-eighteenth of their total income.

(*c*) The final resort of the trade union, if unable to secure its objects by negotiation, is to proclaim a strike

90

and call its members out. This weapon is not available to the medical profession, and the same remark applies to many of the most effective methods of the trade unions which depend on what is euphemistically called ' moral suasion.' Not only are they not available, but they are repugnant to the great majority of the profession.

" 17. . . . There is no doubt that there is something superficially attractive about the idea of a trade union which has appealed very strongly to the members of a profession smarting under a sense of defeat, and ready to snatch at any course which seems to offer a guarantee against the repetition of such a collapse as recently occurred. . . . The Council has arrived at the conclusion that the formation of a medical trade union offers no such guarantee."

After the judgment against the Association in 1918 in what is known as the Coventry Libel Case, the question was again very carefully considered. The counsel consulted, one of whom was Mr. (now Sir) H. Slesser, then standing counsel to the Labour Party, were decidedly of opinion that even if the Association could be registered as a trade union it would be in no better position as to liability to pay damages than that in which the Association had found itself in the recent action.

No history of the evolution of the Constitution would be complete without reference to the subject of the admission of women to the membership. This question did not become prominent until 1875.

In the earlier rules and regulations of the Association nothing had been mentioned as to the sex of members, because it was assumed that all medical practitioners were male. Owing to a similar assumption, it was no doubt intended that in the By-laws of the Society of Apothecaries " persons " should not include females. That assumption, however, was successfully challenged in 1865 by Miss Elizabeth Garrett (afterwards Dr. Elizabeth Garrett Anderson), who then became a Licentiate, and in the following year obtained registration of her qualification by the General Medical Council. In 1870 she obtained the Diploma of Doctor of Medicine from the University of Paris.

The Articles of the Association in force in the early 'seventies contained no clause specifically ruling out the rights of women to membership. Any qualified person with a registrable diploma was eligible for membership.

Dr. Garrett Anderson, as she had then become, was elected a member by the Metropolitan Counties Branch in 1873, being the first woman to become a member. The same branch in the early 'seventies elected another lady, Mrs. Hoggan : these two ladies were elected under the By-laws existing before 1874, that is to say, before the Association was incorporated, and their election was looked upon at that time as valid.

At a special meeting of the Committee of the Council held on March 13th, 1878, a letter was read from Sir William Jenner threatening to resign in consequence of " Lady Members being permitted to attend the meeting of the Association " (Dr. Elizabeth Garrett Anderson is the one referred to in all the correspondence). The Committee of Council thereupon decided that women should *not* be admitted as members : and the consideration " of the privileges of Lady Members " was referred to a special meeting to be held in Birmingham on April 2nd, 1878. At this meeting, however, the consideration of the question was postponed, so that the Committee of the Council could take the opinion of counsel as to the rights of Lady Members and report to the Annual Meeting.

On March 21st, 1878, the South-Eastern Branch passed a resolution to the effect that the admission of women to membership was not desirable. The Edinburgh Branch reported that the introduction of women into the Association involved such fundamental changes that it was *ultra vires* of any Branch to admit women without the sanction of the general body. Similar resolutions were recorded from the North Wales and Reading Branches. In consequence of this opposition, on May 14th, 1878, a Sub-Committee *re* Election of Lady Members met to consider a series of questions " upon the privileges of Lady Members," which had been approved by the Solicitor (Mr. Upton). The following is a copy of the questions :—

" 1. Was the Metropolitan Counties Branch legally entitled to elect Lady Members under the By-laws existing previous to August, 1874 ?

2. Was Committee of Council legally entitled to elect Lady Members under the then By-laws existing in January, 1875 ?

3. How did the incorporation of the Association under the Companies' Acts interfere with the rights of ladies previously elected ?

4. Has the Association any power under Articles of Association to turn out the two existing Lady Members elected previous to the Incorporation ?

5. Has the Association any power under the Articles of Association to restrict the rights of the two existing Lady Members ?

6. Has the Association any power under Articles of Association to pass By-laws prohibiting the election of ladies in future ?

6A. Has the Association any, if so what, power to alter its Articles of Association, so as to enable the Association to make a By-law prohibiting the election of ladies in future?

7. Has the Association any powers under the Articles of Association to prevent Branches from electing ladies ?

8. Have they power under the Articles of Association to prevent their election, except by unanimous vote, or by a majority of four-fifths, whilst men may be elected by a bare majority ? "

The questions were submitted to the Solicitor, with instructions to refer them to Mr. Bosanquet, of the Oxford Circuit, for settlement. Then, as settled, to Mr. Benjamin, Q.C. The Committee of Council, on July 10th, 1878, approved a report of the foregoing Sub-Committee, which contained counsel's opinion and categorical answers to the above questions. The following is a synopsis of counsel's opinion dated July 3rd, 1878 :—

" Counsel advised that Dr. Garrett Anderson as a member of the old unincorporated Association, is a member of the incorporated Association ; but that Mrs. Hoggan, whose election took place *after* the incorporation of the Association at a period when no election could be legally made is *not* now a member of the Association."

Counsel answered Question 1 by stating that Mrs. Garrett Anderson "is undoubtedly a member of the Association."

No persons, male or female, presumed to have been elected between October 21st, 1874, and August 3rd, 1875, were really elected, as no powers of election were in existence during that period. It was pointed out that the Committee of Council could pass a resolution declaring elected all the *male* persons who were elected by it, or by any Branch Council, during the interval between the incorporation of the Association and August 3rd, 1875, whose election was invalid on account of there being no provision then in existence for the election of members. The Committee of Council on October 9th, 1878, thereupon passed a resolution legalising the election of all male persons who had been elected during the interval between the incorporation of the Association and August 3rd, 1875, whose election was declared invalid owing to there being no provision (then) for the election of members. At Bath in 1878 a new clause declaring that " No female shall be eligible for election as a member of the Association " was adopted after a plebiscite in which 3,072 voted for and 1,051 against. At Nottingham, in 1892, the words " No female shall be eligible for election," etc., were expunged, and thereafter women have continued to be elected, and there has been perfect equality between the sexes in the Association.

The Representative Body decided in 1907 " that the principle that no distinction be made on the grounds of sex, as regards the amount of the emoluments to be paid to lady practitioners be affirmed by the meeting," and in 1914 " that the salaries paid to medical women be the same as those paid to men." Since 1907 the Association has done much work in championing the cause of equality as between the sexes in regard to all medical appointments.

As a matter of history, it may be interesting to record that Mrs. Garrett Anderson (then Miss Garrett) was the first woman to receive a medical diploma in England. She took the L.S.A. in 1865 and the M.D. of Paris in 1870, being the first woman graduate in that university. The first English woman to obtain a medical degree was Miss Elizabeth Blackwell, of Bristol, who graduated M.D. in the University of Geneva in New York State, U.S.A., in 1849. Upon returning to England she was able to get her name on the first British Register published in 1858. Miss Garrett was the next to appear in 1866. She married in 1871 and adopted the surname " Anderson."

94

THE ASSOCIATION AND THE POOR LAW

AT the Annual Meeting held at Oxford in July, 1835, the subject of the new Poor Law and its effects on the poor and on the medical profession was raised by Mr. Griffiths, of Hereford, who proposed that a Committee be appointed in accordance with the recommendation contained in the report of the Council, to consider the best means of affording medical relief to the sick poor, and more especially with reference to the operation of the new Poor Law Act. The resolution was carried unanimously, and thus the first shot was fired in the long drawn out battle between the medical profession and the bureaucrats and Guardians, in which the Association championed not only the rights of the general practitioner, but also the best interests of the sick poor.

The chief allegations made at this meeting were that many Boards of Guardians, having in view almost exclusively the pecuniary interests of the ratepayers, were anxious to simplify their arrangements and adopt the smallest possible expense ; that in their endeavours to do so they necessarily legislated on medical subjects to the great detriment of the sick poor, and that the power to decide on the necessity of medical relief was left in a marked way to the discretion of non-medical officers. Another great cause of just complaint was the practice in some Unions of dividing them into districts of great extent, comprehending many parishes and a large population, all confided to one medical officer, thereby placing him at a distance from the sick. Delay in attendance must necessarily follow, and danger in illness had thereby been increased.

Moreover, in some Unions a charge per case had been adopted at the very low rate of 2s. 6d., varying a little to 3s. 6d., according as the number of cases in the parish per annum diminished: a "case" implying any description of illness and of whatever length short of six months, or any accident requiring surgical attention—midwifery excepted : these terms being pressed upon the practitioners by threats of the introduction of young adventurers, fresh from the medical schools.

To realise the enormity of the parsimony and inhumanity of such Guardians it must be observed that the charge of 2s. 6d. was a charge per sick person requiring immediate treatment and not a charge per head of all paupers, sick and well. It is therefore not to be compared even with the contract rate of friendly societies, and still less with the 11s. per patient on the panel of our days.

At the next Annual Meeting of the Association held in Manchester in July, 1836, the Report of the Poor Law Committee thus elected was read, and it was resolved that it be immediately printed and published in a separate form and circulated. This Report became and long remained authoritative on this subject.

It was further resolved that a petition stating the evils arising out of the Poor Law Amendment Act as regards medical relief and praying for redress should be immediately presented to both Houses of Parliament.

The Report, which occupies thirty-six pages of Vol. V of the *Transactions*, fully bears out the allegations made at the Oxford Meeting. The following passages are deserving of reproduction :—

" To refuse help to those who in the time of absolute need and destitution apply to the authorities for medical relief, or to delay it by interposing unnecessary distance and official impediments between the patient and the advice he seeks ; or to supply it from an inferior or a distrusted source, and all this under the specious plea that the poor must be driven by these obstacles and this second-rate relief *to depend on their own resources*, constitutes a theory and practice deserving only of universal reprobation. . . .

" The office of parish surgeon should combine the highest qualifications of the medical body, it being clear that no professional responsibility whatever, public or private, equals it in variety or extent. It embraces and presents in daily profusion cases in medicine, surgery and midwifery, requiring as profound knowledge and diligent care as any public institution affords for each of these

96

branches singly. *It should unite, therefore, an acute percep-tion of the incipient stages of disease with well-directed efforts for its prevention* accompanied by the most diligent and scientific treatment."

The words italicised seem almost prophetic in their wisdom. Sir James Mackenzie took the same point of view, and urged the same argument in speaking of the rôle of the general practitioner in our own time.

A Committee formed at Warwick in 1827 had pointed out that somewhat similar abuses existed under the old Poor Law, such as sweating of the medical profession. Its report stated :—

" In these transactions there is often such a total disregard for fairness and so entire and evident a sacrifice of the well-doing of the sick poor, that parishes contain-ing five or six hundred paupers have been taken for five or six pounds ; twenty or thirty parishes have been farmed by one practitioner, and even a large parish actually farmed for one guinea per annum."

The Committee (of the Association) thus dwelt on the evils of the former system, not merely because they had been so frequently lost sight of in recent observations and remarks on the subject, but because they had evidently been the source of the more numerous and flagrant abuses which prevailed at the time of reporting.

This Report did not mince matters. It stated plainly that it appeared :—

" that hardly had the New Law come into action, when a prejudice was conceived by its administrators against the medical profession, and although they were neces-sarily and totally unacquainted with the various bearings of this important subject, not less than with the best mode of effecting an alteration, yet in general they distrusted and sternly resisted the suggestions of those who alone were able to assist them, viz., the medical practitioners. Nothing is more clearly borne out by the evidence your Committee has collected than this circum-stance ; though it is gratifying to them to state that in *some Unions* and in the sphere of operation of *some Assistant Commissioners*, a more conciliatory spirit has been evinced."

The Report further gives instances of cases in which Boards of Guardians had evinced a desire to meet the fair demands of the professional body, and in these cases it had almost invariably happened that the Assistant Commissioners on the Central Board had refused to ratify the appointments made.

The degrading system of tender by candidates for Poor Law medical posts was emphatically condemned by the Committee.

In addition to the grievances complained of at the last Annual Meeting, some Boards of Guardians had introduced a new one, viz., the institution of medical clubs " intended to provide medical relief for two classes of the poor : the independent labourer and the pauper. The Assistant Commissioners in Essex, Gloucestershire, etc., proposed ' Clubs ' of this kind." At Epping " the Guardians were to have the privilege of adding to the pauper schedule any name they might think proper, during the contract, paying only at the same rate as for those originally included." As the Committee remarked, such Clubs were entirely different from the recently established Medical Clubs, which had nothing to do with pauperism. If and when such clubs were established by the Guardians, wholesale abuse of the rates would be certain to follow until a position might have been reached such as was to be found in Ireland in later years, where in many places all the population below the gentry were the recipients of gratuitous medical treatment through the Poor Law Medical Officers, who were thus robbed of a considerable part of the income which they ought to have received.

The evils of too large medical districts may be exemplified by one case quoted in the Report :—

" In the Wheatenhurst Union comprehending *fourteen* parishes and necessarily much travelling, the Commissioners induced the Guardians to waive a contract with the established practitioners and to engage *one* young man from the schools who had neither a horse nor instruments."

It is noteworthy that in this case, as well as many others, the authorities in London, probably actuated by doctrinaire theories, were even worse sweaters than the Guardians on the spot, who considered their own and their friends' pockets.

98

But if the treatment of the profession by the Poor Law Authorities was scandalous, the treatment of the poor was even more so.

Sick paupers had in many cases to go long distances to the Relieving Officer and then to the Medical Officer, should the former in his wisdom think the case a fit one for medical relief. "In those Unions where a payment per case had been adopted the Relieving Officer had a stronger inducement to refuse an Order than when a contract at a fixed sum existed, because by so doing he saved the parish money. Several instances have occurred where a disorder, in its incipient stage, has been denied medical aid, because the Relieving Officer thought the illness not sufficiently serious for attendance. Protracted disease, or death, has occasionally been the consequence."

After complaining of the indignities often put upon medical officers by Boards of Guardians, "Lastly," the Report states, "those medical men who have presumed to express an opinion unfavourable to the new medical arrangements, have frequently been marked for oppression by the authorities, and some have even been induced to withdraw or withhold their names from petitions to Parliament against the system, from apprehensions of injurious consequences to themselves."

As regards remedies for the abuses complained of, the Committee confessed that it was very difficult to suggest any, but they plainly stated one great principle that should be observed in future legislation on the subject, namely, that the remuneration should not be determined between the interested parties, one of which was interested in reducing it below par and the other in raising it above par. A third party should be called in and the scale of remuneration fixed by legislative enactment. The Committee also recommended the separation of charges for drugs from those for professional services, and that wherever it was possible a Dispensary should be fitted up for the supply of medicine to the sick paupers of all the parishes within a reasonable distance, at their joint expense, while the medical officers should be paid only for the duties which they performed, viz., for attendance, with a graduated charge for journeys, according to the distance and the number of patients.

It will appear from the above that the chief recommendations of the Committee were in principle identical with the arrangements made under the Insurance Act nearly three-quarters of a century later. They were manifestly right in saying, in conclusion, that a more intricate and important subject could scarcely have been submitted to their consideration.

A second Report of the Poor Law Committee of the Association was made to the Anniversary Meeting at Cheltenham in 1837, and published in Vol. VI of the *Transactions*. The most important recommendation was the following :—

That there should be a general professional superintendence of the whole body of Union Medical Officers by a Poor Law Medical Board, or by one or more Poor Law Commissioners, exercising powers similar to those with which the heads of the Army and Navy Medical Departments were invested.

The Committee, in a spirit of prophecy, looked forward with hope to a period when a *Poor Law Medical Board* might form a section of a grand *National Board of Health*. Many things were to happen, and generations were to pass away, before we, the successors of those committeemen, were to see this prevision fulfilled by accomplished fact.

They repeated their former recommendation that the provision of medicines should be separated from that of medical attendance, and they strongly recommended the entire abolition of the system of determining the amount of remuneration by " Tenders." The form and amount of remuneration came in for much discussion, which settled down into the recommendation of payment by salary based on a certain percentage of the poor rate in each parish. The ratepayers in each parish should elect their own medical officer. A Petition to Parliament embodying these opinions in the name of the Association was signed by the President.

Dealing with the profession itself, the Poor Law Committee says (*Transactions*, Vol. V, p. 31, 1837) :—

" Your Committee are led, by present occurrences, to regret the want of some general discipline, some presiding influence over the members of our profession : an influence which is exercised in every profession except

the medical. It is true that a higher standard of qualification would ultimately accomplish the desired end ;
but, in the meantime, something should be done to
check the wretched spirit of rivalry and speculation,
the under-bidding, and the jobbing, which unfortunately are but too frequently to be found among medical
men.

"The prospect which this Association holds out is
almost the only one upon which we can at present look
with satisfaction and hope.

*   *   *   *

"But your Committee cannot omit some notice of the
inconsiderate encouragement which a few of the Lec-
turers in the London Schools have given to these dis-
reputable proceedings, by recommending their pupils to
avail themselves of the openings afforded by the altered
arrangements in parishes ; and by supplying the Poor
Law Commissioners with lists of names from which to
select fit and pliant instruments for their purposes. The
difficulty of making a successful stand against the
oppression and degradation under which the medical
body are now suffering, will hardly be wondered at, when
it is remembered that we have influential traitors in our
camp."

In 1842 a special Report of the Poor Law Committee
of the Association was published, in which, while congratulating the profession on the measure of success
attained, they discussed the *general medical regulations
and explanatory circular* issued by the Poor Law Commissioners and recommended by the President of the
Royal College of Surgeons. The following reforms were
welcomed :—

"Tenders " for medical attendance were now abolished (but it was regretted that the Guardians were
still left at liberty to fix the price of medical duties
without reference to any fixed scale or any principle of
computation).

Qualifications in both medicine and surgery were
henceforth to be required of candidates for union appointments.

The regulations as to maximum areas of districts were
an improvement, but still subject to criticism. Some
areas were much too large.

The Committee urged their objections to the still recognised practice of contracting for medical services.

A Government Bill for amending the new Poor Law was promised to be introduced shortly, and the Committee hoped that the result would be satisfactory if the *principle* on which salaries were to be calculated was to be determined by Parliament.

The attitude of mind of the Poor Law Commissioners may well be judged from a passage in their *Eleventh Annual Report*, which ran as follows :—

" In fixing this amount (of salary of the Medical Officers of Poor Law Unions) it is necessary that we should keep in view the value at which the services of a medical man are attainable for the purpose under the existing circumstances of the profession."

In a leading article on this Report, *The Provincial Medical and Surgical Journal* for October 29th, 1845, quoted with approval from *The London Medical Gazette* a passage which applied the *argumentum ad hominem* to the Commissioners, and expressed the belief that were this same system adopted in the selection of Assistant Poor Law Commissioners, many *competent* men would be found willing to discharge the duties of that office for one-half the salary at that time attached to it.

A lurid light is thrown upon the conditions of medical relief in Scotland by a Report on the Medical Relief to the Parochial Poor of Scotland under the old Poor Law by Dr. Alison, read by Dr. C. Taylor before the Section of Statistics of the British Association for the Advancement of Science in September, 1846. The information given in the Report may be summarised as follows :—

" An Association of medical practitioners had been formed in Edinburgh in 1845 to collect information on the subject, from whose investigation it appeared that in Edinburgh there was no provision for medical relief from the Poor Funds, except for the indoor paupers of the City Workhouse. Previous to 1815, no assistance was ever given to the sick poor at home ; and though since that period the duty had been gratuitously undertaken by the officers of several dispensaries, it had not been effectually or regularly performed. In the Canongate, the dispensary aid to the poor came to a sudden close in the midst of the late epidemic fever, in consequence of the death of one of the medical officers who had acted as treasurer. By the recent Act 10 duly qualified and paid officers have been appointed to take charge of the sick paupers in the different districts. In Glasgow relief has been given by paid medical attendants for some years. Returns were obtained from 40 towns, exclusive of Edinburgh and Glasgow, from which it appeared that in 16 of these towns there was absolutely no *requited* medical relief, either from the public authorities or from voluntary subscriptions. In 4 an occasional payment, never exceeding a few shillings, had been made on special occasions. In Campbelltown £10 was allowed to the professional men during the epidemic fever. In Kirkintilloch a similar sum was given, but by a private individual. In Dundee during the same fever £5 was allowed to 6 dispensary surgeons. In some other places £2 was given to a surgeon, and in others a small allowance was made for drugs. In anticipation of the new Poor Law, £10 has been allowed annually for medical relief in Alloa ; in Dunbar £6 6s., but this includes the supply of drugs ; in Dunfermline £20 a year not including drugs ; in Greenock £25 per annum has been paid to each of 3 district surgeons ; in Kilmarnock £10 each to 3 surgeons ; in Wick £15 is divided between 2 surgeons ; in Dumfries £10 to 1 surgeon. The unrequited medical labour is stated by 25 gentlemen, and ranges from £5 to £220 annually in value, giving an average of £40 per year. But this is not the only tax levied on the charitable feelings of medical men. In 90 per cent. of the cases they had to furnish wine, food, etc., out of their own substance, and in 33 of the 40 towns brought under review no change has been made in this system. Passing over the returns of infirmaries and dispensaries supported by voluntary contributions as rather imperfect, we come to the medical relief in the rural districts. The number of returns made amounts to 325. Out of these 94 have received some remuneration, but only 39 annually. Of these 39, only 13 have received sums above £5 ; 26 above £1 and less than £5 ; and nine £1 or under. Ten are paid by the bounty of private individuals, and of these one is paid £60 by a nobleman, and another £40 by a landed proprietor ; both, however, have the charge of extended districts, and as there is no fund on which they can draw for drugs or necessaries, there are large drawbacks to be made from the remuneration. Twenty-three have received gratuities for their services, chiefly during the prevalence of epidemics. In one case this gratuity amounted to £20 ; in 14 it was under £5 ; in two cases it was only 3s. In one of these cases this 3s. was the only remuneration for 12 years' attendance on paupers, averaging 70 constant and 13 occasional patients ; in the other, the 3s. was a remuneration for passing paupers of other parishes, and *nothing was allowed for 21 years of attendance on resident paupers*, averaging 44 constant on the district roll. Two hundred and eleven, or above 60 per cent., have never received any remuneration of any kind for their professional attendance on the parochial poor, or for the drugs which they have deemed it necessary to supply to them ; and 208 add that they have had occasion to give wine, food, etc., out of their own limited funds, and that they had occasion to defray all travelling expenses when they made distant visits. One hundred and thirty-six have estimated the money value of the unrequited labour which they have bestowed on the parochial poor ; it amounts to £34,447 annually, or an average of £283 each. The complaints of inattention to sick paupers by the parochial authorities are all but universal ; and when applications were made for the repayment of different outlays they were almost invariably refused. It was stated that since the abstract presented to the British Association had been compiled, several additional returns had been obtained, but they in no degree tend to weaken the general impression likely to be produced by the preceding statement, and it was therefore deemed unnecessary to tabulate them."

This Report has been here quoted at length, not because it very directly concerns the history of the Association, but because it includes much independent and detailed evidence as to the scandalous manner in which the benevolence of the profession was abused, and because it was prepared not for an audience of inevitably biassed medical men, but for an assemblage of critical statisticians. It bears out, as concerns Scotland, statements made in the Report of the Committee of the Provincial Medical and Surgical Association.

More than thirty years afterwards Scottish Poor Law Medical Officers still had grievances. At the Annual Meeting of the Association in 1875 the following resolution was passed in the Section of Public Medicine :—

" That, in the opinion of this Section, the interests of the sick poor in Scotland would be furthered, and the system of parochial relief would be placed on a more satisfactory footing if the following measures of reform were adopted universally throughout Scotland ; namely, that the cost of medicines be supplied by every parochial board, exclusive of the salary of the medical officer ; that medical officers be removable from office by the Board of Supervision only ; that the parochial board be required to superannuate such officers ; and that the parliamentary grant in aid of medical relief be placed on the same footing as in England and Wales."

It was resolved by the meeting that an influential Committee be appointed, of which Dr. Matthews Duncan was appointed Chairman, to carry out the resolution of the Public Medicine Section referring to the system of poor relief in Scotland, with power to add to their number.

A meeting of Medical Officers of Poor Law Unions, with a view to an amelioration of the present system of Poor Law relief, was held on Wednesday, October 28th, 1847, at the Hanover Square Rooms, London, in which about 200 medical men took part. The Secretary stated that meetings of medical practitioners had previously been held in various parts of the country to discuss this subject.

The first resolution, which was carried unanimously, was to the effect :—

" That the medical men charged with attendance on the poor are required to be thoroughly and practically acquainted with every branch of their profession ; that they are liable to be called at the shortest notice, and without assistance, to treat the severest forms of disease, and the most formidable injuries which every species of accident may produce, as well as to attend the most difficult and appalling cases which obstetric practice can present. That in the discharge of these duties

H 2

they have not only to contend with the anxieties inseparable from such weighty responsibility, but are brought into situations the most trying and repulsive, not only from the multiplied annoyances which attend them, but from concentrated contagion and other causes of disease, to which many of this valuable class of men have been victims ; that the sacrifice of time, labour and rest, which they are required to make, is great and unlimited ; and that the pecuniary expenses necessarily incurred in visiting their patients and supplying the means of relief are unavoidably heavy. That, in addition to these trials, inherent to their office, there are others of a moral character very liable to be concomitant with them, and of a kind most painfully to affect minds of a highly honourable and sensitive class, to which it is sufficient merely to allude. That the mode in which these services are required to be performed, and the scanty remuneration awarded to the medical men engaged in them, constitute a grievance which cannot be too strongly stated, and for which redress should earnestly be sought. That in so many instances the number of persons among whom the casualties of disease and accident may occur, and the area to be traversed in visiting the patients, are so great as to render early, constant and satisfactory attendance physically impossible. That the pecuniary remuneration being granted on no fixed principles or scale, varies greatly in different localities ; but that in almost all it is so disproportionally small, and in very many of them falls so far short of the expense incurred, as to render a large portion of the medical relief bestowed on the sick poor a tax on individual members of the medical profession, instead of resting like clothing, food, and other forms of relief, upon the rate-paying parishioners in general."

Many instances were quoted by the proposer and seconder in support of the resolution, which, though rather long-winded, beyond question truly represented the facts. A second resolution pointed out that the present system was in the long run uneconomical. The Commissioners, as Mr. Tasker, of Melbourne (Derbyshire), said, had in 1839 stated that the fixed remuneration for permanent paupers in rural districts should be such as to afford the practitioner 6s. or 6s. 6d. a case, to be

106

augmented if necessary up to 10s. But the Guardians disregarded the instructions of the Commissioners—in the Holborn Union the Guardians would not pay the medical officers for midwifery cases.

A Committee was appointed by this meeting to watch events and further the interests of Poor Law Medical Officers. This Committee and the Convention, as it was at first called, became the Poor Law Medical Officers' Association.

A deputation from the Committee had an interview with Mr. Buller, the Chairman of the Poor Law Commission, in April, 1848, and submitted 15 resolutions, which were received sympathetically, and a month later Sir George Grey received at the Home Office a similar deputation accompanied by representatives from the Royal College of Surgeons of England, the Society of Apothecaries, the Provincial Medical and Surgical Association, and the National Institute of Medicine, Surgery, and Midwifery (a short-lived body, long since defunct).

Sir George Grey, in reply to the arguments adduced by the deputation, stated that the question of expense was one subordinate to what was necessary to secure efficient medical relief, and said that he would confer with the President of the Poor Law Commission.

In February, 1849, Lord Ashley, who had been Chairman in 1844 of the Committee of the House of Commons on the subject of medical relief to the sick poor, presided over a meeting of the Convention of Poor Law Medical Officers, at which it was decided to present a petition to Parliament. Among other grievances it was pointed out that new sanitary duties had been imposed upon Poor Law Officers by the " Nuisance Removal and Diseases Prevention Act " without the provision of any remuneration. The celebrated Dr. Thomas Hodgkin, of Guy's Hospital, was appointed Chairman of the Committee ; Mr. Thomas Martin, of Reigate, Treasurer ; and Mr. F. J. Lord, of Hampstead, Secretary.

In 1850 a Bill was introduced into Parliament, designed to provide for the payment of superannuation allowances to officials of Unions, but excluding medical officers on the ground (so it was said) that they were part-time officers. It was pointed out, however, that

107

Clerks of Unions, who were equally part-time officials, were to be admitted to the benefits of the measure. It was strongly urged at this time by many Poor Law Officers that they should be transferred from the control of the Poor Law Commissioners to that of the Board of Health.

In 1851 a deputation from the Convention had an interview with Lord John Russell, at which Sir George Grey was present. They presented a memorial setting forth the grievances of three thousand Poor Law Medical Officers who were responsible for medical attendance on three million poor. It concluded by suggesting the following principles :—

(1) Permanence of office during competency and good conduct ;

(2) Remuneration proportioned to the extent and nature of the duties ;

(3) Responsibility to professional authority under medical inspectors.

They prayed his Lordship to introduce a Bill into Parliament embodying these provisions.

Lord John Russell promised that he would specially communicate with the President of the Poor Law Board with reference to the objects sought by the deputation.

In 1854 a Committee of the House of Commons, which had been appointed to inquire into the mode in which medical relief was then administered in the different Unions in England and Wales, and to ascertain whether any additional facilities might be afforded to the poor in obtaining medical aid, made a report in which they deprecated an entire change in the system as administered under the general consolidated order of 1847.

Although the terms of reference seem to have contained no allusion to the grievances of medical officers, some of the recommendations did incidentally bear upon them. For instance, a reduction of the areas of too large districts was recommended, as were security of tenure of office and increase of inadequate salaries.

The Report also made some recommendations which might possibly affect the interests of medical officers to " purely medical clubs," and that which advised that persons not in receipt of parochial relief, other than medical, should not be placed on the list of paupers.

Charles Dickens, who had always taken a deep interest in the administration of the Poor Law, published in *Household Words* in 1854 an article which, when quoted in the Association *Journal*, took up more than five columns of close print. It was entitled " Medical Practice among the Poor," and purported—as no doubt it did—to give the experiences of a Poor Law doctor, defending himself and his colleagues as a class against charges of neglect and inhumanity, and exposing the grievances and difficulties under which they suffered. It is an eloquent but withal fair-minded article.

In 1859 and 1860 the *Journal* contained many letters and reports of meetings on Poor Law medical reform, and a deputation to the President of the Poor Law Board was received.

In a leading article *The British Medical Journal* (May 12th, 1860, p. 363) said :—

" It must be understood that we have to fight the Boards of Guardians for every penny of increased remuneration we wish to give to the miserably underpaid Poor Law Medical officials. Those engaged in this struggle should remember that as far as its opponents are concerned, the battle will turn upon the mere question of pounds, shillings and pence. It may be all very well for us to descant upon its humane aspect as regards the poor, but neither the Poor Law Commissioners nor the Boards of Guardians will view it for one moment in this light."

Mr. Piggott's Bill for Reform of the Poor Law as regards medical relief was so strongly opposed—Boards of Guardians having brought pressure to bear upon many Members of Parliament—that he withdrew the Bill.

In 1862 the Association drew up a memorial to the Committee of the House of Commons on Poor Relief, setting forth the grievances and needs of Poor Law Medical Officers, and making recommendations for their remedy. This memorial was signed by Sir Charles Hastings as President of Council, and by the General Secretary, Dr. Philip H. Williams, and dated from Worcester.

This Committee issued its Report in 1864, and its effect was discouraging to the friends of the Poor Law Medical Service. In a leading article the *Journal* quoted largely from Mr. Richard Griffin's commentary on the Report, and pointed out that it was hopeless to ask Parliament for redress of grievances. Referring to the underbidding for Poor Law appointments it said :—

"It seems to us hoping beyond hope to expect a free-trade House of Commons will ever force ratepayers to pay more for the services of an official than the official himself demands for his services. . . . Why not attempt one great united movement ? Success would as certainly follow thereon, as it will follow in the case of the Army Medical Officer. If candidates presented themselves in abundance at the Army Medical Board, what chance would there be of any improvement of the Army Medical Service. Yet| the doctor places himself at the service of the pauper and finds him physic during thirteen weeks for four shillings. As long as there were a number of candidates willing to take Poor Law Medical appointments at unremunerative rates, in the hope of getting into other paying practice, there was no hope of improvement. It was the old story of want of union in the profession."

In 1868 the columns of the *Journal* were full of letters and reports on Poor Law Medical Reform, and on the grievances of individual officers. In this year the Poor Law Medical Officers' Association wrote a letter formally asking for the co-operation of the British Medical Association. It was resolved at the Annual Meeting that a committee be appointed to confer with the Council of the Poor Law Association and to co-operate in promoting the interests of Reform.

In August, 1870, the Poor Law dispensary system was the subject of questions in the House of Commons, when Mr. Goschen explained its details to Sir Michael Hicks-Beach. In the same year the *Journal* recorded the fact that a petition to the House of Commons in support of Dr. Brady's Poor Law Officers' Superannuation Bill was extensively signed, and that the Royal College of Surgeons of England presented a petition to the same effect signed by its President and two Vice-Presidents showing that the College repudiated the doings of the "influential traitors in the camp" referred to in the 1837 Report of the Committee of the Association.

110

The result was that in the Superannuation Act of that year a clause made it permissible to grant pensions to Poor Law Medical Officers, though, as Mr. Russell Coombe has noted, it was not until some time later, and after much pressure, that such officers became entitled to pensions as a right.

The subject of dispensaries came to the front again in 1872, when the Poor Law Committee reported a conference with the Poor Law Officers' Association and the interview of a joint deputation with the President of the Local Government Board. Especial attention was directed to the importance of establishing dispensaries, and the objections to making Poor Law Officers Medical Officers of Health of large districts was pointed out.

No great agitation has since been required, but the two Associations have not felt able to relax their vigilance on behalf of the sick pauper and his doctor. Although Dr. Joseph Rogers, who had done so much for his fellow Poor Law Medical Officers, pointed out in a paper read before the Social Science Association at Birmingham in 1884, that as medical relief was made more efficient, so the cost of pauperism decreased, some Boards of Guardians were incapable of realising this fact, and persisted in attempts to deprive medical officers of their rights, so that from time to time the Association had to intervene. In the Retrospect for 1884 instances of successful action are recorded, but the Editor of the *Journal* thus summarises the situation :—

" In no previous year has there been exhibited by Boards of Guardians generally so great a disposition to deny their liability and to absolutely refuse to pay extra fees to which medical officers considered that they were entitled, and we have further to point out that, on appeal to the central department, the views of the Guardians have either been upheld, or it has declined to interfere."

The writer concluded by expressing the belief that the only hope of improvement lay in an increase in the number of medical Members of Parliament.

In 1885 the disputes which had been frequent as to the disposal and treatment of lunatics in workhouses were settled by an Act which rendered it legal to admit

111

and detain for a certain time persons alleged to be of unsound mind. In the same year Mr. Jesse Collings, M.P. for Ipswich, succeeded in annulling the disfranchisement of paupers, thus assimilating English with Irish paupers, who have never been so disqualified. The Editor's comment on this was : " It will be interesting to note whether the English Poor will now be less averse from seeking parish relief." It now seems doubtful whether the English pauper felt the least interest in the question.

In the same article it was noted that the abuse of the issue of dispensary tickets in Ireland was carried to such an extent as to annihilate completely all private practice among the small shopkeepers, tenant farmers and others who in England and Wales have always paid for such medical attendance.

In 1892 the Parliamentary Bills Committee made an effort on behalf of the Irish Dispensary Medical Officers " enabling them to obtain redress for their manifold and serious grievances," which have already been specified. In 1894 and 1895 a committee of the B.M.A. made exhaustive inquiries into the nursing in workhouse infirmaries in England and Ireland, which disclosed many defects and led to salutary reforms.

Since 1895 the Association has not had cause to agitate for any general reform, but has continued to support the causes of individual officers when unfairly treated, and to put practitioners in possession of the facts when Guardians have attempted to fill vacancies under unfair conditions. Co-operation between the British Medical and the Poor Law Medical Officers' Associations has been maintained.

The Poor Law in Ireland had been administered through Boards of Guardians who largely represented the gentry and well-to-do classes, but the Irish Local Government Act of 1898 revolutionised the system and democratised the Boards of Guardians, to the detriment of the Poor Law Medical Service. In 1904 there appeared in *The British Medical Journal* (Supplement, 26th March) the report of a special correspondent who had been sent to inquire thoroughly into the medical relief of the poor in Ireland. The condition of things revealed was shocking. The medical officers of the dispensary service generally

112

complained of ridiculously low pay, heavy and exhausting duties, no clear regulations as to leave of absence, uncertain prospects of superannuation allowances, unsympathetic treatment by the Poor Law Guardians and want of due protection by the Local Government Board for Ireland. The dispensaries in general consisted of miserable rooms, cold in winter and unfit for the examination of patients. The distances to be covered were great, and as every Guardian had the right to issue " red tickets " authorising home visits, private practice was almost non-existent. Much red-tape office work was required in connection with the supply of drugs and the making of returns. The report ended as follows :—

" XVII. Conclusion. At first, on visiting Ireland the matter seemed to be a small affair, easily dealt with. After travelling through the country and meeting many people, the magnitude of the question was clearly perceived.

" It is not the mere question of the well-being of a group of dispensary medical officers. The very existence of the medical profession as an effective factor in the national life of Ireland is at stake. The Poor Law Medical Officers are so considerable a body in Ireland that anything that affects their well-being affects the medical profession as a profession more than in most countries. The State is brought into closer relations with the medical profession in Ireland than in most countries.

" From the statements made in the report, the reader can form an opinion of how far the State, through its responsible officials, has understood its duties and its responsibilities towards that profession.

" It has not understood the responsibility aright, and hence it stands blamable for the existing conditions in Ireland, conditions of great gravity and highly injurious to the Irish people as a nation.

" Personal inquiries were made of all classes of the community. Many Bishops of the Protestant and Catholic Church, landlords and tenants, guardians and electors, priests and parsons, officials and non-officials, the chance visitor met in the railway carriage or at the hotel table, the views put forward are the result of conversations with these many men. The leaders of the medical profession have been fully consulted in all the centres where medical men form any important group of the profession. They all agree as to the need of reform.

"With the medical officers of the workhouse infirmary and the dispensary relations have been close and thorough. I have seen their devoted service and driven with them in the storm and the rain round the battlefield of their splendid struggle against disease and insanitation.

"I have learned to respect them deeply, and I can never forget their many grievances, their splendid devotion to Ireland, their humanity, their broad views in the land of narrow views. The medical profession in Ireland contains the most level-headed, the least bitter in religious animosities, and the most just-minded men in the land, and with just treatment they must come to the front. The struggle will be long and trying, but they must never despair, and as the years go on, victory will surely come if they stand up as they do for humanity, progress, and all that means betterment for the Irish people.

"In all my efforts to see correctly in the land where vision is liable to constant error, I have had before me only one hope, but that is a splendid hope ; that, as the result of this inquiry, some help may come to him—the ultimate Irish peasant—who has suffered in the past and still suffers so much. If my work tends in any way to his betterment, I shall not have laboured in vain. I say with fervour : ' God save Ireland.' "

In a leading article (*B.M.J.*, 1904, Vol. I, pp. 737-8) on the Poor Law Medical Service in Ireland, it was pointed out that the average size of a dispensary district was 42 square miles with an average population of 6,000 scattered over that wide area. Many districts were much larger, and it was no uncommon thing for a medical officer to have charge of two or more branch dispensaries, with a sphere of work extending over 60 or 70, or even 100 square miles.

Politico-religious considerations influenced elections as much as or more than professional fitness.

The teachers of the Medical Schools of Ireland had done their best to dissuade newly qualified men from entering the service and the Irish Medical Association, which included in its membership 52 per cent. of the profession in Ireland, took similar action, which was answered by an attempt of the Guardians to import men from England and Scotland. The public Press and all classes except the Poor Law Boards sympathised with the doctors, but the Local Government Board was hostile or indifferent.

In the same year (*B.M.J.*, 1904, Vol. I, p. 1029) a leading article on Poor Law Medical Relief in Scotland appeared, based on the report of a Departmental Committee. This dealt chiefly with the difficulties met with in the sparsely populated Highlands and Islands, and the scarcity in numbers of medical officers. In 1900 nearly 400 persons in these districts died without being seen by a doctor, and the majority of deaths were uncertified in some, especially in the Hebrides.

In 1905 the Poor Law again came to the front, when in December of that year a Royal Commission was appointed to inquire into the Poor Laws and the Relief of Distress. As far as its work was concerned with medical relief its proceedings were closely watched by the Association, which tendered evidence on the subject of the sick poor, and on whose behalf Dr. MacVail made a careful investigation, the results of which were laid before the Commission. The Report, a folio volume of 1,252 pages, consisting of a majority report of 670 pages, a minority report of 518 pages and some other details, was issued in February, 1909. It dealt with Scotland and Ireland, as well as England, and was preceded and followed by a host of volumes of evidence and appendices.

Both reports recommended the abolition of Boards of Guardians. The majority report recommended among other things that medical assistance should be reorganised on a provident basis in accordance with the recommendations of the report of the Association on Contract practice and with Dr. MacVail's special investigation. The minority report, which was largely the work of the Socialist theorists, Mr. and Mrs. Sidney Webb, advocated a whole-time medical service, by salaried medical civil servants. As the *Journal* remarked, it was " a discursive document containing many passages of fervent eloquence, even its summary of conclusions reading more like an article in a monthly magazine than the various recommendations of a Royal Commission for fresh legislation."

Some of the changes which were recommended have since been made ; such as the formation of a Ministry of Labour, one of the duties of which would be to organise a National Labour Exchange.

There had been nearly one hundred reports to Parliament on Poor Law matters since 1834, but none of them like this, including pauperism as a whole.

Soon after the earliest reports of the Commission were issued a special Poor Law Reform Committee of the Association was formed which studied the subject and reported from time to time to the Council.

The introduction of the National Insurance Bill of 1911 diverted attention for a while, and dealt with a large part of the field covered by the Commission's researches. After the passing of the Act, the War and post-War troubles occupied the Legislature. The formation of the Ministry of Health and the passing of the Local Government Act of 1929, which came into force in April, 1930, have deprived many of the recommendations of the Commission of more than historical interest. The Boards of Guardians are now abolished, and the administration of poor relief of all kinds placed in the hands of County Councils and County Boroughs.

THE ASSOCIATION AND PUBLIC HEALTH AND STATE MEDICINE

WHEN the Association was founded such a science as that of public health was non-existent, and could not exist, for at that time there were no correctly ascertained facts on which it could be based. For the City of London and its immediate suburbs the Bills of Mortality supplied some information as to the causes of death, on which, in 1662, John Graunt, F.R.S., wrote the first book on vital statistics, entitled " Natural and Political Observations . . . upon the Bills of Mortality." (See *The British Medical Journal*, 1926, Vol. II, p. 645.)

The sanitary condition of the country as a whole, and especially of the larger towns, was so deplorable that it might have been thought that it had only to be recorded to be remedied. Hardly any place had a water supply, except from local wells. Sir Francis Drake had set an example at Plymouth out of public spirit, and Sir Hugh Middleton had supplied the City of London with the design of making money as well as of benefiting the citizens. There were, however, no sewers, and the cesspools in the basements of houses too often communicated more or less directly with shallow wells. It must not be thought, however, that these conditions were peculiar to England. As Dr. John Conolly, of Warwick, pointed out in his address to the Provincial Medical and Surgical Association in 1834, the sanitary condition of Paris was even worse than that of London, while the epidemic death-rate in Novgorod was 1 in 25, and that in Leysin 1 in 60.

In 1831, under the threat of cholera, a Consultative Board of Health consisting of a number of physicians had been formed, but its advice was hardly more useful than that of the College of Physicians at the time of the Great Plague, and it was soon superseded by a Central Board of Health, which in its turn could do little more than make recommendations and rules for quarantine and isolation. These were bodies hastily formed to meet the emergency, and had no permanent effect on sanitary reform or vital statistics.

In 1840 a Select Committee of the House of Commons reported on the health of the inhabitants of large towns, and in the same year an Act was passed authorising gratuitous vaccination against smallpox under the control of the Poor Law Commissioners. The year 1842 was notable as that in which Mr. (afterwards Sir Edwin) Chadwick, then Secretary to the Poor Law Commissioners, made his classical "General Report on the Sanitary Condition of the Labouring Population of Great Britain," which was circulated widely, and had a very great effect in arousing national attention to the evils existing, so that in 1843 a Royal Commission was appointed to inquire into the public health generally, with very wide terms of reference. Legislation followed on the Commission's reports in 1844 and 1845, culminating in 1848 in the establishment of the General Board of Health for a period of five years, at the end of which term the Government were defeated on a Bill intended to prolong its existence. The Board was unpopular, and the very qualities which distinguished Mr. Chadwick had rendered him obnoxious to a great many persons whose interests and prejudices were interfered with. The Board was reconstituted without Chadwick, and in 1858 and 1859 a new Public Health Act was passed and a Medical Department under the Privy Council established, which continued to act under the skilled guidance of Sir John Simon until the formation of the Local Government Board in 1871. The Act which constituted this Board abolished the Poor Law Board, and the Local Government Board took its place as well as that of the Medical Department of the Privy Council. This Board, of which the President was always a member of the Government of the day, continued in control until 1919, when the Ministry of Health took over its functions, together with the administration of the Insurance Acts and other duties. Meanwhile the first appointment of a Medical Officer of Health had been made by the City of Liverpool under a Private Act in 1846, and the City of London had followed suit in 1848 with the appointment of Sir John Simon.

EDMUND BEADON TURNER,
F.R.C.S., CHAIRMAN OF
REPRESENTATIVE BODY,
1915–1919.

GUY ELLISTON,
GENERAL SECRETARY,
1902–1918.

The foregoing brief catalogue of the chief events in the history of public health legislation seems a necessary introduction to an account of the Association's activities in this connection. The reader who wishes to go more deeply into the matter is recommended to consult Sir John Simon's excellent treatise on English Sanitary Institutions,* of which he might well have said " Quorum pars magna fui." In the conditions outlined above it is little wonder that one of the chief objects sought by the Provincial Medical and Surgical Association in its earliest days was the study of topographical medicine, which included what are known as epidemiology and vital statistics. At its first Anniversary Meeting in 1833, the secretaries of the Association were directed to address the House of Commons Committee on Parochial Registers, submitting " that great benefit might be expected to accrue to medical science, and consequently to the community at large, if arrangements could be made for recording *causes of death* in the provincial registers of mortality." Three years later the Act of 1836 for the Registration of Births, Deaths and Marriages supplemented the decennial census inaugurated in 1801, and laid the foundation for the first serious efforts in the study of public health.

Another aspect of public health and State medicine occupied the Association in 1834, when the Council commended Dr. Barlow's investigation into the incipient stages of diseases and recommended such studies to the members. In 1837 influenza claimed attention. The epidemic had been at its worst in January, complicated by pneumonia, and in some cases accompanied by gastro-intestinal symptoms. In 1838 vital statistics were promised as the subject of the retrospective address. Caspar and Quetelet were given as authority for the statement that the percentage who reach 70 years of age varied from 24 for medical men to 42 for theologians. The " Medical Topography " of Copenhagen, Swansea and Exeter was also compared. The *Transactions* of the Association for 1839 included an elaborate paper on " Variola," by Dr. Ceely, and the

* " English Sanitary Institutions." Reviewed in their course of Development, and in some of their political and social relations, by Sir John Simon, K.C.B. (London, Cassell and Co., Ltd., 1890).

same year the report of a Vaccination Section of the Association recommending the practice of inoculation for smallpox for the poor paved the way for the Vaccination Act of 1840.

Meanwhile the most urgent need was still a sound system of recording vital statistics. The Registration Act of 1836 had satisfied some, but not all, of the demands of the Association, which continued to ask for some extensive and precise information. At the 1865 Annual Meeting, Dr. Ransome, of Manchester, moved for the appointment of a committee "to encourage the registration of disease, and to devise the best means of obtaining the evidence of members upon medical questions having a practical bearing." A strong committee was appointed, which reported the next year, and recommended that the members of the Association should themselves undertake the registration of disease and of death coming under their notice in public practice.

In October, 1866, Mr. Rumsey called the attention of the Committee of the Association on the Observation and Registration of Disease to a letter from Dr. Farr, and the Committee thereupon passed the following resolutions :—

" 1. That this Committee, recognising the importance of Dr. Farr's proposition for the appointment of a registration medical officer in every Superintendent Registrar's District, strongly urge him to press it to a successful issue and assure him of their hearty co-operation.

2. That in the opinion of this Committee such a medical officer would be the suitable authority for collecting and publishing periodical returns of disease, obtained by local associations.

3. That the districts for the registration of disease should be based on the division of the country for the registration of births, deaths and marriages.

4. That it is desirable that voluntary associations should be formed in each of the above districts to carry out the scheme of registration of disease, adopted by this Association." (See *B.M.J.*, August 25th, 1866, p. 229.)

In the following year, at the Dublin Meeting (the first Annual Meeting held in Ireland) the Association recorded its decided approval of Dr. Farr's plan, namely, the appointment of a registration medical officer in every registration district or group of districts, with medicolegal and sanitary functions, and pledged itself to support the measure as the initiative step to a national organisation for purposes of State medicine.

In 1872 the support of the Social Science Association was secured for the Association's policy, and that policy was pressed upon the Government at every available opportunity, and in 1873 a memorial was addressed to the Local Government Board and a petition to Parliament embodying the case for comprehensive registration of disease, and pointing out that the Association's scheme had already been successful during ten years in Manchester and Salford and St. Marylebone, five years in Birmingham, four years in Newcastle-on-Tyne and for a shorter time in Preston, and that the appointment of registration medical officers would not only facilitate the registration of disease but would greatly improve the services of State medicine.

The question of notification of infectious diseases was necessarily connected with that of the observation and registration of disease in general. This was frequently discussed by the Association, which decided in 1876 that compulsion was necessary for successful notification, and that the medical attendant should be required to declare the nature of the disease while the duty of notification should be imposed on the householder himself in order to avoid appearance of any breach of confidence on the part of the medical attendant.

In 1879 the Registration of Diseases Committee, under Dr. Arthur Ransome, made its last report, which was not in favour of notification by the medical attendant. In the same year various local Bills legalising notification were introduced in Parliament. In 1881, at the Annual Meeting at Ryde, considerable opposition to compulsory notification by attending practitioners was apparent, but ultimately it was decided to support a Bill introduced into the House of Commons by Mr. G. W. Hastings and then under discussion. The subject continued to engage the attention of the Association until the passing of Mr. Ritchie's Act in 1889, which provided for the compulsory notification of certain infectious diseases, and laid the responsibility on the householder as well as the practitioner.

Meanwhile other aspects of public health policy were not neglected. In 1867 the Committee of Council were instructed "to direct their early and special attention to the amendment of the sanitary laws; to invite the co-operation to this end of the Council of the National Association for the Promotion of Social Science, and to urge the Branches of the Association to promote the same object by local efforts, by representation to individual Members of Parliament, and, if need be, by deputation to Her Majesty's Government." A committee was also appointed to collect information. In 1868 the report of the joint committee of the British Medical Association and the National Association for the Promotion of Social Science, which had made a critical examination of the report of the Royal Sanitary Commission, was adopted and a Public Health Committee appointed.

The Association early recognised the close connection between the problems of the unsound public health services and the existing provision for the medical care of the sick poor, then a subordinate activity of the Poor Law authorities, and the matter was taken up in 1870 by a joint committee on Public Health and the Poor Law. The activities of this Committee are dealt with in another chapter; but one of its recommendations may fitly be quoted here as a sufficiently clear formulation of the principles vindicated after many years by the creation of the Ministry of Health in 1919 and the Local Government Act in 1929.

The smoke nuisance has always been with us, and in the same year we find that the Association was already alive to its importance, for the following resolution was passed at the Annual Meeting in 1870 :—

"That in future sanitary legislation the smoke nuisance and other gaseous pollutions of the atmosphere should be dealt with by compulsory measures to be carried into effect by authorities independent of the district and instructed by local surveyors unfettered by local interests and feelings."

It was not until 1926 that public opinion was sufficiently informed to secure the passing of the Public

Health (Smoke Abatement) Act, a belated measure which naturally commanded the support of the Association.

Meanwhile the qualifications and conditions of service of the personnel of the public health services had become a matter of increasing importance, and at the Annual Meeting in 1873 the Section of Public Health recommended " that a Committee should be appointed to consider the best means of providing for the adequate qualification in State Medicine of all public medical officers." The Annual Meeting appointed a strong Committee accordingly, which included among its members Dr. E. A. Parkes. This Committee reported in 1874, making various suggestions and recommending that the General Medical Council should be empowered and required to prepare a scheme for examination in the subject. The Council was slow to act in this matter, and while it hesitated the licensing bodies, led by Trinity College, Dublin, instituted examinations and diplomas on their own account. Regulations for examinations in this subject were not issued by the General Medical Council until 1896. A diploma in public health is now necessary for every medical officer of health whose authority extends over 50,000 inhabitants, and it has become practically a *sine qua non* for all whole-time medical officers of health.

The gradual improvement in the powers and status of medical officers, and their consequently increased usefulness to the public, have been jealously watched and fostered by the Association from the very first, when a medical officer of health might be, and sometimes was, dismissed because his recommendations affected the pockets of influential members of municipalities, until security of tenure and a right to superannuation allowances were established by law, no dismissal of an officer being possible without the approval of the Local Government Board or its successor, the Ministry of Health. Besides these important achievements, the Association has established minimum scales of salary which are generally accepted.

Numerous references to special committees and their reports have appeared in the foregoing pages, and much useful work was done by these bodies ; but for many

123

years their doings were overshadowed by the activities of the Parliamentary Bills Committee. This Committee, first appointed in 1863, did not finally discharge its reference until its work was merged in that of the Medico-Political Committee in 1903. From 1872 to 1897, under the chairmanship of Mr. Ernest Hart, who was at the same time Editor of *The British Medical Journal*, it took a leading part in influencing legislation on public health matters and in making known the opinion of the profession, which the Association could claim to represent in an ever-increasing degree as its membership grew from year to year. During his tenure of office Hart made the activities of his Committee and its reports seem the most important non-technical matters dealt with in the *Journal*, as indeed they often were. Hart's own position in the public estimation as a sanitary authority may be gauged by the fact of his election to the chairmanship of the National Health Society in 1892. Three years later, while still chairman of the Committee, he visited India and made a considerable impression there also in speaking about cholera, which was prevalent at Hardwar and Mecca, and likely to be spread by pilgrims to those places. From its inception the Committee also owed much to three medical Members of Parliament, Dr. Lyon Playfair (afterwards Lord Playfair, F.R.S.), M.P. for the Universities of Edinburgh and St. Andrews, and at one time Postmaster-General ; Dr. Walter Balthazar Foster (afterwards Lord Ilkeston) ; and Dr. (afterwards Sir) Robert Farquharson, who acted as exponents of the medical point of view, and from their official positions were able to obtain the serious attention of the Governments to which they belonged to grievances and projects of reform in which the Association was interested. The period of Hart's chairmanship was one of considerable legislative activity, a fact which contributed to the leading part which his Committee took at this time in almost all the major activities of the Association. Amongst these, the promotion of notification of infectious diseases, already referred to, the agitation for medical reform (discussed in detail in another section), the movement for registration of midwives (of which more will be said below), and the perennial struggle, still in

124

progress, for more adequate defence of the public against the activities of quacks and charlatans, and more especially the vendors of secret remedies, deserve special mention. For this last topic reference should be made to the section on Quackery. On occasion the Committee collaborated not only with other committees of the Association, but with outside bodies, as, for example, when it supplemented the efforts of the Inebriates Legislation Committee and the Society for the Study of Inebriety in 1888-9 in an endeavour to secure more effective provision for the treatment of inebriates, notably arrangements for compulsory admission to retreats of such as were not willing to apply voluntarily, a less intimidating reception for voluntary patients, and special medical care and treatment for the impecunious. Its activities were not limited to the United Kingdom, for in 1892 we find it dealing with a Medical Ordinance for Sierra Leone, and another for regulating the sale of drugs and poisons on the Gold Coast and at Lagos. On more than one occasion it was able to voice the grievances of militia surgeons and army medical officers who were unable to express their opinions except through the Association. In this connection it had the support in 1890 of the Royal Colleges of Physicians and Surgeons throughout the kingdom, and succeeded in securing the appointment of a committee to consider the rank, pay and status of army medical officers. In the same year it advocated in vain the Royal College of Surgeons of England Bill, which attempted to widen the franchise for the election of the Council of the College—a question still unsettled. For the rest, a mere catalogue of some of the matters which fell within the Committee's sphere must suffice to illustrate the range and vigour of its activities. They included various public health and local government Bills (including local sanitary Bills, which required careful watching) for England, Scotland and Ireland ; lunacy legislation in both England and Ireland, pharmacy and poisons legislation, the status of ship surgeons, the housing of the working classes, railway servants' eyesight, the administration of anæsthetics, the Alkali Works Regulation Act, the Plumbers' Registration Bill, the Oaths Act, coroners' law and death certification, and factory legislation. Particularly notable under these heads was the work done in the protection of the Irish dispensary doctors, in resisting proposals made by factory owners for reducing or abolishing the part taken by certifying factory surgeons in carrying out some of the most important provisions of the Factory Acts, and in endeavouring to secure adequate protection for medical practitioners called upon to take action under the lunacy law. In this last connection a considerable measure of success has ultimately been secured under the Mental Treatment Act, 1930, though the protection is even yet less complete than that advocated by the Association.

A comprehensive account of such multifarious activities as those so far enumerated is beyond the compass of our review, and what has already been said must suffice at once to suggest the breadth and variety of the Association's activities in those early days, and the value of its practical contribution to the development and application of the new science of state medicine, and to rebut the charge sometimes made that, prior to the reorganisation of 1902, its interests were exclusively scientific. Other aspects of the work may be found in a more detailed study of the development of some particular branch of the Association's policy which may be taken as typical of its general aims and methods. For this purpose no better example can be chosen than the Association's contribution to the development of the national provision for the care of maternity, infancy and childhood. Since the essential prerequisite of this, as of all other branches of state medicine, is clearly the existence of a sound system of recording vital statistics, the Association's advocacy of registration in 1833 may be taken as the starting point of the story. Particular aspects of the protection of infant life have received attention from time to time as occasion offered. For example, the Association was active in promoting the Act of 1871 for the regulation of baby farming, and in 1873 took up the important question of the certification of stillbirths, the principle of which was embodied in several Bills subsequently drafted by the Association. The principle was conceded by the Select Committee on Death Certification in 1893 after consideration of its evidence, and again by the Departmental Committee on Coroners' Law in

126

1909, but did not receive legal sanction until the Births and Deaths Registration Act of 1926. Later it secured effective action for the elimination of ophthalmia neonatorum in a manner which supplies an apt illustration of the connection between its scientific and medico-political activities. In 1906 ophthalmia neonatorum was chosen by the Council for the Middlemore Prize, and in 1907 it was discussed in the Section of Ophthalmology, which recommended the appointment of a committee to consider steps for the prevention of the disease. The Committee reported two years later urging the necessity of notification, and, largely owing to the publicity obtained by its report, a considerable number of authorities had adopted notification by 1910, when the Council of the Association issued a model scheme for administration in areas where notification was in force. The Central Midwives Board altered its Rules to conform with the Committee's recommendation that purulent vaginal discharge requires medical assistance, and the Association's policy was fully endorsed in 1914, when notification was made compulsory by statutory Order. It has been fully justified by the event. By 1920 the Chief Medical Officer to the Ministry of Health was able to state that good results had been reported from certain large towns, and that the large proportion of total cures, the almost complete absence of total blindness, and the relatively few cases of damaged vision spoke well for the care with which the disease was treated and nursed. A still more recent inquiry into cardiac disease in children, carried out between 1923 and 1927, has already had its effect in promoting the adoption of notification of this disease by a number of local authorities. An extensive inquiry into the incidence of rheumatic heart disease in childhood carried on from 1927 to 1930 in Gloucestershire, Somerset and Wiltshire, led to the provision of special treatment centres. To the work of some of these the Association has made direct financial contribution.

These activities, however, were by the way. The first aspect of the main problem to secure public attention was the need of a supply of qualified midwives. Clearly, the profession was in a particularly advantageous position for estimating the effects of incompetent midwifery, and in 1873 it urged upon Mr. Stansfeld, then President of the Local Government Board, the necessity of the education and control of midwives, subsequently at his request co-operating with the Obstetrical Society in drawing up a scheme for the education and registration of midwives. For the next thirty years the subject was frequently before the Association and the public, and only the main stages in the development of its policy and the long drawn out Parliamentary struggle for reform can be noted here. In 1879 attention was directed to the question by a Medical Acts Amendment Bill, which touched incidentally upon the regulation of midwifery, and this led to the preparation of the first of a series of Midwives Bills drafted by the Association itself. The Bill provided for the training, examination and registration of midwives under the control of a Board which was to include at least three general practitioners, and limited the sphere of independent action of the registered midwife to cases of normal labour. The underlying principle of the Bill being that of the Medical Acts, namely, the distinction between the qualified and unqualified practitioner, it contained no prohibition of unqualified practice. By 1883 the Association had secured the approval of the Privy Council and the General Medical Council for a revised edition of this Bill, and it was actually adopted in that year as a Government measure, but ultimately lapsed through pressure of Parliamentary business. Later, the attitude of the Government seems to have changed, for Lord Carlingford considered the Association's Bill too complicated and " too compulsory " for acceptance, and a number of efforts to promote legislation were unsuccessful. In 1890 a Midwives Bill was introduced by Sir Walter Foster and Dr. Farquharson, together with several other private members. It was shorter and less complete than the Association's, but directed to the same end, and its history constitutes a curious interlude in the development of the Association's policy, for its withdrawal was directly occasioned by the attitude of the Association at its Annual Meeting in August, although, according to *The British Medical Journal*, the whole profession was by this time in favour of its basic principle. The fact was that a considerable amount of opposition to the

128

actual legislative proposals so far formulated had by this time developed within the profession, as well as in lay circles. Lay opposition was apparently still inspired by a general dislike of interference with individual freedom, fostered by a convenient ignorance of prevailing conditions. Professional opposition seems to have been due to a growing realisation that registration must fail of its avowed object in the absence of complete prohibition of unqualified practice, and a conviction that the actual proposals for controlling the practice of qualified midwives were inadequate. From this arose a fear that the practice of registered midwives could not, in fact, be confined within the specified limits, so that their statutory recognition must entail the creation of a new class of partially qualified practitioner which would compete with the profession in an important field of medical practice. The body of professional opposition based on these criticisms had acquired such force by the date of the Annual Meeting that, although the Midwives Bill had by that time been largely remodelled in accordance with the accepted policy of the Association, the meeting demanded and obtained its withdrawal with a view to giving more time for its discussion amongst the profession. This does not mean that the Association wavered in the support of the general principle of control. Indeed, for the next ten years it never ceased to press the point, however severely it might criticise successive proposals, and it had considerable success in securing the amendment of a number of measures introduced during this period. None of these, however, reached the Statute Book.

In 1899 an important advance was made when the Association, in opposition to an inadequate Bill framed by a committee of nurses and a few specialists interested in midwifery, put forward a new Bill of its own, which embodied for the first time an absolute prohibition of unqualified practice in midwifery. In 1902 the Government introduced a Bill so defective from the point of view of the Association as to be characterized by *The British Medical Journal* as " the worst yet submitted to Parliament." It was no small tribute to the growing strength of the Association that its work in and outside Parliament was successful in securing such amendments to

129

this measure that when it became law it embodied the main essentials of the Association's policy, more particularly the prohibition, under penalty, of unqualified practice. Even so, the Act was by no means perfect ; and the experience of the next few years showed the need of adjustment. In 1909 the Association gave evidence before a Departmental Committee which accepted its more important suggestions and recommended a number of amendments. Legislation, however, lagged, and it was not until 1918 that a new Midwives Act imposed on local authorities the duty of paying the fee of medical practitioners called in by midwives. Provision for the effective supervision of maternity homes, long demanded by the Association and now required by the Nursing Homes Registration Act of 1927, was first made by the Midwives and Maternity Homes Act of 1926. This last Act also strengthened the original prohibition of unqualified practice. This had applied only to unqualified women who " habitually and for gain " attended women in childbirth otherwise than under the direction of a qualified medical practitioner. On the one hand, the unqualified male accoucheur, not altogether unknown, was not touched by the clause ; on the other, a conviction of practising for gain habitually was necessarily a matter of some difficulty. The Act of 1926, therefore, placed upon the accused person the onus of proving that attendance in any given case was rendered as a matter of sudden or urgent necessity, and extended the prohibition of unqualified practice to men.

While the Association did not secure the statutory representation of general practitioners on the Central Midwives Board for England, it nominates a member of the Scottish Board under the Act of 1915.

The influence exerted by the Association upon the development of the existing system of maternity and infant welfare clinics is hardly comparable to that described in connection with the Midwives Acts on the one hand, or, on the other, with the development of the school medical service which will be discussed later. This may be accounted for in part by the fact that the period of most rapid development of this service coincided with the Great War, and in part by the predominantly educational character of the service. During the latter

130

years of the nineteenth century a number of philanthropic agencies came into being for the amelioration of conditions of maternity and infancy amongst the poor, and the humanitarian movement which they represented received a considerable impetus at the opening of the twentieth century from the general interest aroused by the falling birth-rate and the light thrown upon public health conditions by the experiences of the Boer War. To this interest the findings of the first school medical inspections contributed, and the adoption of a system of notification of births, permissive under the Act of 1907, and compulsory under the Act of 1915, laid the foundations for a national scheme of maternity and infant welfare work. The incorporation of what had been primarily a voluntary movement in the national system of health services was marked by the first exchequer grant for maternity and child welfare work in 1914, and provision for orderly development followed with the Maternity and Child Welfare Act of 1918. In these earlier years of the movement there was a real danger that it would fail to secure the co-operation of the private practitioner, so essential to its full fruition. In 1916 the Representative Body called attention to this danger, and emphasised the need for the fullest possible utilisation of the services of local practitioners in connection with the new centres, but the drain of the War upon the profession hindered the desired development.

In 1921, however, the Association was free to devote its energies to the work of reconstruction and development, and a review of the value of maternity and child welfare work in relation to the reduction of infant mortality was carried out by a Medico-Sociological Committee, appointed experimentally in 1920 " to consider social and economic questions affecting the public welfare as to which the medical profession has special knowledge, and to take such steps as may be found necessary in order to create or develop public opinion thereon." Whatever the ultimate verdict on the value of the report issued by the Committee, it cannot be denied that these terms of reference emphasise an important aspect of the Association's responsibility for promoting public education in health. In addition, the

Committee's co-option of representatives of a number of bodies interested in the work but not exclusively medical, and its association with these bodies in the report published in 1921, tended to establish closer and more cordial co-operation in the work than had before obtained ; while the report itself served a useful purpose, both in directing the attention of private practitioners to the urgent necessity for taking a fair share in the activities of the centres, and in checking the tendency of the day to divert the activities of those centres from the legitimate task of education to that of treatment. Meanwhile public attention had been attracted by the contrast between the stationary figures of maternal mortality and the decreased infant mortality rates. In 1924 a report on Maternal Mortality by Dame Janet Campbell, published by the Ministry of Health, conveyed the impression that the persistence of high puerperal mortality rates might be primarily assigned to the inadequacy of the professional attention during pregnancy and at the time of child-birth. This suggestion gave rise to considerable controversy amongst general practitioners, and occasioned the appointment of a Special Committee of the Association to consider and report on the Causation of Puerperal Mortality and Morbidity, and the administrative action, if any, which should be taken in connection with the matter. The survey made by the Committee was comprehensive. Considerable pains were taken to obtain information from the Overseas Branches of the Association, and to examine all available material, and several suggestions for action were obtained from a conference at which representatives of the central Government Departments and the several professional bodies interested met the Association's Committee. It is, of course, impossible to make any final estimate of the value of the Committee's reports after so short an interval. Their main feature was the emphasis laid on the necessity for further experimental research in specified directions, the supreme importance of ante-natal work as a factor in reducing puerperal mortality, and the need of further institutional provision for maternal cases and increased facilities for training both medical students and midwives, more especially in ante-natal work. One of the

132

Committee's recommendations, the compulsory notification of puerperal pyrexia, has already been adopted. Apart from this, the immediate outcome of the Committee's work was the creation of a special committee to formulate practical measures for the reduction of puerperal mortality and morbidity rates, to keep in touch with research work and to assist Divisions and Branches of the Association in educational work in connection with ante-natal services, the conduct of confinements and the post-partum care of mothers and infants. This important work and the extensive collection of records of midwifery is now entrusted to the Maternity and Child Welfare Sub-Committee of the Association's Public Health Committee.

The work of the Association from the early days of the campaign for the registration of midwives to the publication of the reports on puerperal morbidity and mortality had its logical issue in 1929 in the publication of a memorandum outlining a comprehensive scheme for a national maternity service for England and Wales. In this scheme the old theme of the importance of due co-operation between midwife and medical practitioner finds its place beside the new one of the importance of ante-natal and post-natal care. The three principles underlying the scheme are that the normal case can be safely treated at home ; that maternal mortality and morbidity can be greatly reduced if proper ante-natal care and supervision during confinement is provided in all cases, together with institutional accommodation for cases of complicated labour ; and that maternal morbidity can be greatly reduced by proper post-natal care and treatment.

While the Association can fairly claim to have made a substantial contribution to the development of the maternity and child welfare service, its connection with the creation of the school medical service was even more intimate. In 1888, on the recommendation of Dr. Warner, in a paper read to the Section of Psychology at Glasgow, a committee was appointed to investigate the average development and condition of brain power among children in elementary schools, and from then on the Association took a leading part in the numerous inquiries which resulted in the establishment of special schools for physical and mental defectives, and later in the creation of the school medical service itself and the development of its far-reaching activities. The first report of the Committee, on the examination of 5,440 children by some of its members, published in 1889, attracted considerable attention and stimulated further inquiries in which the Association collaborated with a number of scientific and philanthropic bodies. Amongst these inquiries was an examination of 100,000 school children by a committee appointed in 1891 by the International Congress on Hygiene to investigate the requirements of child life, and the recommendations based on that inquiry deserve special mention. But even before their publication the earlier pioneer work had begun to bear fruit. In 1891 the London School Board and five large provincial centres established the first special schools for feeble-minded children. Some school boards appointed medical men to examine day-school children and the National Association for Promoting the Welfare of the Feeble-minded began to provide voluntary homes for defectives. A number of Governmental inquiries were now undertaken, and valuable material was supplied for their purposes by the various reports referred to. Throughout this period of investigation and experiment the *Journal* was active in urging the necessity both for the creation of special schools and for regular medical inspection of schools. In 1896 the Council of the Association considered that the establishment of the Childhood Society for the Scientific Study of the Mental and Physical Condition of Children relieved the Association of further responsibility for investigation in this direction, and the reference of the Association's committee was therefore terminated.

The quickened interest in public health due to the falling birth-rate and the South African War was greatly stimulated by the report of the Inter-Departmental Committee on Physical Deterioration, which recommended that school authorities should be required to institute " a systematised medical inspection of school children." The recommendation fell short of the policy of the Association, as the proposal was limited to the inspection of the class of school in which the presence of ill-health might reasonably be expected! The

134

EDWIN RAYNER, M.D.,
F.R.C.S., TREASURER,
1907–1916.

G. E. HASLIP, M.D.,
TREASURER, 1916–1924.

SIR JENNER VERRALL,
M.R.C.S., CHAIRMAN OF
REPRESENTATIVE BODY,
1913–1916.

J. A. MACDONALD, M.D.,
CHAIRMAN OF
REPRESENTATIVE BODY,
1907–1910 ; CHAIRMAN OF
COUNCIL, 1910–1920.

Association, therefore, continued to urge its views upon the Government by memorandum and deputation, and ultimately succeeded in securing the insertion in the Education (Administrative Provisions) Act of 1907 of a clause making provision for the medical inspection of elementary school children obligatory and permitting arrangements for " attending to their health and physical condition." The principle having been conceded, the Association turned to administration, and the Medico-Political Committee drew up a form for the record of medical inspection which was published in the *Journal* in December, 1907, and adopted without any significant modification by the Board of Education thereafter. The Association was represented on the Special Sub-Committee appointed by the London Education Committee to consider the treatment to be provided under the Act. This Sub-Committee recommended the establishment of school clinics, a scheme rejected by the County Council in favour of arrangements with voluntary hospitals, in which the Association found grave defects. The chief objections to the scheme, and to the alternative policy recommended, were laid before the Board of Education by a deputation which stressed the importance of three points, viz., adequate and complete inspection ; the provision of treatment for cases not otherwise cared for by means of school clinics financed by the authority, as opposed to the transfer of public responsibility to charitable institutions ; and the appointment of specialists and the provision of a dental service.

In 1911 the Association presented a complete scheme for school clinics in the metropolitan area, to be staffed with the co-operation of the Metropolitan Counties Branch of the Association. No better comment upon this phase of the work can be found than the remark of Mr. Runciman to a deputation to the effect that " the Board of Education had been in communication with the London County Council ever since August, 1908, and some of its communications had been condemned as being high-handed and so forth, merely because they expressed in rather milder language exactly what Sir Victor Horsley and Dr. Addison had said that morning." In conclusion, Mr. Runciman thanked the deputation for strengthening the hands of the Board of Education.

K

From the very outset the Association was alive to the danger that the school medical service might, if carried out through whole-time officers, be run in competition with private practice rather than as supplementary to private practice when the services of a family doctor were not available. It was, therefore, primarily concerned to ensure that the service should be conducted, as far as possible, through the agency of private practitioners, and in all cases with their full co-operation. It did not, however, neglect to urge that whole-time officers of the service should be suitably qualified for their work and obtain adequate status and remuneration. It also held conferences with the Society of Medical Officers of Health and the National Union of Teachers, and repeatedly circularised the Divisions calling attention to the need for adequate co-ordination and the fullest possible measure of co-operation between all branches of the educational service. The work of obtaining general agreement in principle was slow, and it was not until 1916 that a detailed policy covering both inspection and treatment, the terms of employment of members of the service, and the machinery as well as the principles of co-operation between the service and private practitioners was approved. In 1918, when the Fisher Act extended the obligation of education authorities to cover treatment as well as inspection of children in elementary schools and inspection of children in a number of other educational institutions, and gave power to provide treatment in these latter cases, the Association secured a valuable safeguard by the inclusion in the Act of a proviso that, in the exercise of the powers indicated, a local education authority shall not establish a general domiciliary service of treatment by medical practitioners for children or young persons, and that in arrangements for medical treatment they shall consider how far they can avail themselves of the services of private medical practitioners.

With the development and expansion of the service the Association has always kept closely in touch. The position at the present time is indicated in the proposals for a General Medical Service for the nation, published by the Association in 1930. These proposals afford

136

an invaluable commentary upon the whole history of the Association's contribution to State medicine, and should be examined in detail by any serious student of the Association's policy. They include a review of the resources now available for the health services of the nation and an outline programme for their ordered development on the lines suggested by a century of progress in the science of preventive medicine, and of experiment in public health legislation and administration and in collective action by the profession. As a manifesto addressed primarily to the public, the proposals illustrate the part played by the Association in bringing to bear upon the development of public policy the experience of the profession as a whole. Their origin in a review of the relationship between private and salaried practice ensures that due value has been given to all shades of professional opinion. Here for the first time the policy developed over a long period, as circumstances demanded, first for one section of the profession, then for another, is set out as an ordered whole, in which the functions of each branch of medicine are seen in due proportion and relation. The fact that it was possible at a critical period in the development of the national administrative machinery to meet the growing public demand for a comprehensive scheme of health services by so complete a statement, not of new but of agreed policy, is in itself a sufficient vindication of the earlier work of the Association. Of that work some account, however fragmentary and incomplete, has already been given, but it may not be out of place to try, in conclusion, to distinguish some of its main characteristics ; a task the more necessary because the Association is frequently charged with neglecting the public interest in the promotion of narrow and short-sighted professional policy.

In the first place, then, it is noticeable that the policy of the Association has in the main been in advance of public opinion, provoking considerable opposition when first formulated, but receiving the sanction of legislation after the lapse of years. In the second place, while the details of the policy put forward for immediate application have necessarily varied from time to time with contemporary social and economic conditions, the advance

K 2

of science and the growth of administrative experience, both Governmental and professional, the main objects in view have never varied. These may roughly be defined as the advance of knowledge of the incidence, cause, prevention and cure of disease ; the provision of adequate health services for the whole community, irrespective of individual economic circumstances, by methods adjusted to the needs of different groups ; and the maintenance of conditions conducive to progressive standards of efficiency in medical practice and in the services auxiliary to medicine. This last aim clearly implies the protection of the material interests of all sections of the profession ; but it has consistently been interpreted as covering also the elaboration of the most effective means of co-operation between the profession and auxiliary health services, thus avoiding the tendency to any narrow professionalism.

THE ASSOCIATION AND THE DEFENCE FORCES

THE Association stands in a position of peculiar responsibility to its members in the Services. By the nature of their employment they are subject to regulations and discipline, and are not allowed to combine in the way open to persons engaged in practically every other form of employment. It is therefore necessary that there should be some outside responsible body which is able to take a comprehensive view of the conditions of employment inside the Services as compared with those outside, and be both able and willing when necessary to make representations to the Department concerned or to Parliament, when questions of principle arise which are incapable of being settled by internal regulations, or where it seems likely that the conditions, if not improved, will lead to a deterioration in the quality of the medical services. The Association has tried to do this duty for many years, and the record shows that it has not been unsuccessful, in the teeth of many difficulties.

It has, however, always been unwilling to intervene in cases of grievance of individual officers until the individual concerned has exhausted all the usual internal machinery of his Service, and only then if it appears that injustice is likely to be done.

Intervention, backed by the unrelenting logic of facts, has been successful, time and again, in improving not only the conditions of service of medical officers as a body, but also of the lot of the sick and wounded sailors and soldiers under their care. Instance of each form of action will be found in the sections dealing with the Naval, Army and Indian Medical Services.

The medical service of the Royal Air Force is in the happy position of having as yet hardly any history, for it was not definitely established until 1920. The conditions of service in this Corps were settled by an

139

Inter-Departmental Committee of all three Services, which reported in 1926 (*B.M.J.*, 1926, Vol. II, p. 41). The Representative Body expressed its satisfaction with the recommendations of this Committee at Nottingham in the same year. The Association has, however, in the past twelve years frequently had to consider and deal with questions affecting the Services, as will be seen by reference to the separate sections.

THE ASSOCIATION AND THE
NAVAL MEDICAL SERVICE

IT is very much to the credit of a former Editor of
The British Medical Journal that, while still a medical
student, he started an agitation in the metropolitan
medical schools which led to a great improvement
in the treatment of surgeons' mates in the Navy. In
an obituary notice of the late Mr. Ernest Hart, published
in January, 1898, Mr. Timothy Holmes, who had been
his fellow student at St. George's Hospital, described
how Hart's influence on his fellow students led to a
boycott of the Naval Medical Service until the enactment of new rules regulating the accommodation allotted
to young surgeons on board Her Majesty's Ships.
Hitherto they had had to share the cockpit with midship-
men, but from this time they were given cabins of their own.

The conditions of service at sea are so different to
those in the land forces that naval surgeons have never
had quite the same grievances as their military brothers.
The regimental system, with its subordination of the
surgeon to the officer commanding his unit, could be
abolished, as it was, by a stroke of the pen, but the
naval surgeon, like everyone else on board ship, must
necessarily be under the orders of its captain or other
commanding officer.

Until the year 1875 naval surgeons had grievances
similar in some respects to those of their Army brethren.
In that year an Admiralty Warrant abolished most of
these grievances, granting to medical officers wardroom
rank and privileges, whatever their seniority. Subsequently, titles resembling those of executive officers
were granted, as in the case of the officers of the Army.
A letter to the *Journal* from a naval medical officer in
1875 well exemplifies the feeling of the Service at that
time :—

" A young man now enters the Service with befitting
rank, exceptionally good pay, and every requisite to

141

make him feel that he is in the position of a gentleman. One word in conclusion as to the part played by the Association and your *Journal* throughout the struggle. We all feel that had it not been for the powerful assistance we derived from our professional brethren, who so kindly espoused our case and made their voice heard, we might long have remained unemancipated, and it is to be hoped that Naval Medical Officers will never forget what is due to the British Medical Association for what it has done during the eventful years 1874–1875."

But the blissful state of things here described did not last long. In 1881 the Parliamentary Bills Committee reported that it had been necessary to intervene in the year before, with the satisfactory result " that the Naval Medical Warrant which has been published during the year carries out the majority of the suggestions put forward by Mr. Ernest Hart in the memorandum which he drew up on the subject last year at the request of the First Lord of the Admiralty. . . . It does confer a considerable boon upon the Service generally, both in respect of rank, pay and promotion . . . and has had the effect of attracting to the Service a greatly improved supply of efficient candidates." (*B.M.J.*, 1881, Vol. II, p. 241.)

The note of caution in this recommendation of the Service was justified by events. By the year 1903 the authorities were in difficulties again, for want of candidates for vacancies. The *Journal* (1903, Vol. I, p. 38) bluntly asserted that the Service was no longer popular.

As related in a leading article in the *Journal* (1904, Vol. I, p. 679) with a view to improving the conditions of service, the Government, in March, 1902, appointed a Consultative Board consisting of Mr. (now Sir George) Makins, Dr. Allchin and Dr. (now Sir Humphry) Rolleston, with the Director-General of the Naval Medical Service as Chairman, the intention being that this Board should bear the same relation to the First Lord as the Medical Advisory Board of the Army had to the Secretary of State for War. New regulations were promulgated on October 31st, 1903, under which promotion was materially accelerated, and special promotion was promised in cases of distinguished service or conspicuous professional merit. Permission was given to surgeons to withdraw from the service with a gratuity at the end of four years if they should so desire. As the writer pointed out, " The prospect of a gratuity of £500, after enjoying an opportunity of seeing the world under exceptionally favourable conditions, is an inducement to young men of spirit such as is scarcely likely to present itself in the ordinary course of civil life." Rates of pay were improved, the right to study leave was granted, and fees and lodging allowance for postgraduate study were allowed. Charge pay was authorised at from 10s. to 2s. 6d. a day, according to rank. The writer admitted that " there is now no difficulty in getting candidates," but pointed out that there were still drawbacks to the Naval Medical Service. One of the greatest was the inferior position of the Director-General, who had no right of access to the First Lord except through one of the Naval Lords. " He is merely a figure-head. His position as head of a department is recognised merely when his official superiors find it convenient to make him a whipping post for their own shortcomings." What countless thousands of lives might have been saved had Sir James Lind, in the eighteenth century, been free to introduce the use of lemon juice into the Navy as an antiscorbutic ? " Everywhere the proper activity of the Medical Officer is hampered by the interference of the executive branch." The same difficulties in the Navy were found as formerly in the Army, owing to the surgeons' lack of disciplinary power over sick-bay attendants and hospital personnel. The frequent practice of keeping a number of medical officers of a fleet in port on duty at once, instead of instituting a system of medical guards, under which only one or two would be constantly on duty, had been adversely commented on again and again. The absence of definite rank, and the consequent bad treatment of medical officers, in the allotment of cabins was an old and rankling sore, together with certain social disabilities due to the snobbishness of certain executive officers, which only definite rank could check. The justice of the *Journal's* criticisms was shown by experience. By the year 1906 the Admiralty had found it necessary to appoint the Durnford Committee, which reported in 1909.

143

In 1909 the *Journal* found it necessary to condemn in strong terms the state of things exposed by the Court Martial on Fleet Surgeon Matthew. This officer was accused by his Commander (his junior in years and only his equal in rank) of behaving with contempt towards him and wilfully disobeying his commands. Fleet Surgeon Matthew was honourably acquitted, but soon afterwards retired.

Later in the same year the Naval and Military Committee of the Association successfully urged the right of naval medical officers to receive coroners' fees for evidence and post-mortem examinations at inquests. This anomaly was removed by an amendment to the King's Regulations in 1910.

The Durnford Report was not favourably received at the Admiralty, and only the shortage of candidates for commissions and the probability that if it were held back much more sweeping changes would be forced upon them, induced the authorities to give effect to its recommendations in the new regulations of 1911. (*See* Supplement to *B.M.J.*, 1911, Vol. II, p. 329, for text of Admiralty Circular Letter, No. 24.)

In a leading article (*B.M.J.*, 1911, Vol. II, p. 1116) the Editor welcomed the new regulations. The most important change was the formation of a medical school, at the Royal Naval College, Greenwich, and at Haslar, and the introduction of compulsory post-graduate instruction. Another excellent reform was the regulation that the Principal Medical Officer of a Fleet should have a place on the staff of the Commander-in-Chief. Promotion to administrative grades was to be by selection, and promotion to Staff Surgeon to be subject to examination with compulsory retirement after two failures to pass. An extension of charge pay was provided for. Notwithstanding these improved conditions, some of the old causes of dissatisfaction remained, such as rank and the allotment of cabins, control of sick-bay staff, etc., and within three years there was once more trouble. In the *Journal* (1914, Vol. I, p. 497) an article under the heading " The Increased Shortage of Medical Officers for the Navy," explained that, owing to the concentration of our naval forces in home seas, " The Navy is no longer the pleasant and varied service it

144

was when the country had considerable squadrons on all the seas of the globe," and, consequently, while the Army Medical Service had for several years been up to or over its full strength of upwards of 1,000 officers, and there was keen competition for vacancies, in the Navy there was a great shortage.

A report, of which the following is the gist, was drawn up and approved by the Council, and forwarded to the Admiralty. It pointed out that in the Army there was one medical officer to every 244 personnel, in the Navy one to 390, although there was much greater isolation of units in the latter. The complaints made of over-work in shore medical establishments and consequent lack of leave, and of study leave for all, must therefore be well founded. The following were the remedies suggested (Supplement to *B.M.J.*, 1914, Vol. II, p. 34) :—

1. Improved remuneration. The Navy, which out of consideration of its hardships used to be better paid, was now worse paid than the Army.

2. Increased opportunities for professional study.

3. Creation of a comparatively fair number of appointments for specialists, carrying extra pay, in such subjects as Operative Surgery, Electro-Therapeutics, Bacteriology, Venereal Diseases, Physical Training, State Medicine ; additional professorships at the R.N. Medical School, Greenwich, at present glaringly understaffed.

It is now a matter of common knowledge what a great and far-reaching economy such appointments have effected in the Army. In the words of Lord Haldane, " They have repaid the outlay over and over again."

4. Medical officers should be placed on half-pay only at their own request, or on account of misconduct.

5. Fixed headquarters, known in the Navy as " Port of Division." This would reduce frequency of uncertain and expensive movements of homes.

6. Suggested roster, from which officers could get longer notice of changes of station, etc.

7. Graduated charge pay, securing such pay for medical officers in ships having smaller complements than 650.

8. Leave. At present the R.A.M.C. has 60 days' leave in the year, the Navy only 42, and abroad only 14 days a year is allowed to accumulate.

9. An increased number of higher appointments, for which there is plenty of useful work.

10. Relative rank.

11. Withdrawal on gratuity.

12. Improved widows' pensions—on at least as good a scale as in the Army. Good service pensions on as good a scale as in the other branches of the Naval Service.

13. Diminution of executive interference in medical affairs.

14. Courts Martial. Representation of the Medical Service on such when medical officers or other personnel of the Medical Branch are on trial ; as in the Army.

The remaining three sections dealt with the old but real grievances connected with boats, cabins, and mess presidencies, etc.

Within a month of the date of publication of this report the country was at war, and all questions of peace reform were necessarily postponed indefinitely. The Association busied itself with helping the Admiralty to find medical officers " for the duration of the war " as described in another section of this work.

In 1919 new rates of pay for naval medical officers were promulgated, but nevertheless by the year 1920 the naval shoe was beginning to pinch the medical foot again. A letter appeared in the *Journal* (1920, Vol. II, pp. 917-18), signed by " Six Naval Medical Officers," detailing their grievances and stating that in their opinion " all candidates would be well advised to steer clear of the Naval Medical Service."

In 1919 the Admiralty introduced a regulation which provided that as from January 1st, 1920, Commanders (including Surgeon Commanders) were to retire at the age of 50 instead of 55 (Supplement to *B.M.J.*, 1925, Vol. I, p. 160). This meant a loss of about £440 for each year of service lost, and it was felt that these officers had been unjustly treated. The feeling was aggravated by the small increase in pension (about 10 per cent.) given to Surgeon Commanders in the 1919 revision. Repeated representations were made by the Association to First Lords, the Parliamentary Secretary and Members of Parliament, but failed to obtain even an acknowledgment of the existence of a grievance, and the Council placed the full facts before the profession through the *Journal*, and advised members of the profession who might be considering joining the Navy seriously to consider the disadvantages to which they would be liable.

This position was approved by the Representative Meeting in Glasgow in 1922, and no statement concerning the conditions of service in the Royal Naval Medical Service appeared in the educational numbers of the *Journal* for the years 1922 to 1924.

As a result of the shortage of medical officers, the Admiralty received a deputation from the Association in January, 1924, and in November made an offer that was considered inadequate. The Admiralty then offered to increase the gratuity offered to Surgeon Commanders from £250 to £300, and the Council, after consulting the officers affected, accepted the terms and decided no longer to discourage candidates.

Notwithstanding these improvements and those effected on the recommendation of the Interdepartmental Committee of the three forces appointed in 1925, the Service did not succeed in attracting suitable candidates, and in 1930, when the Association undertook an exhaustive inquiry into the position of all three branches of the medical service of the defence forces, much anxious consideration was devoted to its needs. As a result of this inquiry the Council of the Association made urgent representations to the Admiralty, which it reinforced by giving evidence before the Committee appointed by the Prime Minister in June, 1931, to investigate the causes of the shortage of officers and nurses in the medical and dental branches of the three Defence Services. The matter is still under consideration by this body.

THE ASSOCIATION AND THE ARMY MEDICAL SERVICE

THE Association quite early in its career championed the cause of the medical officers of the Army, and did its best to obtain removal of their grievances. This for a long time appeared to be likely to prove but a labour of Sisyphus, for as soon as the Government of the day had granted a measure of reform and redress the War Office and the higher " combatant " officials set to work to whittle it away to nothing or next to nothing by administrative measures and orders. It has only been by untiring vigilance and persistence that the profession, chiefly through the Association, has succeeded in improving the rank, pay and status of the medical officers of the defence forces. Indeed, the record of Parliament and the politicians in this connection has not been one of which the nation can be proud. The medical service of the Army has in former times been prevented from officially placing its requirements before the Government in peace time, and has been unjustly blamed for failures in the treatment of the sick and wounded— especially the sick—in time of war. This has been the case again and again, until the last war, when the lessons of South Africa were too recent to have been forgotten. The awful experiences of the Crimean War, redeemed by the heroism of surgeons and nurses, helped by the fortunate fact that the reformer of hospital nursing was on intimate terms with the Secretary of State for War, were borne even more by medical officers than by the combatants of the Army. Many medical officers succumbed to evils which they must have foreseen, but were powerless to prevent.

In the words of Mr. Russell Coombe, in a short history of the Association, published in the *Handbook* of the Association in 1921 :—

148

THE ARMY.

" Even prior to 1850 the Association had begun to act in the interests of Medical Officers in the Army. Attention had become attracted to the want of recognition from which they suffered by the action of George James Guthrie, who was at the time of the incident one of the leading surgeons in London, a member of the Court of Examiners, and afterwards President of the Royal College of Surgeons. He, as a younger man, had served 10 or 12 years as an Army Surgeon, and in common with many others who had served with distinction in the Peninsula Campaign and early Indian Wars, had received no recognition beyond that of mention in Despatches. He deliberately refused the honour of a Companionship of the Bath, when he found that it was proposed to place him in the Civil division, and pointed out that, if he were entitled to the honour at all, it was the Military C.B. that he should receive.

" Even mention in Despatches was an innovation, said to be due to the friendship existing between Wellington and his principal medical officer, McGrigor, the latter having pointed out that medical officers should at least be mentioned in Despatches, since while combatant officers had to remain in the trenches for only eight hours, the surgeons had to remain in them for 24 hours at a time.

" The Association took the matter up and made representations to Parliament.

" Beyond this, Army Medical Officers suffered from other injustices. Despite the fact that deaths from wounds and disease were quite as high as amongst other officers, and that a surgeon habitually accompanied storming parties and other dangerous services, there was a tendency to regard them merely as a kind of camp follower. They were classed, for instance, as civilians, and in contrast to combatant officers got no pensions for wounds.

" Moreover, the conditions of admission to the Service, and of promotion and so on, were highly unsatisfactory. Thus, in 1837, a successful candidate in the examination might have to wait years for a commission as Assistant Surgeon, with the rank and pay of a lieutenant, plus 1s. a day.

" In 1840, out of 310 Assistant Surgeons on the list, 30 had served more than 20 years without promotion.

" Thus it came to pass that in 1850 the Association presented a memorial to Parliament on the subject.

" The Crimean War and Indian Mutiny were a time unsuitable for urging changes and reformation, but the highly unsatisfactory occurrences (scandals is probably a more appropriate word) connected with those campaigns led the Association to present, in 1857, a much more comprehensive memorial than had been previously drawn up.

" It was claimed that the Medical Services, both of the Navy and of the Army, should be thoroughly re-organised and the conditions of service entirely altered ; that none but regularly educated medical men should ever be engaged, that once commissioned, they should enjoy absolute equality with other officers, that they should have like authority over those serving under them, be equally well provided in respect of pensions, reception of honorary distinctions and other rewards for good service.

" The presentation of this memorial was followed by the issue, in 1858, of a Royal Warrant and new Army Medical Regulations. This did not, however, bring peace, for the fact that the Warrant had raised the Army Medical Department from a subordinate position to one of relative independence and power was bitterly resented by combatant officers of all ranks, and they set themselves to neutralise the effect of the Warrant as much as possible, and it must be confessed they largely succeeded."

The Association was much occupied in the year 1864 with questions of Army medical reform, and the pages of the *Journal* are full of notices of memorials by Branches and deputations to Ministers and to the Commander-in-Chief. The last deputation was introduced by the President of the Royal College of Surgeons, and included many distingished physicians and surgeons in its membership. The deputation asked for various reforms, but particularly for the full restoration of Clause 17 of the Warrant of 1858, with clear definition of the precedence of the medical officer in accordance with his rank, and some guarantee for the enforcement by the Executive of the Warrants which define the terms under which medical men enter the Army ; also some security that principles recognised and regulations issued after long

150

and careful deliberation should not be modified in their essential features without an inquiry at least as comprehensive as that on which they were originally founded.

The British Medical Journal for 1864 (Vol. II, p. 16) gives the following extract from Lord Dalhousie's minute of the Report of the Commission on the Sanitary State of the Army (1858) :—

" 35. But the most galling, the most unmeaning and purposeless regulation by which a sense of inferiority is imposed upon medical officers, is by the refusal to them of substantive rank. The Surgeon and Assistant Surgeon rank invariably with the Captain and Lieutenant ; but the rank is only nominal whenever medical officers and others are brought together on public duty ; the former has no rank at all, and the oldest surgeon on the list must, in such case, range himself below the youngest ensign last posted to a Corps.

" 36. It is impossible to conceive how such a system as this can have been maintained so long on the strength of no better argument than that ' it has been,' therefore ' it ought to be.' It is impossible to imagine what serious justification can be offered for a system which in respect of external position, postpones service to inexperience, cunning to ignorance, age to youth ; a system which gives a subaltern, who is hardly free from his drill, precedence over his elder, who perhaps has served through every campaign for thirty years ; a system which treats a member of a learned profession, a man of ability, skill and experience, as inferior in position to a cornet of cavalry, just entering on the study of the pay and audit regulations ; a system in fine which thrusts down grey-headed veterans below beardless boys."

That part of Mr. Russell Coombe's Historical Sketch which deals with the relations of the Association with the Medical Service of the Army at this period is so admirable, yet concise, that it has been thought best to quote it *in extenso* :—

" In the early 'seventies the Minister unfortunately took counsel of a personal friend who was not in a position to give informed advice, and thereon a fresh Warrant was issued, one, as *The British Medical Journal* immediately remarked, foredoomed to failure.

L

"Surgeons were therein classed as either Administrative or Executive Officers, but the unified corps to which they were supposed to belong practically did not exist, and some of the regiments to which they were attached declined to recognise them as their fellows.

"An Army Surgeon was, in effect, no longer either a civilian or a soldier ; his relative rank brought no advantage ; his promotion was blocked ; his retiring terms were bad ; he might be forced to keep a horse, but was not certain to receive forage allowance ; he had no mess room of his own, and if attached to a regiment, he had no definite right in the mess room of its officers ; his time was liable to be entirely occupied by returns, and except as a possible witness, he played no part on boards even when they dealt with strictly medical subjects. When he worked in hospitals it was under the command of a combatant officer, and he had no authority over his own orderlies.

"The Association was not long in taking steps to remedy matters. It drew up a complete list of the evils which existed, and presented this to the Minister at an interview. A short extract from the Minister's reply is worth quoting :—

' The Medical Officers of the Army were very fortunate in having a civil power of magnitude and influence like this Association to represent their interest in deputations, and this was what other parts of the Army had not. The advantage in being thus represented was very great.'

"A few concessions were made, but the fight continued and was carried on by the Association with such intensity that, shortly before the Government was forced to give way, a semi-official attack appeared in the *Army and Navy Gazette*, accusing the Association of having seriously injured the Army by depriving it of Medical Officers.

"Nevertheless, in 1879 a new code of Army Regulations unified the Army Hospital Corps with the Army Medical Department, abolished the remains of the old regimental system, ousted combatant officers from control of hospitals, provided for trained male nurses under the command of the surgeons, and in many other ways improved the position of Medical Officers.

" Still it left some questions, including that of rank, unsettled, and so the warfare continued until in 1887 the Director-General attended the Annual Meeting of the Association, and while expressing the indebtedness of the Service to the Association, endeavoured to dissuade it from pressing this particular claim.

" The Meeting was, however, not satisfied and decided to make personal inquiries from all Medical Officers at home and abroad. The Association received some 800 answers, and on the result of the analysis thereof it decided to press for this particular reform.

" This resulted in a Departmental Committee being appointed which recommended the composite title scheme ; the Army Medical Service was still a ' department,' the ' camp-follower ' idea still prevailed. In the evidence before the Camperdown Committee great stress was laid on the fact that the combatant branches of the Service tended to treat the Medical Officers as civilians. Even so late as 1897 an instance is quoted in the *Journal* of the relative treatment of the Army Surgeon :—

' At one of our foreign stations a road was being made in an unhealthy district. All the men received extra pay. The officers, whose duties consisted in mustering the men and marching them to work, received special allowances. The Medical Officers had to visit each man once or twice every day, which involved making a circuit of from 8 to 10 miles. They received no allowance whatever.'

" The Association returned to the charge, and the next few years were years of strenuous endeavour on the part of the Association.

" In 1896, owing to matters having apparently reached a deadlock, the Parliamentary Bills Committee, on the motion of Dr. W. Gordon, of Exeter, instructed by the South-Western Branch, appointed a Sub-Committee to consider the question of Army Medical Reform. Dr. Gordon was appointed Chairman, and to his personal efforts are to be attributed the great success of the Association in achieving the creation of the Army Medical Corps. It is not to be wondered at that, at the succeeding Annual Meeting, the thanks of the whole Association were awarded him on the success of his efforts.

" On investigation by this Sub-Committee it became quite clear that, without Army rank and Military titles, Medical Officers could not maintain their authority either in peace or in war, since neither junior ' Combatant ' Officers or their men understood any other sort of rank or title. Accordingly a Report was drawn up and submitted confidentially to forty Army Medical Officers of all ranks. Their replies were full and important and a Memorandum was prepared embodying them. The Report was modified to accord therewith, and forwarded to Lord Lansdowne, then Secretary of State for War.

" In January, 1897, this Report was sent to the Dean of every Medical School in the Kingdom, with a letter to ask him, without actually dissuading any candidate, to bring it to the notice of every man contemplating entering the Service.

" In February, 1897, Mr. Brodrick announced in the House of Commons the concession of some minor points, e.g. :—

Increases of pay whilst on service in India.
Indian tour reduced from six to five years.
Study-leave on return from foreign service.

" He stated, however, that ' none of the proposals which have been submitted to the Secretary of State for giving new forms of Army rank to the Medical Staff ' appeared to him ' advisable for adoption.'

" After the February Examinations the Report was brought up to date and re-issued with an appendix. Copies were sent to every Medical School, and on this occasion a further important step was taken in also sending copies to the Editors of all the leading newspapers in the Kingdom.

" The Senatus of the University of Edinburgh was the first to record and forward a minute approving and supporting the Report, and many favourable leading articles appeared in the Press.

" After the August Examinations the Report was again brought up to date and re-issued as on the previous occasion, but with the important points emphasised by heavy type.

" This time the result was most remarkable. The Report had such a ' good Press ' as to be practically unanimous in calling for the reforms advocated therein.

154

"Lord Lansdowne agreed to receive a deputation, which he did in January, 1898. The deputation included representatives deputed by the Universities of Cambridge, Edinburgh, Dublin and Aberdeen, the Royal College of Physicians of Ireland, the Royal College of Surgeons of Ireland and the Society of Apothecaries.

"The deputation was very favourably received, and a little later on a message was received from the War Office offering to concede all the reforms demanded if only the title of 'General' were waived. The alternative suggestion was then made by a well-known Surgeon-General that the hard-won Army rank should be bartered for 'relative rank' and the title of 'General'! This suggestion could obviously not be entertained, and the terms of the War Office were accepted.

"The formation of a Royal Army Medical Corps with Army rank and Military titles was announced by Lord Lansdowne at a banquet at the Mansion House on May 4th, 1898, and a Warrant was issued in due course. Thus the Royal Army Medical Corps came into existence.

"After the South African War considerable reconstitutions, with a view to still further improving the conditions of service and increasing the popularity of the Corps, took place, and it is no secret that the changes adopted were, in the main, points that had been put forward by the Association. The first step was the appointment of an expert Committee of the War Office in 1901 by the Secretary of State for War (Mr. Brodrick). This Committee reported on September 30th, 1901. Certain reforms were recommended, but the representations of the Association with regard to the reforms most urgently needed had been ignored. From the date of the publication of the Report the Association threw its full weight into an effort to secure adequate status and authority for the Service, and certain minor reforms. When the Royal Warrant was issued in March, 1902, the success of this campaign became apparent.

"The *Journal* commented on the situation as follows :—
'Questions relating to the position of the Medical Service of the Army have been before the Association almost without intermission for nearly fifty years, and although there have been periods of retrogression, on the whole very distinct progress

155

has been made. Some points still remain for settlement, but it is hoped that the Service now organised in a Royal Corps with improved pay and increased facilities for professional advancement, may become contented, and, therefore, prove attractive to young medical men.'

" The Association had, indeed, been successful in securing a place for the Director-General on the Army Board. The more important recommendations with regard to promotion had been accepted ; pay had been increased, and pension rights, threatened for a time, secured. The more important recommendations with regard to the examination system had also been conceded. Unfortunately, the Esher Committee undid an important part of the work of the Brodrick Committee. The whole administration of the War Office was brought under review, and in the newly constituted Army Council the Director-General had no place. The position attained under the Brodrick scheme has consequently to be fought over again."

A great step in advance was taken when the Director-General of the Army Medical Department was by the Brodrick Committee given a seat on the Army Board, but this step was retraced when the Esher Committee recommended the formation of the Army Council, from which the Director-General was excluded. It is true that during the Great War the Director-General was invited to attend meetings of the Army Council, but he had no voice in its decisions, and after attending one meeting he took no further part in its work.

At present (1932) the R.A.M.C. is under the Adjutant-General, and is represented by him on the Army Council.

Improvements in the status and consequent usefulness of the Medical Officers of the Army have, generally speaking, only been granted when it became clear that candidates for commissions were not coming forward, and would not come forward, until the conditions of service were improved. By means of articles in the *Journal*, and by putting the facts clearly before the Medical Schools and leaving them to speak for themselves, the Association has had a very powerful influence in improving the rank, status and pay of the medical officers of the two older Services. Deputations to

156

Ministers and agitation in Parliament have no doubt had their effects, but most of the great reforms have only been granted when a reluctant War Office found itself face to face with such a dearth of candidates that a breakdown of the system seemed to be in sight.

At the time of writing the Army under present conditions has evidently lost its attraction for recently qualified men. There is a great shortage of officers, especially in the junior ranks, so much so that in many cases Majors have to do Orderly duties which normally should fall to the lot of Captains. Entry by competitive examination has had to be temporarily suspended, and selection after interview substituted, but even this desperate resource appears to have failed to provide enough aspirants for commissions. And this in spite of the fact that in 1929 the Association felt justified in recommending the Services in the following terms :—

" The rates of pay and conditions of service for the Royal Naval Medical Service, the Royal Army Medical Corps, the Royal Air Force Medical Service, and the Indian Medical Service are considered by the British Medical Association to be satisfactory. In point of fact, the present conditions of service, more particularly in the case of the R.A.M.C. and I.M.S., are largely the result of the action of the Association. In fulfilment of the desire of the Association to assist in recruiting these services we publish below full particulars.

" There still appears to be considerable difficulty in getting a sufficient number of young medical officers to enter any of these Services, and the Association desires to point out that in its opinion the prospects in them are both financially and professionally good, and that there is no reason why young men recently qualified should not enter them. In the case of the R.A.M.C. the prospects of rapid promotion are particularly good, owing to the prolonged shortage of candidates since the War. Another important point should be noted, namely—the concession, in the case of the R.N.M.S., R.A.M.C. and the R.A.F.M.S., by which a newly qualified medical man can hold a hospital appointment for one year before entering the Services, counting it as a year of service towards promotion, and retirement."
(*British Medical Journal*, 1929, Vol. II, p. 430.)

157

The continued dearth of candidates could not fail to attract the attention of the Association, and a comprehensive inquiry into the position was undertaken in 1930. Recommendations based upon this inquiry were submitted to the Committee already referred to in connection with the Naval Medical Service, appointed by the Prime Minister, and met with a favourable reception. The Committee has not yet reported, and the present conditions are hardly conducive to any effective action in the near future.

It has not only been in assertion and defence of the rights of Army Medical Officers as a body that the Association has exerted itself. It has intervened with great effect in the causes of individuals who have been unjustly treated. One example of such action will suffice.

The case of Surgeon-Major Briggs was referred to in the Report of the Council in 1892. It was an astonishing instance of foul play in high places, such as was unfamiliar to a public which had not yet heard of the Dreyfus case. This officer, who had distinguished himself in the Soudan campaign, was ordered to go to India fifteen months before he was due to serve in that country. It may have been only a coincidence that he had just been cited to appear as a co-respondent in a suit for divorce brought by Lord Connemara against his wife. Surgeon-Major Briggs appealed to the military authorities against their order, representing that his honour was involved and that of Lady Connemara, and that he felt bound to remain in the United Kingdom until the suit should be decided. He was met with a firm refusal. Thereupon he felt that no other course was open to him but retirement from the Service. Lord Connemara's petition was dismissed and Lady Connemara and Briggs were exonerated. The latter applied for reinstatement in his former rank in the Service. This was granted, but with loss of pay and seniority. Urged by the British Medical Association and the Medical M.Ps., Dr. Farquharson and Sir Walter Foster, the Secretary of War (Mr. Stanhope) overrode the decision of the Horse Guards and reinstated Surgeon-Major Briggs in his proper rank and seniority. Without the pressure applied in the House of Commons there would have been no hope of justice for this officer. In announcing his decision, in reply to a question put by Dr. Farquharson in the House of Commons on March 22nd, 1892, Mr. Stanhope said : " I am of opinion that Surgeon-Major Briggs should not suffer any loss as regards position or promotion in consequence of an act which any gentleman was bound to perform, and which he performed under a pressure which no one could have resisted. Dr. Briggs will, therefore, be restored to the seniority which he held before retirement." This was all very well as far as it went, but no public censure was officially passed upon those persons of high rank in the Service who must have been to blame for instigating, or at least countenancing, what appeared to have been the persecution of a meritorious officer.

THE INDIAN MEDICAL SERVICE

THE Medical Service of the Indian Empire has not been without its troubles, although they have differed in character from those of the British Army. Questions of relative and substantive rank have been far less prominent in India, but questions of pay and promotion and the preservation of privileges acquired before the Indian Mutiny have been of great importance.

During the twenty-five years that passed between the foundation of the Provincial Medical Association and the outbreak of the Mutiny, the Association found no cause to intervene between the Honourable East India Company and its medical officers. The Service dated from the year 1786 according to an "apologia" by Surgeon-Major Cornish, which was quoted at some length in a leading article of *The British Medical Journal*. No influence had been so strong in reconciling the masses of India to British rule as that of the Medical Service, which also had trained and educated Indians to become physicians and surgeons fit to carry on the treatment of their fellow countrymen. The reputation of the Service was very high, whether as military surgeons or as medical officers to civil hospitals, or administrators and governors of prisons and so forth. They had opportunities of improving their professional skill and knowledge which were, unfortunately, denied to their brethren of the British Army, and an enormous field of experience, especially in ophthalmic and urinary surgery, lay open to them, of which not a few officers fully availed themselves. In the civil branch, which included nearly half of the officers of the Indian Service, there were lucrative opportunities of practice among Europeans and natives.

After the Mutiny, when the Company ceased to rule and the Crown took over its duties, the European Artillery and Infantry in the Company's service were incorporated in the British Army, carrying with them all their combatant, but none of their medical, officers, to whom, by Act of Parliament, 21 and 22 of Queen Victoria, all the advantages they enjoyed under the Company were guaranteed by the Crown. But through misunderstandings—for it is incredible that the breach of faith was intentional—these fair promises were not kept. In 1864 rumours of amalgamation of the Indian and British Army Services were current and recorded in *The British Medical Journal*, which roundly asserted that the provisions of the new Royal Warrant were breaches of the undertaking, being alterations of existing rules for promotion, the continuance of which had been guaranteed by the Act. After question in Parliament, a Royal Commission was appointed " to inquire whether the guarantee given to the Officers of the late East Indian Army had or had not been departed from." Later on, the Secretary of State for India, Sir Charles Wood (afterwards Lord Halifax), said in the House of Commons that a plan of amalgamation had been adopted and that he hoped that before long it would be promulgated. But there were unaccountable delays in issuing the Warrant, partly no doubt due to the slowness of communication between London and Calcutta.

But perhaps, unfortunately for India, the scheme of unification of the Indian and British Medical Services fell through. " The then Director-General of the Medical Department of the Army, the late Sir James Gibson, an honourable and estimable man, but a narrow-minded and prejudiced official, was bitterly opposed to a measure that, if it had been carried out at the time on the just and liberal terms proposed by Sir Charles Wood, would have saved a very large sum of money to the finances of India, have promoted the interests of both Services, and for ever have extinguished paltry jealousies which, very little to their credit, were encouraged by some who put Service interests first and the public weal nowhere " (*British Medical Journal*, Vol. I, 1880, p. 134). The writer quoted instances of duplication of offices, waste of money, and inefficiency resulting therefrom.

Notwithstanding this expression of opinion from a distinguished Indian Officer, it seems now, on looking back at the subsequent history of the two Services, that the amount of autonomy which was enjoyed by the Indian Service was beneficial to that Service and to the Europeans and natives of India who came under its care. To this view the Association as represented by its journal came round before many years. Meanwhile, in 1864 discontent and distrust of the Government's intentions was general, and Indian Medical Officers, writing in the *Journal*, warned young surgeons not to enter the Service, on account of the non-fulfilment of the promises of the Warrant as regards rank and pay and allowances. Instances were quoted which were described as breaches of faith—being alterations of pre-existing rules for promotion, the continuance of which had been guaranteed by the Act of Parliament passed on the transfer of the administration of India to the Crown. The sore was merely scabbed over and not soundly healed. By 1880 discontent was widespread, as the correspondence and editorial columns of the *Journal* showed. Early in that year (*B.M.J.*, 1880, Vol. I, p. 405) a leading article described how " on January 3rd the Government of India with one stroke of the pen had swept away all the Surgeons-General of the Indian Service, and decided that in future the head of the Service in each of the three Presidencies is to be an officer of the British Medical Department—thus converting the Medical Service of India into a subordinate branch of the Medical Department of the British Army." The writer asserted with truth that this was a distinct breach of the promises established by Act of Parliament under which the Company's officers entered the Royal Service, and condemned the change in the strongest terms. Probably as a result of such protests and the action of the Parliamentary Bills Committee, what was officially called a " continuation order," dated March 15th, 1880, was promulgated, yielding to the complaints of the Service and the profession, and restoring the Indian Medical Service to a great extent. There still remained, however, unfair conditions of pay, promotion and pension which needed revision. The *Journal*, however, approved of the separation of the civil from the military branch which had been effected, as far as administration was concerned. But although deprecating the putting of the claims of the Service before the public weal,

162

it pointed out (*British Medical Journal*, 1880, Vol. II, p. 746) that the popularity of the Service had been rudely shaken. " For a long time the Indian Service commanded the best-qualified men in the medical market, but at the last examination the Army Medical candidates took higher places than the Indian Medical Service. It was so right through the list." " Nothing like this state of things has been known since the Army Medical School was established. Is it the beginning of the end ? "

Among other grievances the *Journal* instanced these :—

" Placing Indian medical officers in arduous and responsible positions, often on active service and in some of the worst climates in the world, as in the Passes of Afghanistan, on what is insolently called ' unemployed pay,' whilst their juniors in the British Service merely doing duty with their regiments draw the full allowance of their rank. No notice of this is ever given to Indian candidates by the India Office ; they are left to find it out when they arrive in India. The attention of our readers has more than once been called to another, perhaps the greatest, affront ever put upon a body of officers : the names of Indian medical officers who had distinguished themselves in Afghanistan, and were mentioned in despatches, were withheld from the Gazettes. . . . It would be well for intending competitors unless the above inequalities are removed between this and the next examination to think once, twice and thrice before they commit their fortunes to an Indian career."

In the year 1900 the Indian Medical Service was put to a severe strain. As an editorial in the *Journal* stated, the expeditionary force which was sent, together with troops of other powers, to China, took with it a large number of the Indian medical staff, for the Indian troops formed the bulk of the British contingent and were very properly accompanied by an unusually large number of medical units. In order to find the officers required, 87 officers in civil employ had to be lent by local governments and probably more would be wanted.

This strain came upon an already sorely tested Service, which had been overworked owing to cholera, plague and famine, for the last five years, so that obviously some augmentation of the establishment had become necessary, and even the separation of the civil and military duties, by the creation of a separate sanitary service, might have to be considered.

A number of well-informed correspondents communicated to the *Journal* their opinions and records of their experience, from which it appears that the opportunities offered in India had much depreciated of late years. Private practice, which formerly had been lucrative, was passing or had passed into the hands of civilians, both European and Indian, and well-paid appointments were scarcer than of old. It was therefore not strange that candidates for commissions were not coming forward in sufficient numbers.

There was still unrest in the Service in 1903, as correspondence and editorial articles in the *Journal* showed, but it was pointed out in a leader (*British Medical Journal*, 1903, Vol. II, p. 375) that the Association was handicapped in its attempts to improve the position of the Indian Medical Service by the divergence of views among the members of that Service as to the causes of complaint and the measures necessary to restore it to a happy and contented state. The Council of the Association presented a full report on the situation to the Annual Meeting held at Swansea.

This diversity of opinion was partly due to the dual functions of the Service, which consists of two branches— Civil and Military. Their duties differ, and their grievances likewise, but some of the latter are common to both. For instance, loss of private practice, due to the education of a number of native gentlemen, affected chiefly the civil branch; the appointment of R.A.M.C. officers to the most important military appointments was a grievance to the military branch. The depreciation of the rupee and increased cost of living affected both. There were other troubles which made the Service as a career unattractive and prevented the best men from coming forward as candidates.

New regulations had adversely affected the civil branch. One of the most offensive of these put severe limitations on private practice, so that no officer was allowed to accept a larger fee than Rs. 50 (£3 6s. 8d.) for a single visit, no matter at what distance, or more than Rs. 1,000 (£66 13s. 4d.) for a whole year's attendance,

164

without the permission of the Provincial Government. The Indian papers were full of instances of the mean and apparently envious spirit in which the Government officials executed these ordinances.

These and many other grievances were set forth in the Report which the Council forwarded to the Secretary of State. Lord George Hamilton, however, showed no sympathy with them. His attitude was a strictly commercial one, and amounted to the contention that as long as candidates came forward there was no need of change. The *Journal* warned him that if he persisted, he or his successor would find himself in a similar position to that of the Secretary of State for War some years previously, when the profession practically boycotted the Army Medical Service, so that he was obliged to surrender to its moderate demands. But, as in August, 1903, there were 41 candidates for 16 appointments, the Minister probably thought he could afford to disregard complaints. In October the India Office issued a memorandum (*British Medical Journal*, 1903, Vol. II, p. 861) on the position of officers to be appointed to the Service as affecting the military branch, which showed a more conciliatory disposition on the part of the authorities. The memorandum, however, showed no intention of improving the position of the officers in civil employment, who were nearly half the officers in the Service.

The Order of 1907, severely restricting the conditions under which fees might be accepted from natives of India by members of the Indian Medical Service and limiting their amount, which had been so strongly resented by the Service as a breach of the regulating Act of 1857, was revised and modified on the representations made by the Association in 1911.

In 1913 there was still trouble, and the India Office, brought face to face with the fact that the standard of ability of the candidates for commissions as well as their numbers had fallen off, consulted the Association, which reported on the question through its Council to the Secretary of State in October of that year.

This report had been drawn up independently, and was intended for publication in the *Journal* in a series of articles, but it was withheld till February, 1914, when

165

it appeared in the Supplement. It was a masterly document, which dealt with the subject under a number of headings without exaggeration or rancour. Shortly stated, the reasons for the then existing state of things were much the same as those formerly stated. Some of the circumstances were due to causes beyond the control of the Government. Others were the result of the deliberate policy of the India Office and the Government of India, such as the restrictions placed upon private practice, which were intended to encourage Indian-born civilian practitioners, and had had that effect to the detriment of the members of the Service. The further suggested curtailment of private practice was looked upon as a breach of solemn undertakings given to the Service and confirmed by Act of Parliament. Inadequate pay, considering the fall in the value of the rupee, scarcity of leave and a number of vexations which might seem petty to civilians in Europe, but which mounted up to very serious burdens on an overworked Service, were carefully and temperately stated. The inferior position of the Surgeons-General in their relations to the local governments affected only a few individuals, but, through them, militated against the prestige and efficiency of the whole Service. The status of District Medical Officers was at the same time unsatisfactory. The report pointed out that in the Civil Branch of the Indian Medical Service the Government had a war reserve of medical officers which was unequalled anywhere and was the envy of foreign governments, and that in lowering the position of these officers it was endangering the efficiency and the very existence of this valuable asset.

The outbreak of the World War prevented action on the Council's Report to the Secretary of State, and it was not till four years later that the question was re-opened.

In the summer of 1918 the Association warmly supported the officers of the Indian Medical Service in their efforts to get their grievances redressed. A deputation, led by the President, Sir Clifford Allbutt, Regius Professor of Physic at Cambridge, waited on the Secretary of State for India, Mr. Montagu.

The chief points dealt with were :—

166

THE GREAT HALL
BRITISH MEDICAL ASSOCIATION HOUSE
LONDON

THE GREAT HALL
BRITISH MEDICAL ASSOCIATION HOUSE
LONDON

1. The inadequate scale of remuneration.
2. The difficulty in obtaining leave and study leave.
3. The constant, irritating and damaging interference with private practice. ‑
4. The unsatisfactory position of the Director-General and Surgeons-General in relation to the Government of India and the Local Government.

Lieut.-Colonel R. H. Elliot, I.M.S. (ret.), the vigilant Chairman of the Naval and Military Committee of the Association, obtained permission to read a statement on the action taken by the British Medical Association with regard to the Indian Medical Service. It recalled the fact that in September, 1913, the Secretary of State for India asked the British Medical Association to assist him to ascertain the causes of the very serious falling off in the number and quality of the candidates for positions in the Indian Medical Service. The Association prepared a memorandum on the (then) present position and future prospects of the Service, which was forwarded to the Secretary of State in October, 1913 (*B.M.J.*, Supplement, February 7th, 1914). This memorandum had been placed before the Royal Commission on Public Services in India during its session in London in July, 1914. When the Commissioner's report had been published in January, 1917, the Association had recorded its profound concern and disappointment with the whole trend of the report and its recommendations. In his reply the Secretary of State recognised the condition of affairs in the Service and promised consideration of the questions raised. In 1919 the following statement by the Secretary of State as to the future of the Service was made public. Grade pay to be increased $33\frac{1}{3}$ per cent. Promises were made as to leave and study leave and private practice, etc. Lieut.-Colonel Elliot, on behalf of the Association, promised "that we will do what we can to support you in getting officers for that Service." But however sincere in his promises the Secretary of State might be, the administrative officers behind him were not going to yield without a struggle. In 1919 it became necessary for another deputation to wait on the Secretary of State for India to complain of the delay in carrying out the promises made by Mr. Montagu to the deputation of the previous year.

Lieut.-Colonel Elliot said that officers still found leave closed to them. " They have become increasingly exasperated, and consequently difficult of persuasion." With regard to pay, " the Financial Department of the Government of India have contrived so to deal with the figures that the concession you (the Secretary of State) made has not, in fact, fulfilled the hopes and expectations with which it was received."

Criticism in the Service was very active. Three points were raised by the critics of the Services Committee of the Association.

1. The question of free passages to and from India.
2. That the pensions of Indian Medical Service officers have not been raised and are very unsatisfactory ; and
3. That the increase of pay recently granted is insufficient.

Mr. Montagu, who had to listen to some very plain speaking, was conciliatory. An early decision was pressed for by Lieut.-Colonel Elliot.

After years of struggle the Government of India was forced by hard facts to capitulate, and in 1920 new and improved terms were announced to the profession.

The Secretary of State had agreed :—

" 1. To increase the pre-War minimum pay by approximately 50 per cent.
2. To grant, in addition, allowances for station hospitals.
3. To maintain the existing allowances to holders of professional and bacteriological appointments and certain other special classes of appointment on the civil side.
4. To increase pensions.
5. To give the same facilities for passages :—
(a) To Indian Medical Service officers in military employ as to combatant officers in the Indian Army.
(b) To Indian Medical Service officers in civil employ as to officers of other Civil Services in India.
6. To give to the Director-General and Surgeons-General the same rights as the Secretary for the Government in the matter of :—
(a) Direct access to the Viceroy or Governor as the case may be ;

168

(*b*) Access to documents and opportunity of forwarding their views to the Viceroy or the Governor as the case may be.

7. That the cadre of the Indian Medical Service should have a reserve of 25 per cent. for furlough and $2\frac{1}{2}$ per cent. for study leave whenever this may be practicable."

Thereupon the Annual Representative Meeting, recognising that the announcement of terms was the crowning success of a struggle which has been waged since 1913, passed the following resolution :—

" That the terms offered by the Secretary of State for India in satisfaction of the demands made by the British Medical Association be accepted, and that the Association now use its best endeavours to help recruiting for the Indian Medical Service.

" The Association promised the Secretary of State for India that as soon as the terms asked for were granted it would do its best to help in obtaining recruits for the Service, and this undertaking will be fulfilled. We now appeal, therefore, to all the officers in the Indian Medical Service who are members of the Association to honour the bargain made on their behalf and to encourage young men to join the Service."

Although the grievances of the officers of the Indian Medical Service had been attended to, no radical reform of the organisation has taken place. The Association had moved in this matter, and in a leading article of the *Journal* the question was dealt with as follows (*B.M.J.*, 1920, Vol. II, p. 535) :—

The Medical Services in India.

" The position of the Indian Medical Service as the pioneer in the teaching and practice of Western Medicine in India had interested the British Medical Association long before the fresh crisis brought about by the War led it to take the matter up again with the Secretary of State for India. In consequence of the representations made to him by the Association, Mr. Montagu, in a despatch of October 11th, 1918, asked the Government of India to examine into the whole mechanism by which the medical needs of India and especially medical education are to be satisfied in future. The Government of India thereupon appointed a Committee, with Sir Verney Lovett as president, to report on the reorganisation of the medical services in India, both civil and military.

" It was a body of experts and took evidence in various parts of India. Its report is a very able State Paper clearly argued from abundance of knowledge, and written with a sense of responsibility that goes far to carry conviction. It very definitely recommends that the only satisfactory scheme in the circumstances is the unification of the medical services in India. It proposes the formation of an Indian Medical Corps, to take the place of the Indian Medical Service, doing the civil and military work now done by it, and also the work now done for the British Army in India by the R.A.M.C. ; this new corps would, in fact, recruit for and include the higher civil medical service of India. It would comprise commissioned officers, the military assistant and sub-assistant surgeons with improved training and better terms of service, the Indian Army Hospital Corps and the Indian Army Bearer Corps.

" The Corps would be started by transferring to it a large number of officers of the I.M.S. and R.A.M.C. under specially favourable conditions. There is, the Committee states, at the present day not only a certain degree of friction, between the two services, but a considerable amount of overlapping and reduplication of effort. The plan proposed would lead to economy in personnel and hospital buildings. At present the authorised ratio of officers R.A.M.C. to strength is 4 per mille, of Indian Medical Service 1·28 per mille ; it is considered that the military cadre of officers for the Indian Medical Corps should provide a ratio of 3 per mille of the total strength of British and Indian troops and followers in the Army in India. It is laid down that the training of the R.A.M.C. and Indian Medical Corps should be parallel, so that it would be easy for officers and men of the two corps to work together when they meet outside the boundaries of India. Further, the two services should be so alike that if in the future an Imperial Medical Service for the whole of the British Empire were established, the Indian Medical Corps would fit into it with the least possible disturbance in its constitution.

170

" This is in brief the Lovett Committee's solution of a problem full of difficulty. It has neither shirked that difficulty nor minimised it ; it has dealt with the matter with a mastery of detail, a breadth of knowledge and a clarity of vision that command respect. The solution offered is logical and the reasoning plain to understand, for it is clear that the unification proposed would eliminate much waste, overlapping, jealousy and schism. It has failed to win the approval of the Army. It is perhaps for this reason that its report, though it has been in the hands of the Government since April, 1919, was only issued on the same day last week as the report of the Esher Committee on the Administration and Organisation of the Army in India. That Committee also was impressed by the desirability of unification, and admits that the Lovett Report puts forward the only feasible scheme for a unified civil and military medical service ; it would be reasonable to expect such a statement to be followed by an endorsement of the scheme, but it is not. The Esher Committee is ' unable to support ' that scheme because it would, after the first selection had been made, permanently exclude the R.A.M.C. from India. This, it is considered, would seriously diminish its opportunities for gaining clinical experience and be disadvantageous to British troops in India. These arguments are not very impressive so far as the welfare of British troops is concerned ; administrative difficulties must always arise during a period when alterations are being made in the Constitution of a Government Service, but they could in this instance be overcome with comparative ease.

" The British Medical Association will, we do not doubt, look at the proposals from the broadest point of view, being interested in the matter as it affects the progress of Western medicine in India and the welfare of the British Army and civil services in that country. The really important thing is to get the best possible medical service for India, a service which will attract the right class of man and will give the Indian Empire the fullest possible value—military, civil and educational. There must be no question of rival interests of the Indian Medical Service and of the R.A.M.C., the welfare of the Empire must stand first. The opinions conveyed

171

to the Secretary of State by the British Medical Association in the past have been formed after full inquiry, and have been pressed in measured terms. There is now, we hope, a great chance of getting the whole question settled in a large way, and silencing for ever petty jealousies that have disfigured the past.

"The Lovett scheme would go a long way towards the attainment of the desired end. There are objections to it, but there are objections to every plan, even the Esher Committee's plan of doing nothing. The Lovett scheme has the conspicuous merit also of showing how the legitimate aspirations of Indians for a share in the Service appointments may be met under certain conditions which would eventually allow them to attain to a large measure of participation in both executive and administrative appointments."

The Medical Secretary, in calling attention to these concessions some months later, wrote :—

"The above concessions are the result of a struggle which has been waged on behalf of the Indian Medical Service by the British Medical Association since 1913. I think you will agree that they represent a very great victory, and should go a long way towards allaying the feeling of dissatisfaction with the Service that undoubtedly exists at the present time. You will doubtless appreciate the fact that this struggle has given a very great amount of work and anxiety to the members of the Naval and Military Committee, and especially to the Chairman, Lieut.-Colonel R. H. Elliot, I.M.S. (ret.). I therefore venture to express the hope that you will show your appreciation of the work of the Association on behalf of your Service and its individual members by at once becoming a member and thereby giving it in the future your moral and financial support. If every member of the Indian Medical Service were a member of the British Medical Association it would very materially assist the Association in impressing the views of the Service on the India Office in any future representations that have to be made."

Notwithstanding improved conditions, which are now considered so satisfactory that the Association recommends recently qualified men to enter the Service, it appears to have ceased to attract them. The whole

172

subject is in the melting pot consequent on recent political developments, and at the time of writing it is impossible to prophesy what the future of the Indian Medical Service may be.

THE PRISON MEDICAL SERVICE.

In addition to the great fighting services and that caring for the sick poor, other medical services did not escape notice. For instance, in an article on " The Convict Service " in 1882 (*British Medical Journal*, 1882, Vol. II, p. 331) attention was drawn to its drawbacks and to the hardships of the medical officers of H.M. Prisons. Poor pay and onerous duties of little technical interest rendered the Service unattractive. The article concluded as follows :—

" Let us earnestly warn our younger professional brethren from entering such a Service, where besides inadequate pay, hard work and great responsibility (to say nothing of liability to assaults from prisoners), the brain is frequently worried by petty annoyances which certainly should not be added to the many cares of a professional man."

The condition of this branch of medical service has frequently been the subject of action by the Association in recent years, and certain improvements have been made largely under its influence.

SHIP SURGEONS.

The position and pay of ship surgeons had long been unsatisfactory, and had from time to time called for notice and remonstrance by the Association, which in 1883 presented a memorial to Mr. Joseph Chamberlain, then President of the Board of Trade, calling his attention to the conditions of the medical service on Atlantic steamships, and especially to the incomplete supervision of emigrants. The defective status of surgeons, their small pay and lack of proper quarters and authority, repelled the better class of men from entering the Service, and so deprived passengers and crews of adequate attention.

Conditions have greatly improved, mainly because the great shipping companies, in their efforts to make their facilities more attractive to passengers, have seen the necessity of improving the conditions of service of their surgeons. These efforts have been watched and encouraged by the Association through a special committee partly composed of past and present ship surgeons. In 1931, by means of a committee of the Association on which were representatives of the London School of Hygiene and Tropical Medicine, the Dreadnought Hospital and various other bodies interested in the post-graduate education of ship surgeons, courses of education suitable for these practitioners have been arranged with the active co-operation and sympathy of the large shipping companies.

THE ASSOCIATION'S
JOURNAL

WHEN the Provincial Medical and Surgical Association was first established, it had no weekly or fortnightly periodical to report its doings and represent its interests. Like other medical societies it published an annual volume of transactions, the first of which appeared in 1833, and was followed by eighteen others, ending with that recording the Annual Meeting of 1852, which appeared in 1853. The eighteenth volume contained reports of the papers read at the Annual Meetings for the years 1850 and 1851. These Transactions have been elsewhere commented on. The last eleven volumes were overlapped, as it were, by the volumes of *The Provincial Medical and Surgical Journal*, a weekly publication of which the first number appeared on October 3rd, 1840, under the joint editorship of Dr. Hennis Green, of London, and Dr. R. J. Streeten, of Worcester. There were other contemporary weekly medical journals, for, as Mr. John Green Crosse, of Norwich, stated in his address to the Annual Meeting of the Provincial Medical and Surgical Association in 1836, there were then seven medical periodicals published in Great Britain, of which three appeared quarterly, one fortnightly and three weekly.

THE PROVINCIAL MEDICAL AND SURGICAL JOURNAL.

The Provincial Medical and Surgical Journal may be considered as the direct ancestor of *The British Medical Journal*, for, although at first its editors did not claim any official connection with the Provincial Association, in the Introductory Address in the first number they mentioned among their objects :—

" Second. The affording a special means of communication for the several medical and branch associations which have been formed in various parts of the Kingdom.

" Third. The promotion as far as possible of the interests of those admirable institutions, and, *more* especially, of those of the Provincial Association."

The first issues were in octavo, which measured, when bound in a volume, seven inches by ten, the first issue containing fifteen pages of reading-matter and three illustrations in the text, besides advertisements. As to the Editors, Dr. Hennis Green was a physician practising in London who made a special study of diseases of children, and Dr. Streeten was physician to the Worcester Infirmary, and thus was in constant communication with Hastings and the other local leaders of the Association.

For its size *The Provincial Medical and Surgical Journal* compared favourably with its contemporaries. On the scientific side it was well supplied with clinical records, and with papers on the practice of medicine and surgery. Its leading articles were well written, in a tone worthy of the high aims of the Association, and free from the vulgar abuse and scurrility which disfigured the pages of some of its contemporaries.

The Journal continued to appear under the same editorship until the end of March, 1844, but in March, 1841, John Williams Rumsey, of 6, Wellington Street, Strand, had become publisher. In 1844 the title-page of Volume VIII bore the following information : "Edited for the Provincial Medical and Surgical Association by Robert J. N. Streeten, Secretary to the Association." At the same time John Churchill became publisher.

The following announcement appeared in a leading article in the issue of April 3rd, 1844 :—

" The present number of this Journal is the first of a new series devoted entirely to the interests of the Provincial Medical and Surgical Association, and published under the control of its Officers and Council. The work will from this time be exclusively the journal of the Association, and no other interests, whether of publisher or proprietor, will be suffered to interfere."

In 1847, as announced on the title-page of Volume XI, William Harcourt Rankin, M.D., became Foreign Editor. He became Joint Editor with John Henry Walsh, F.R.C.S., in 1849, as announced on the title-page of Volume XIII.

176

In January, 1853, the title of the paper was altered to the *Association Medical Journal*, and Dr. (afterwards Sir) John Rose Cormack became Editor. Towards the end of 1855 the Association assumed its present title, and in 1856 the Journal bore on its title-page " edited for the British Medical Association by Dr. Andrew Wynter," who had been Joint Editor with Dr. Cormack for a short time, and became sole Editor in 1856.

For its first ten years *The Provincial Medical and Surgical Journal* appeared weekly, until in the beginning of 1847, from motives of economy, it was changed to a fortnightly journal, and continued as such until it was superseded by the weekly *Association Medical Journal*. Nevertheless, the annual volumes of the fortnightly issue contain more reading matter than their predecessors of the weekly issue, each fortnightly number being larger than two of the previous weekly issue. The saving effected, therefore, if any, must have been in postage and covers only.

The metropolitan rivals of the Journal posed at the best as candid friends. Thus, *The Medical Times and Gazette* in 1855 had published a leading article on the decay of the *Association Medical Journal*, and recommended its discontinuance. A month later in the same paper Sir John Forbes, writing on the same subject, recommended the abolition of leading articles. But these were little more than exhibitions of disappointed rivalry and petulance, and were not justifiable by a fair review of the situation.

In the ninety-two years that have passed since the first appearance of the Journal there have been occasions upon which a section of the members of the Association have been dissatisfied with it, whether it were called " Provincial Medical and Surgical " or " Association Medical Journal," or by its present title. This dissatisfaction several times found vent in proposals to abolish it, either on the score of expense or of its alleged lack of interest. Luckily these proposals did not take effect, for without that weekly (at one time fortnightly) bond of union and organ of self-expression and communication between its component parts, the Association must long ago have died out. It was for the Journal alone that nearly all of the unattached members paid their subscriptions, and as at one time such members numbered some two-fifths of the total membership, their loss would have had a disastrous effect. It may be said without exaggeration that the Journal, throughout its long history, has represented the peripheral nervous system of the Association, without which communication with the Branches and Divisions would have been almost entirely non-existent, and paralysis must have resulted.

In its early days the Provincial Association was certainly rather extravagant in its expenditure on publications, and at the Annual Meeting at Norwich in 1846 the Bath and Bristol and East York Branches both brought forward resolutions to the effect that money was being wasted. The former Branch proposed that the publication of Transactions should cease, and that the Journal should appear fortnightly. The latter Branch moved that the Journal be given up in order to leave at the disposal of the Council a larger sum for the Benevolent Fund, and for the general purposes of the Association. A committee on publications was appointed at this meeting, which reported the next year at Derby, when it was decided to publish the Journal " in enlarged form " fortnightly. The publication of Transactions was continued.

Again, in 1853, at Swansea, an animated debate took place on the conduct of the Journal, many members thinking it too expensive. It was pointed out, however, that if the arrears of subscriptions, amounting to £1,093, were paid the financial difficulty would disappear.

Once again, in 1855, dissatisfaction was expressed. Dr. G. W. Dyke addressed a letter to Sir Charles Hastings, which was published in the *Association Medical Journal* for May 11th, complaining that the Editor's election was " informal if not illegal," and alleging that he acted in too partisan a spirit. The question was warmly debated at the ensuing Annual Meeting at York. The General Secretary and Editor, Dr. John Rose Cormack, explained the position and justified his action. He pointed out that the Association commenced the new journal without any cash in hand, and with considerable liabilities. In the end it was decided by the General Meeting " That the Offices of General Secretary and Editor of the Journal shall not be held by the same person." Notice had been given of a resolution by Mr. C. R. Bree, " That in the opinion of this meeting the Journal is not conducted in accordance with the spirit and objects of the Association," going on to complain of the exclusion of communications sent by members, and to state that the Association " never intended to sanction unjust criticisms and *ex parte* statements of the public institutions of the country, or unjust or unfounded attacks against public men," and concluding, " That it is the opinion of this Meeting that the Journal should be discontinued." Dr. Rose Cormack was saved the trouble of answering this formidable attack by the absence of the mover of the resolution and the silence of his sympathisers, if any. However, he shortly afterwards resigned his editorship and was succeeded by Dr. Andrew Wynter, who in his turn gave place to Dr. Markham in 1860.

Ten years later trouble arose again. At the Annual Meeting at Leamington in 1865 a proposal was made to discontinue the Journal and replace it by a less expensive one, directed to increase knowledge and to promote better legislation on questions of public hygiene and State medicine. To this an amendment was proposed that an editorial committee be appointed to help the Editor. This was lost, and finally an amendment in the following terms was carried almost unanimously in a largely-attended meeting :—

" That it is inexpedient to disturb the existing arrangements with regard to the Journal, (*a*) because Dr. Markham has proved himself quite equal to the responsibilities devolving upon him, and (*b*) because the tone and management has gone on improving ; and that general support and sympathy from the members of the Association, especially of those connected with the public medical and surgical institutions of the Kingdom, are alone warranted to make the Journal an organ suited to carry out the principles on which the Association is founded."

This handsome tribute to the Editor's ability and conduct smoothed the troubled waters, and since then there has been no suggestion of the abolition of the Journal, although there have been criticisms of the editorial discretion.

In the first number of *The British Medical Journal,*
dated January 3rd, 1857, the following leading article
appeared :—

" In accordance with the vote of the Association, its
organ this day assumes the title of the ' British Medical
Journal : being the Journal of the British Medical
Association.' With a more comprehensive name, we
trust to be able to present to the Associates a Journal
more comprehensive than it has hitherto been possible to
furnish. We hope that in a few months the many friends
of the Association will enable us to carry on with more
vigour than before several of the departments of the
Journal. As it is not at present thought advisable by
the Council to extend the paper every week to the full
32 pages, we have done the next best thing in our power
by printing the whole of the Journal in a small type,
which enables between two and three pages to be added
to its capacity without increasing the number of pages,
and we think it may be added with benefit to its appearance. The number and variety of the Hospital Reports
have proved not the least of the new and interesting
features presented to the Associates. It is trusted that
this department of the Journal may be made still richer
with the help of the hundreds of our Associates allocated
to hospitals and dispensaries, whom we would earnestly
beg to remember that the strength of the Journal lies in
the practical contributions which they only can supply."

The British Medical Journal in 1857 was edited by
Dr. Andrew Wynter, who, as before stated, had assisted
Dr. John Rose Cormack in the editorship of the *Association Medical Journal.* In 1861 Dr. W. O. Markham was
appointed Editor.

In 1866, on his appointment as a Medical Inspector
under the Local Government Board, Dr. Markham
resigned his editorial duties, and Mr. Ernest Abraham
Hart was appointed his successor by the Committee of
Council, and at the same time a " Journal Reference
Committee " was appointed, consisting of the President
of the Association, the President of Council, Dr. Markham
and Dr. Stewart. Mr. Hart retired in the spring of 1869,
soon after which the Committee of Council appointed
Mr. (afterwards Sir) Jonathan Hutchinson as his successor. At the Annual Meeting at Newcastle-on-Tyne in

1870, Mr. Hutchinson having resigned, Mr. Hart was once more appointed Editor, a post which he occupied with distinction until his death in 1898. In the Report of the Council to the Annual Meeting at Leeds on August 7th, 1869, occurred this passage :—

" The Council have to regret the resignation of the very able Editor of the Journal. Arrangements have been made for carrying on the business of the Journal until the appointment of his successor, which it will be the duty of the new Committee of Council to decide on at its first meeting."

No record remains in the volumes of *The British Medical Journal* for that or subsequent years of the circumstances which led to the sudden and regretted withdrawal of the Editor. It is to be presumed that it was sudden, for else why was the Council not able to announce the appointment of a successor at the same time as it announced the resignation, instead of having rather lamely to state that " arrangements have been made " ? When the report of the Council came to be discussed at the Annual Meeting, if any explanation of the occurrence was asked for or offered, no report of it found its way into the pages of the Journal, either in that year or in the Jubilee year 1882, when a retrospect of fifty years was published. There was, however, a lively discussion as to the expenses of the Journal. The meeting was described by a correspondent of a rival periodical as " verging upon the stormy." Some speakers objected to the item of £802, recorded in the accounts as paid to anonymous contributors, as too high. It was, moreover, pointed out that this sum was placed at the absolute discretion of the Editor. Dr. Singer seems to have expressed a general opinion when he said that the disposal of this large sum placed the Editor in a very delicate position.

In the pages of *The Lancet* there was a fuller report than in *The British Medical Journal*. From this it appears that the Chairman was unwilling to afford information. When Dr. Seaton, of Sunbury, wished to know if it was within the knowledge of the Auditor how this money had been spent, and whether the Editor had had the sole and secret control of it, the Chairman replied, " I do not suppose he will answer that question, even if he can," and when asked himself, "Can you give me any information on this matter ? " he made the surprising reply, " I am here to regulate the meeting and not to answer questions." Mr. Nunneley, of Leeds, said that " there was a principle which ought to guide them, and there ought not to appear on their books a sum of £800 unaccounted for." After Dr. Webster, of Dulwich, who had been the first and only President of a defunct British Medical Association,* had warned the meeting that " they would get into the Gazette if they went on like that," the subject was allowed to drop on the Council's promising that in future no payment should be made to a contributor except through a cheque paid by the Treasurer.

When we reflect that in 1869 there were not many more than 4,000 members, the sum of £800 represents a very large proportion of the total income of the Association. At the meeting of the Committee of Council held in Birmingham on August 24th, 1869, it was resolved " that Jonathan Hutchinson, Esquire, be elected Editor of *The British Medical Journal.*" That distinguished and afterwards celebrated pathologist and surgeon only occupied the editorial chair for one year, for, as already stated, he resigned in 1870, and Mr. Ernest Hart was re-elected and resumed office in the same unobtrusive way as that in which he had quitted it, and, as far as can be ascertained, without any public discussion of the situation at any meeting of the Association.

When, in after years, Ernest Hart came to recapitulate the doings of the Journal in an editorial article, he made no reference to the year 1869, but treated of his editorship as uninterrupted since 1866. Nor does the obituary notice which appeared in the Journal of January 15th, 1898, afford us any more information on this interlude. Rumour—circumstantial rumour—was rife at the time, but those who knew the facts of the case at first hand are now no more, and the generation that followed has nothing but second-hand hearsay left to go upon.

Whatever may have been the trouble which led to his resignation, there can be no question about the success of Hart's editorship. Under the financial care of Francis Fowke, and the keen political direction of the Editor, the Journal and the Association with which its interests were so closely bound up flourished. On the occasion of

* See Chapter on " Other Medical Associations."

THE GREAT HALL
BRITISH MEDICAL ASSOCIATION HOUSE LONDON

THE GREAT HALL
BRITISH MEDICAL ASSOCIATION HOUSE
LONDON

the Jubilee at Worcester in 1882 the following leading article, under the title " The British Medical Journal," appeared at p. 887 of Volume I for that year :—

" When the present Editor came into office in 1866, it was agreed, on his suggestion, to enlarge the Journal and to commence a vigorous development of the several departments. This was commenced in 1867, and from that time the Journal has gone on steadily increasing until the number of pages in each half-yearly volume has risen from about 600 in 1867 to more than 1,000. To increase the utility of the Journal special departments have from time to time been [sic] either developed or newly formed.

" In 1868 a department was created under the title of ' Poor-Law Medical Science ' for the special discussion of all questions affecting the interests of the Poor-Law Medical Officers. This arrangement has had the happiest effect in providing authoritative and powerful support for these meritorious public servants throughout the Kingdom, giving them, as it were, at once a definite *locus standi* in the medical republic, and a common meeting-place in which they can from week to week note any discussion of principle or any detail of facts which affect the interests of this important part of the service. In order to ensure that this department should be conducted with a thorough knowledge and in active sympathy with the needs of the great body of general practitioners employed in the Poor-Law Medical Service, it was placed under the special care of Dr. Joseph Rogers, President of the Council of the Poor-Law Medical Officers Association, whose advocacy of the interests of general practitioners and medical officers may always be depended upon. It is well known that this department has rendered effective service to the Poor-Law Medical Officers as a body by its vigilant defence of their interests, as well as to individual members under circumstances of peculiar hardship.

" When the development of the Sanitary Acts and the creation of the great body of medical health officers indicated that the interests of the practitioners of the country were about to assume a special phase in connection with the service, special attention was devoted to the development of the department of public health in connection with that of the Poor-Law Service. Here, again, the assistance of highly experienced and skilled persons throughout the provinces was obtained, and this department has been so conducted as to afford a survey of the work of the great body of practitioners, who are aiding in the care of the public health and performing public duties in respect of sanitation throughout the country. The analysis of this great body of reports, involving much labour, has been carried out in a manner which we may venture to say has attracted the attention of the most eminent sanitary authorities throughout the world, and reflects no small credit on the gentleman whose services have been available for that purpose.

"Again, the development of cottage hospitals throughout England and the new departures which have been taken of late years in the administration of hospitals indicated the advisability of devoting a recognised department for the reception and study of communications and information from all sides, relating to the progress of provincial hospitals, of cottage hospitals and of provident dispensaries. Such a department was accordingly organised in 1877, with the able assistance of Dr. Fairlie Clark, of Southborough, and others, by whom all documents and communications relating to this subject are systematically analysed.

"The Army and Navy Medical Services have from 1873 also had a special department in our columns. Free use has been made of this space, and the correspondence which we receive is sometimes very considerable, although of course only a very small proportion of that which is received is intended for publication. Of the services which THE BRITISH MEDICAL JOURNAL has been able to render to the Army and Navy, much has been said by leading personages of those services; and constant communication with representative members of all ranks enables us to hope that the sympathy which exists between the editorial department of this JOURNAL and the officers of the Army and Navy may continue to serve a useful purpose in protecting and advancing the interests of those departments on all occasions. Of late years the number of members of the two Services who have joined the Association has greatly multiplied.

"The JOURNAL has sought by the establishment of a department of Clinical Obstetric and similar Memoranda

184

to encourage the busy practitioner in town and in country to record interesting and valuable cases occurring in his practice, but requiring only a brief history. It has set apart columns for the special record of news concerning the profession in Scotland and Ireland, and has established a staff of correspondents in these divisions of the Kingdom, as well as in many of the large cities and towns. It has also widened the range of hospital reports, and of reports of medical societies so as to include all parts of the Kingdom.

"In thus increasing on all sides the editorial labours connected with the JOURNAL, the object has been held in view in all cases of unstintingly devoting the space of the JOURNAL to the interests of the profession at large, and especially to provincial interests and to the interests of practitioners resident in the sister countries.

"In the creation of these successive departments, we have met with that sincere form of flattery which consists of imitation, by the ablest and most powerful of our contemporaries. Such competition we hail with great satisfaction, for it is at once powerful testimony of the justice of the views entertained in these continuous developments of the sphere of influence and work of the JOURNAL, and shows us also a healthy rivalry which, as much as anything else, tends to that constant progress which it is our object to maintain. Of the JOURNAL generally, in respect to its scientific contents, we may be content to quote the statement of Dr. Bradbury in his Address on Medicine delivered at Cambridge. Commenting on the scientific merits of the JOURNAL, he said: ' Speaking on the subject of scientific medicine, I cannot but allude to the benefits which our Association especially has conferred upon this branch of study through her scientific grants, and through our most excellent JOURNAL, which is not surpassed in this or any other country in the scientific material which its pages weekly contain. In preparing this address I have been struck with the very great care which is taken in our JOURNAL to bring before us all that is best in modern scientific medicine.' "

The Editor went on to claim the increase in numbers of the Association since 1867 to a great degree as being the result of the excellence of the Journal. In the last fifteen years the Association had trebled the numbers which it had attained in thirty-five years' growth. Tribute was paid also to the sub-editors, namely, " Dr. Alexander Henry, who has held the office for thirty years ; the late Dr. John Murray, Mr. George Eastes, Dr. Fancourt Barnes, and Mr. Alban Doran."

In the Annual Retrospect at the end of the following year (*B.M.J.*, 1883, Vol. II, p. 1289), a leading article, possibly in reply to some criticism, gave the titles of ninety editorial articles as follows :—

" The staff of editorial writers in *The British Medical Journal* numbers more than 80, most of them being persons of recognised eminence and the greater number extra metropolitan. Among these articles are the following : Mortality at Sea ; the Peltzer Trial ; the Leeds General Infirmary ; Life and Death in England ; the Medical and Sanitary Department of Ocean Steamships ; the Financial Crisis at the London Hospitals ; Army Surgeons and their Hospital Practice in Egypt ; the Influence of Alcohol on Mortality ; Medical Certificates, Coroners and Death Registration ; the Navy and Army Medical Services ; the Medical Officers of Atlantic Steamers as Government Officials ; Sir Spencer Wells' Hunterian Oration ; the Leicester Guardians and Compulsory Vaccination ; Superannuation of Poor-Law Medical Officers ; the Government Medical Reform Bill ; Hospital-Colleges for Medical Students ; Medical Faculties of Oxford and Cambridge ; the Proposed Conjoint Scheme of the Colleges of Physicians and Surgeons ; Yellow Fever and Quarantine ; the Small-Pox Death Rate among Children as influenced by Vaccination ; Indian Medical Service ; Abuse of Lunacy Law ; the Regulation of Tenement Houses ; the General Medical Council ; the Contagious Diseases Acts ; Unqualified Assistants ; the Vaccination Question in Parliament ; the University of Cambridge and Salaries of Professors ; Weather Forecasts ; the Increasing Fatality of Cancer ; Coroners ; Report of the Committee on the Army Medical Service ; the Development of Myopia in Education ; the Ismailia Hospital during the Egyptian Campaign ; Compulsory Re-vaccination ; the Annual Meeting of the Association in Liverpool ; Examinations, Present and Future ; Old Prescriptions ; Official Self-sacrifice in

Vaccinal Research ; Notification of Infectious Diseases ; New Regulations of the University of Cambridge ; Lord Wolseley and the Army Medical Officers ; Typhus Fever at Nazareth House ; the Surgical Arrangements at the Battle of Tel-el-Kebir ; the Election of Members of the Council of the Royal College of Surgeons ; Laws in Germany regarding Poisonous Pigments ; Preliminary Education for the Medical Profession ; Combatant and Medical Officers of the Army ; Re-vaccination in Foreign Armies ; Outbreak of Diphtheria due to Infected Milk ; Honorary Queen's Cadetships ; Servants of the Sick Poor ; Gambling in Life-Assurance ; the Addresses at the Annual Meeting in Liverpool ; Cholera and Quarantine ; the Closing of Schools as a Sanitary Measure ; the Metropolitan Diseases Prevention Bill ; the New By-laws of the British Medical Association ; the Medical Work of the Session ; Registration of Nurses in Philadelphia ; Advice to Medical Students ; New Conference on Cholera ; the Southall Park Catastrophe ; Overcrowding and Crime ; the Walthamstow Murder ; Hospital Accommodation for Infectious Diseases in Liverpool ; Intemperance and Cholera ; the Relation of Drugs to Medicine ; Medical Study and Practice ; the Introductory Addresses at the Medical Schools ; Educational Over-pressure ; Professor Huxley on Medical Reform and Education ; Railway Unpunctuality and Public Health ; Health matters in Liverpool ; the Public and Life Assurance ; the Thornton Heath Murder ; the Remains of Harvey ; the Doctor's Holiday ; Class Mortality and Stratified Statistics ; the Sale of Poisons ; Canvassing for Hospital Appointments ; the Clinical Uses of Nitrite of Sodium ; Legislation for Inebriates ; Quarantine in Australia ; Poisonous Pigments in Austria ; the Use of the title ' Doctor ' ; the Annual Meeting in 1884 ; Foundation of Medical Sick, Annuity and Life-Assurance Society ; the International Health Exhibition ; the Irish Lunacy Bill ; the Results of the Franco-Egyptian Cholera Commission ; Cholera and Small-Pox in India."

The reader of this list will notice the great length of many of these titles as compared with those of 1923. One is ten words long. There is no doubt but that the Council was right in 1869 in speaking of Hart as " the very able editor." His ability was outstanding, and

187

during his long term of office he increased the value and usefulness of the paper and made it known beyond professional circles, even though his many other interests, his journeys abroad, and his long fatal illness necessitated leaving much of the work to his very capable assistant and successor, the late Sir Dawson Williams.

But although the Editor was so successful, some of his activities did not commend themselves to a number of the most prominent and renowned leaders of the profession, especially the teachers in the metropolitan schools of medicine. As Sir Dawson Williams has said ("The Middle Age," *Glasgow Medical Journal*, No. 1, July, 1922, Vol. XCVIII), Hart was never disposed to play second fiddle : the emoluments he derived from his office as Editor were small, and his active spirit found many other outlets, which enabled him to entertain freely in his large house in Wimpole Street. It was generally known that he was largely interested in the sale of a foreign mineral table water, which was well advertised in the Journal. This and other such facts, and the memory of his early career, no doubt prejudiced his critics against him, so that when (*B.M.J.*, 1888, Vol. II, p. 835) an article appeared in the Journal headed in large type, "The Handwriting of the Dying Emperor," and containing a facsimile reproduction of a note written by the German Emperor Frederick casting reflection on the treatment of his case by Professor Von Bergmann, there was at once a very general outburst of protest. In 1888, it will be remembered, the German Emperor died of Cancer of the Larynx. At the suggestion (as we now know) of Prince Bismarck, Sir Morell Mackenzie had been called into consultation with the German Surgeons who had been treating the case. This is not the place to discuss all the quarrels and heartburnings which arose, or the final tragedy. Suffice it to say that Morell Mackenzie had many critics in London as well as in Germany who were not likely to approve of the attitude of the Editor of *The British Medical Journal*. A memorial was drawn up, signed by 186 of the leading physicians and surgeons, members of the Association in London and the Provinces, and presented to the Council, drawing "the attention of the President and Council to the publication in the 1,450th number of the Journal of

188

the Association of a facsimile or ' script ' by the late Emperor of Germany [*sic*]. The publication of this document the undersigned regard as a violation of professional confidence, and its appearance in *The British Medical Journal* as discreditable to the medical profession in this country. They accordingly request the President and Council to take such immediate action as may be required to clear the Association and profession from discredit now attaching to them in respect of this matter." The long list of signatures to this memorial is headed by the names of Sir William Savory and Sir James Paget, of St. Bartholomew's Hospital, J. Eric Erichsen and John Marshall, of University College, Sir William MacCormac, of St. Thomas', Sir Joseph Lister, of King's College, Alfred Pearce Gould, of the Middlesex, George Pollock, of St. George's, and the President of the Royal College of Physicians, Sir J. Risdon Bennett. The Editor defended his action, but expressed regret for the appearance of the script in the columns of *The British Medical Journal*. It was moved by Dr. J. S. Bristowe (London) and seconded by Mr. W. D. Husband (Clifton, Bristol), and unanimously resolved :—

" That this Council strongly deprecates the publication of any details in violation of professional confidence. The Editor of the Journal has given to the Council his assurance that he had reasons which he considered adequate for believing that the publication of the ' script ' referred to in the protest laid before the Council was not a breach of confidence, but he expressed his regret for its publication in the Journal. The Council would express their own regret that under any circumstances that document was published."

A copy of this resolution was sent to Professor Von Bergmann by the President of the Council on January 16th, 1889.

But this severe rebuke did not quell the Editor, nor did it satisfy the signatories of the memorial, who no doubt desired his dismissal. They returned to the charge next year, basing their complaints on the conduct of the advertisement columns of the paper, and also attacking the principle of anonymity of editorial articles. An account of this agitation was published in November, 1889 (*B.M.J.*, 1889, Vol. II, p. 1120), as a special article, headed " Rumoured Resignations," in which it was stated that a paragraph had lately appeared in a number of provincial and metropolitan newspapers announcing that a private meeting had been held in the metropolis of some of the gentlemen in whose names a communication was addressed to the Council of the Association at Leeds, and that they had resolved to carry out their threat of secession. The article went on to say that these gentlemen had in the previous March expressed their opinion in a memorial addressed to the Council that all editorial articles should be signed, and complained of the character of the advertisements admitted to the Journal.

An answer was returned by the Council defending the character of the advertisements, and asking for specific charges. At the same time an Editorial Committee was appointed, consisting of the President of Council, Dr. Bridgwater, J.P., of Harrow ; the Treasurer of the Association, Dr. Holman, J.P., of Reigate ; Dr. Farquharson, M.P., F.R.C.P. ; Dr. Donald MacAlister, F.R.C.P. " To these the proofs of every article prepared for publication in the Journal are forwarded from day to day, and the Committee meets on Thursday to pass the pages for the press."

Despite this concession on the part of the Council, the memorialists were not placated, and in August, 1890, a letter was addressed by them to the Council, expressing their disappointment in their hopes of an improvement, and using the following terms : " So strong is this feeling that a large number of men in influential positions, in the profession, warmly attached to the Association but jealous of its honour and despairing of seeing the improvement they desire, have expressed their determination to resign their membership." Before doing so they made one more appeal to the Council. This letter was signed by Joseph Lister as Chairman, and W. H. Allchin, W. A. Meredith and John Williams as Secretaries. To this the Council returned a defiant reply.

At the ensuing Annual Meeting the following resolution was passed with only one dissentient :—

" That this Meeting desires to express its satisfaction with the result of the present representative system of government of the British Medical Association, and their

190

approval of the steps taken by the Council for the management of its Journal."

The complainants not making any appearance at the Meeting, their cause was allowed to go by default, and they thus laid themselves open to be taunted by the triumphant Editor with despairing of the republic, and of having adopted a high-handed procedure. The article implied that the memorialists had all resigned their membership, but did not definitely say so. We know, however, that for some years to come the leaders of the profession for the most part stood aloof from the activities of the Association. Looking at the question after the lapse of more than forty years, it seems clear that the memorialists do not come very well out of the episode. Feeling as strongly as they did that the honour of the Association was at stake, they should have carried the matter through by attending the Annual Meeting, and there and then proposing a resolution and supporting it with all the strength and influence they could command. As it was, they flaunted some of the dirty linen of the Association before the public, but refrained from sending it to the wash.

The Council at the Annual Meeting definitely affirmed its confidence in the Editor, whose position and influence seems to have become stronger than ever. For over seven years there was peace, and the fame of Ernest Hart increased yearly.

In the Report of the Council for 1895 (*B.M.J.*, 1895, Vol. II, p. 198) the following appreciation of the Journal and its Editor appeared :—

" The Journal has, in addition to usual literary and scientific matter, occupied itself usefully with the thorough investigation of the system of barrack schools as against boarding out. . . . Systematic investigation of a great number of provincial workhouse infirmaries. These reports, 51 in number, have produced already a most beneficent and widespread result not only in the particular places which have been the subject of investigation and report, but also collaterally by their influence on the standards of the Local Government Board and the methods adopted by its inspectors. A circular has been issued by the Local Government Board in accordance with the general views expressed in the reports of *The British Medical Journal.*

" The widespread and favourable reception of *The British Medical Journal* beyond the limits of the United Kingdom has once more been evidenced by the public demonstrations and reception with which the Editor has been received [*sic*] throughout India during his visit there."

At the Annual Meeting of 1897 the question of the conduct of the Journal again came to the front. Mr. Lawson Tait brought forward a resolution declaring it desirable that the Council should exercise a more complete control over the paid editor and not leave matters to the Reference Committee, which Mr. Tait contended to be illegal under the 9th Article of the Association. He complained that Mr. Hart devoted himself to a particular department of the profession, that of public health, and that articles on this subject ought not to be editorial when there were hundreds of able young sanitarians anxious to write them and be paid for them. The Lancashire and Cheshire Branch had complained that they could not get important reports on the midwifery question published in the Journal.

The President of Council having said that the resolution would be taken as a censure on the Council, the matter dropped. The incident was symptomatic of serious dissatisfaction in some quarters.

On Hart's death in 1898, Dr. (afterwards Sir) Dawson Williams, who had long been Assistant Editor, succeeded him, resigning in January, 1928, and being in his turn succeeded by his Assistant, the present Editor, Dr. N. Gerald Horner. From 1897 to 1917 the Assistant Editor was Mr. Charles Louis Taylor, who in 1910 acted for four months as Editor during the illness of Sir Dawson Williams. (For an account of whom and of other officials, see the section on Personalities.)

As the previous pages will have shown, in the first half-century of the Association's existence the editorial chair of the Association's Journal was not always as comfortable as a bed of roses. The work has always been responsible, and with the increase of membership and of the size of the paper it has not become lighter.

In 1898 the conduct of the Journal was again impugned. At a meeting of the Council on January 19th, Dr. Woodcock, of Old Trafford, representing the Lancashire and Cheshire Branch, proposed the following resolution :—

" That this Council condemns the action of the Reference Committee in allowing the Journal of the Association to be used officially in furthering the interests of a particular candidate for a seat on the General Medical Council without consulting the Council of the Association, and considers such action prejudicial to the interests of the Association."

This resolution referred to events following the resignation of Dr. R. Rentoul of his membership of the General Medical Council in the previous September, at a time when the Editor of the Journal was lying ill in a Nursing Home. The Acting Editor at this time was not the Assistant Editor, Sir Dawson Williams, but Mr. Louis Taylor. The resolution was rejected by the majority of the Council.

Attention was then called by the Council to the terms of the resolution passed by the Journal and Finance Committee on October 21st, 1896, and ratified by the Council, which ran as follows : " That the Reference Committee shall guide the policy and control the contents of the Journal." Nevertheless, in 1899 an editorial statement reminded readers of the fact that the Reference Committee was no longer in existence, not having been re-appointed by the Council in July, 1898.

In the year of *Sturm und Drang* 1900, the conduct of the Journal was once more in question. At the Annual Meeting the President praised the rapidity with which the reports of the last Annual Meeting had been published, compared with the long delays of previous years. Surgeon-Colonel Ince commended the Journal, and compared it favourably with what it had been when the editorship was in other hands " and the contents were not always of a highly professional character." But this concert of approbation was suddenly disturbed by a very jarring note. Mr. Victor Horsley wished to move an amendment, after the manner of the House of Commons, to reduce the Editor's salary by £100. When told that the General Meeting was not competent to do this, he moved an amendment to the resolution approving the Council's Report, in which he roundly accused the Editor personally of *suppressio veri* and *suggestio falsi* in a leading article on the Exeter Hall meeting. Dr. Dawson Williams successfully rebutted this accusation, but Mr. Horsley further complained that the Journal " does not do all it should do to promote the interest of the profession." To this the Editor very truly answered, " That is a charge which is easy to make, but exceedingly difficult to meet." After some heated protests in favour of the Editor from Dr. James Barr and others, Mr. Horsley was allowed by vote to withdraw his amendment.

The contents of the Journal increased from 1,058 pages in 1859 to 3,640 in 1910, and the gross increase was really more than is shown by these figures, for in addition a Supplement containing Association news and notices, and other medico-political information, has been published separately since the beginning of 1903. Besides this, an *Epitome of Current Medical Literature* has been issued with the Journal, beginning with the first number of the year 1892. This useful report of progress in the whole realm of the Medical Art probably arose phœnix-like from the ashes of another publication. Notwithstanding his numerous and very various activities, Mr. Ernest Hart found time in 1873 to edit a new paper, published at his suggestion by Mr. George Smith, entitled *The London Medical Record*. This paper, after 1875, was changed from a weekly periodical to a monthly one, and its title changed in 1888 to *The London Medical Recorder*, but apparently, although a useful publication, its circulation was not large enough to make it profitable, and it ceased to appear after 1891. In the next year the Epitome, as a part of *The British Medical Journal*, more than took its place, and still continues to afford a useful guide to contemporary cosmopolitan medical literature.

A series of articles on subjects connected with the history of medicine was begun in the 'nineties under the title of " Archæologica Medica," and ran through a number of half-yearly volumes, to be succeeded by the " Nova et Vetera" series, instituted by and freely contributed to by Mr. C. L. Taylor, but of which the first article was contributed by the present writer in January, 1900. From time to time special numbers of the Journal have been issued, such as the Jenner number, published to celebrate the centenary of his first vaccination from Cow-pox in 1796, which number was, in the words of the Council's Report for 1897, " a considerable literary effort, in which the services of a great number of

194

distinguished writers were utilised, and which redeemed in some measure the Country and the profession from the reproach of neglecting to do suitable honour to the memory of this great physician and benefactor of mankind, such as has been done in other countries than that of his birth." On the occasion of the Diamond Jubilee the " Victorian Number " paid tribute to the glories of Her Majesty's illustrious reign. Among other noteworthy special numbers or supplements must be mentioned the Lister Jubilee number of December 13th, 1902, the special commemorative number of July 18th, 1925, on the occasion of the opening by King George of the Association's new House in Tavistock Square, and the Lister Centenary number of April 9th, 1927, besides special articles and reports of the Lister celebrations in Edinburgh and Glasgow.

The various reports in the Journal of inquiries into workhouse infirmaries in England and Ireland had great effect, and those on the health and physical condition of the pauper children of the State and on Barrack Schools led to the appointment of a Special Commission, which reported in 1896 strictly in accordance with the conclusions and recommendations set forth in the Journal.

THE JOURNAL IN WAR-TIME.

A Leader in the first issue after the fateful Fourth of August, 1914, struck the right note and rightly appreciated the gravity of the situation in the following words : " It is a clear duty of all members of the Medical Profession, who remain at their ordinary civilian work, to see that those medical men who have pledged themselves in advance to serve the Country in any such emergency as has now arisen shall not suffer in their civilian practices, and that their patients shall be looked after." The article ended with this grave warning : " No man can say what that future has in store, nor how great the sacrifice we may be called upon to make in the life and death struggle which has been forced on the Country."

Through the next four and a quarter years the Journal was carried on with a more and more depleted staff in the editorial and printing and publishing offices, and in the last year of the War with a most inadequate supply of paper of questionable quality. Owing to the rationing

195

by the Government of this most important material, each issue was reduced so that, instead of having as in pre-war times 60 or 70 pages of literary matter and as many of advertisements, the weekly issue now consisted of 64 pages, divided about equally between literary and advertising matter. The bound volumes on the shelves of the Library remain as mute witnesses of the progressive atrophy from which the paper suffered. From 1,440 pages (exclusive of Supplements and Epitome) in the first volume for 1914, each succeeding one was smaller until Volume II of 1918, which was little more than half that size, containing 732 pages only. Some part of the shrinkage was no doubt due to the much-reduced reports of Annual Meetings, but on the other hand a good deal of interesting War matter had to be curtailed or excluded as the difficulties of publication increased. But despite all obstacles, the Journal continued manfully to give to the members and the medical world a good account of events, and to provide them with reports of the latest doings and advances in medicine and surgery. In 1917 the Association published " British Medicine in the War," being a collection of essays which had appeared in the Journal on problems of medicine, surgery and pathology arising among the British armed forces. The Epitome contained numerous " War Numbers " and contrived to give information, despite the blockade, of what was being done on the Continent, while the Supplements gave news of administrative and medico-political affairs.

It was evident in recent years, in the course of some of the journalistic campaigns in favour of unqualified practice, that the Association had not " a good press," partly owing to the fact that even the first-class journals were unable to distinguish between the General Medical Council and the Council of the British Medical Association. Consequently the Association received some of the controversial brick-bats which were intended for the Statutory Body. Nevertheless, when Sir Dawson Williams resigned his editorship in 1928, the leading daily papers which had not been behindhand in criticism of the profession, paid handsome tributes to the conduct of the Journal under its retiring Editor. *The Times*, in a leading article headed " Medical Journalism," said : " The B.M.A. is able to-day to uphold the traditions of the profession of medicine in the face of any opposition to these traditions," and " the Association is ready to lend its help to every public body charged with the care of health."

The first volume of *The Provincial Medical Journal* bore the imprint " London 1840 " on its title-page. It was published by William Bull at No. 34, Paternoster Row. The volume for 1841 was " Published by John Williams Rumsey, at his Residence, No. 6, Wellington Street, Strand, in the precinct of the Savoy." The next year there was another change, and Volume 3 for 1841–42 was published by John Churchill at his residence, No. 16, Princes Street, in the Parish of S. Anne, Westminster. Volumes 4 to 7 were published by Henry Renshaw at 356, Strand, but in 1844 John Churchill published Volume 8, and continued to publish successive volumes up to and including Volume 16 in 1852. These volumes (9 to 16) bore the additional publishers' names of " Deighton and Co., Printers, Worcester." The editorial address was that of Dr. Streeten, Foregate Street, Worcester. In 1852 *The Provincial Medical Journal* came to an end, as did the transactions of the Provincial Medical and Surgical Association. These two publications were succeeded by the *Association Medical Journal*, which was " Published for the Association by Thomas John Honeyman at the office, 37, Great Queen Street, Lincoln's Inn Fields." Thus began a long and honourable connection between the Association and the family of Honeyman, for the son of the first official printer of the Journal succeeded to the service of the British Medical Association as Librarian, and built up the Library to the condition of importance in which he left it at his resignation in 1927. Mr. T. J. Honeyman continued to print the Journal under the name of *British Medical Journal* until 1867, in which year Thomas Richards succeeded him as printer at the same address, and continued to print the Journal until Volume II of 1879 was " Printed and Published at the Offices of the British Medical Association, 161A, Strand." From 1874 to 1878 the Journal was published for the Association by Francis Fowke, 36, Queen Street, a house adjoining the printing office, where the Journal occupied two rooms. The frequent changes in the management of the publication

of the Journal are symptomatic of the troubles which
beset its youth and adolescence. In 1878 the Association
decided to undertake the printing of its Journal, and
premises were leased at 161A, Strand. In 1886 the lease
of 429, Strand was acquired, and to this the neighbouring
premises in Agar Street were added in 1888 and 1896.
In 1907 all the houses were demolished, and during the
process of razing the old building and erecting the new,
the work of the Association and its Journal was carried
on in temporary premises next door to Drury Lane
Theatre. These moves, and the transfer in 1925 from the
Strand to Tavistock Square, called for a great deal of
foresight and hard work on the part of officials and staff.
In January, 1911, there was an impending strike of
employees at the firm of machine printers who had for
many years " machined " the Journal each week after
the type had been set up in the Association's printing
office. This crisis was met and overcome by the prompt
action of the Editor and the Financial Secretary ; within
five hours arrangements were completed to transfer the
machining and distribution of the Journal to Messrs.
Odhams, who have since then continued this work,
their high-speed rotary machines enabling larger and
larger issues to be printed rapidly as the Journal's
circulation increased year by year.

Another landmark in the typographical history of the
Journal was the change over from composition by hand
to mechanical typesetting. The first four linotype
machines were installed in the printing office at 429,
Strand, in the spring of 1923, and others have since been
added. The photogravure process for the reproduction
of illustrated insets was introduced in November, 1930,
and the type face used for the literary pages was completely changed at the end of that year, the first issue for
1931 being printed throughout from the legible and
agreeable type known as " Bookprint." Many difficulties
had to be overcome in planning and effecting these various
changes so that the weekly issues of the Journal might
proceed without interruption. Indeed, the only break that
has ever occurred in the regular sequence of publication
was during the General Strike. Owing to the stoppage of
all work at the machine printers, two issues were sand-
wiched into one, bearing the date May 8th and 15th, 1926.

CONTRACT PRACTICE AND THE ASSOCIATION

COMPLAINTS of the evils of contract medical practice are older than the Association. In the earliest medical periodicals objections to clubs were made, and after the Poor Law Act of 1832 the profession resisted the attempts of the Guardians to force clubs upon them, and the " Battle of the Clubs " had been chronicled in the medical journals for a good many years.

Contract practice was of two kinds. The least objectionable was that of the private club, in which a practitioner agreed to attend his poorer patients for a small annual sum to be paid weekly, whether the patient were well or ill. No outside body intervened between the doctor and his patients, but, in fact, this was a form of charitable relief coming out of the doctor's pocket, for he knew that these club patients could not afford to pay adequate fees. It was for the doctor and for him alone to settle the terms on which he would admit patients to his club, including in terms the question of wage limit. If his terms were too high he not improbably lost his patient.

The other and much more formidable kind of contract practice was that carried on through the medium of friendly societies, who acted as intermediaries between the doctor and his patient, and were in fact his employers, whom he contracted to serve at a certain rate of pay per patient. In this kind of contract practice the doctor had to treat whatever patients the society chose to allot to him. The before-mentioned clubs, fostered by some Boards of Guardians, were of this kind.

It was with the friendly societies and their later developments, the Medical Aid Associations, that all the trouble, which lasted for the best part of a century, occurred.

An example of the kind of conditions which the societies attempted to impose will be found in *The*

Provincial Medical and Surgical Journal of January 26th, 1848, in a leading article commenting upon a meeting of Dorset practitioners at which the rules and regulations of the Dorset County Friendly Society were considered. Two shillings and sixpence per head from each benefit member was to be paid to the medical officers ; 2s. for a wife or child above 16 years of age ; 1s. each for the first three and 9d. for each additional child under 16 years, and 10s. 6d. for confinements. There was no restrictive clause as to the election of benefit members, and no income limit was fixed. A meeting of practitioners concerned held it desirable to restrict medical relief to the labouring population and journeymen mechanics and proposed a conference with a Committee of the Society.

The strength of the position of the societies lay in the lack of union among medical men. As in the similar case of the Poor Law Medical Officers, the societies relied, and too often justifiably from their point of view, on finding one among the local practitioners whose poverty or whose anxiety to get into practice induced him to accept their niggardly terms. Not only were the rates of pay extremely low, but the societies obstinately refused to allow a wage limit to be fixed above which members should be ineligible for medical benefit. Cases occurred of members whose prosperity increased so that they became wealthy, or at least too well-off to be attended on the same terms as day labourers, and the medical officers of the societies contended that no one whose income exceeded a certain sum should be admitted to medical benefit, and that if and when, after admission, his income increased to above that sum, he should cease to be so eligible. The medical profession has always adjusted its fees to the financial status of its patients, but the commercially-minded authorities of the societies professed themselves unable to see why the same advice and medicine given to a rich man should cost more than when given to a poor one. Perhaps their lack of vision was excusable, but it was certainly affected by the spectacles of self-interest through which they looked at the question.

The wrangle between the doctors and the societies went on for years and decades, and at one time the

"Battle of the Clubs" was a regular heading in *The Lancet*, but in time it seems to have become so chronic that in the index of *The British Medical Journal* for 1890 no entries are to be found under "Contract Practice" or "Friendly Societies." There are, however, some references to clubs and to the absence of a wage limit in some cases.

In answer to an inquiry in the *Journal* the Editor touched the sore spot when he alleged "that the practitioners themselves are chiefly to blame therefor; indeed, it is within our knowledge that in several instances in which medical men have entered into a medical (signed) agreement not to take any new club for a less sum than 5s. per annum for each member, first one and then another have withdrawn therefrom, with the view to accept such appointment at 4s. and 3s." (*British Medical Journal*, 1900, Vol. II, p. 1039.)

The question once more became a burning one when medical aid associations were formed. To the old friendly societies, medical benefit was only one of many interests. Sick and unemployed benefits were, generally speaking, more important, and, moreover, it was the existence of these latter which largely prevented the societies from consenting to a wage limit because they could not exclude a member from one form of benefit and admit him to others. The medical aid associations were formed to provide only medical and surgical treatment to their members, and they rapidly grew into powerful societies with medical officers who were often unmercifully sweated. Some practitioners employed by large societies undertook more patients than they could properly attend personally, and therefore employed unqualified assistants, who would accept a lower wage than a qualified man. This system had the advantage from the employer's point of view that it obviated the danger of an assistant setting up on his own account and attracting to himself some of the patients of his former employer. But the practitioners who acted in this way were not regarded with favour by their colleagues, and the great majority of the profession cordially supported the attempts of the Association to get the evil system mended or ended.

In 1892 the General Medical Council took action and summoned a practitioner from Stourport—that

Worcestershire town where Sir Charles Hastings had his introduction to medical practice—to answer a charge of " covering " in connection with a medical aid association, in that he " by placing his services and registered qualification at the disposal of such persons (the Stourport Amalgamated Friendly Societies and Medical Aid Association) had enabled and did enable a medical practice for profit to be carried on by unqualified persons to the detriment of the public." A second charge was that of employing a certain unqualified assistant on his own responsibility as though he were duly qualified. After two days' hearing the Council came to the conclusion that the charges had not been proven, but they cautioned the practitioner to be more careful in future " to avoid associating himself with an unqualified person in the treatment of patients." The result of this case was a disappointment to the critics of the medical aid associations.

In June, 1893, a Committee of the General Medical Council on Medical Aid Associations made its report. Among other recommendations it submitted the following :—

" That the rules as to covering do apply to medical officers of medical aid associations which employ unqualified assistants. That the Council should record its opinion that a medical practitioner is acting in a reprehensible manner (a) if he holds a medical aid appointment the duties of which are so onerous that he cannot do justice to the sick under his care ; (b) if he consents to give certificates where in his opinion they are not justifiable on medical grounds ; (c) if he accepts or retains employment by an association in which canvassing is used to attract members."

But the majority of the Council shirked responsibility, and the Committee's report was not adopted.

An editorial article in *The British Medical Journal* in 1894 (Vol. II, p. 831) commented on the increase in number of medical aid associations. It attributed the success of such ventures largely to the fact of the impecuniosity of medical men. It alleged that during the previous ten years the ratio of medical practitioners per 1,000 of the population had steadily increased, and that at the same time the charitable medical relief

202

supplied in our large towns had continued to assume larger and larger proportions ; consequently the struggle for existence generally within the ranks of the profession had become annually more and more keen.

In the same year (1894) a fund was opened by the Association for the support of the practitioners of Cork, who had resigned their positions as officers of clubs and benefit societies rather than submit to their terms.

All over the country the profession was protesting against the oppression of the societies and the aid associations in particular, and in 1900 the *Journal* (Vol. I, p. 928) started a column headed " Contract Medical Practice," in which news on this subject was published and discussed in editorials and letters.

At the Annual Meeting at Swansea in 1903 Dr. Alfred Cox put forward a motion, of which notice had been given by the Gateshead Division of the North of England Branch, of which the following is an abstract :—

A. That the Medico-Political Committee be instructed to investigate Contract Practice.

B. That the Ethical Committee be instructed to investigate the ethical position of medical men engaged in various kinds of contract practice as to canvassing and holding posts which their colleagues generally have declined.

C. That the Medico-Political Committee be asked to consider the advisability of placing the services of the Organising Secretary at the disposal of Divisions requiring his help.

The motion was carried.

The result was the publication of the Contract Practice Report, which with its appendices occupied the whole of a special 96-page Supplement to the *B.M.J.* in 1905 (Vol. II, Special Supplement, July 22nd, 1905).

This important document, including as it did a Special Report on Provident Dispensaries, and another on Public Medical Services, may be considered to have pronounced the last word on this difficult subject (which though no longer a burning question is yet of great historical interest) as it put on record the facts and also many expressions of opinion by a large number of members.

The chief points in the Report were :—

1. An acknowledgment that there are districts where contract practice is necessary.

2. That the profession is the best judge of the classes and individuals who are entitled to such a concession on their part, and that therefore the ideal system is that contract practice in every area should be arranged by and under the control of the medical profession itself.

3. That such a system should be open to all practitioners who care to take part in it, and that there should be no private contract arrangements competing with the general arrangement.

This Report formed the basis of many of the negotiations which ended with the passing of the National Health Insurance Act in 1911, and although this Act excluded the creation of such a Medical Service as was contemplated in the Report, the investigation supplied valuable evidence upon which to negotiate.

The Medico-Political Committee of the Association were fully justified in drawing attention to the valuable services of the Medical Secretary, Mr. (now Sir James) Smith Whitaker, in the preparation of the text. As the Editor of *The British Medical Journal* stated in a leading article on July 22nd, it would be a mine of information in the future, as all the facts had been gathered at first hand, and the main conclusion was that the first principle must be that the medical profession should itself prescribe the rules and conditions under which it will enter into agreements to give medical attendance by contract. It was largely over this principle that the unequal battle between the profession and the Government of the day was waged in the discussions of the Insurance Act.

The Report was referred to the Divisions in 1905 and approved by the Representative Body at the next meeting in 1906.

Meanwhile, after the refusal of the General Medical Council to act on its Committee's Report, numerous Branches of the Association took the matter up and convinced the Council that it had not sufficiently considered the fact that these commercial undertakings depended to a great extent for their success on advertisement and canvassing. This view of the matter was pressed home by the direct representatives on the Council, which at last decided that medical practitioners serving canvassing societies would be acting in an infamous manner in a professional respect. As the Council had already decided that the employment of unqualified assistants amounted to " covering," the Association found two weapons placed in its hands which it did not fail to use with effect, until the Insurance Act put an end to these Medical Companies altogether.

It may be of historical interest to put on record that according to the Secretary of the Medical Alliance (of Medical Aid Associations) the first one was opened in 1869 at Preston, and that in 1911 he could boast of the existence of upwards of 100 of these institutions in the country, of which 75 had formed an alliance.

PERSONALITIES

IN preparing these notes on the personalities of some of those whose influence has made itself felt on the growth and welfare of the Association, much use has been made of the obituary notices which have appeared in the pages of the *Journal*. The subjects of these notes are none of them now living, and it seemed that there could be no better sources of information than the contributions of their friends and contemporaries written when their memories had had no time to fade. For some of the most outstanding personalities other sources were available, and they have not been neglected. Particularly valuable were the recollections of Sir Dawson Williams which were the basis of his brilliant article on "The Middle Age."

The reader who wishes for fuller appreciation is referred to the numerous and full obituary notices, which are to be found in the volumes of *The British Medical Journal*.

LANDMARKS AND PERSONALITIES.

Among the persons whose influence has made itself felt on the development and conduct of the Association there is little that can be said as to the personal characteristics of the associates and immediate successors of Sir Charles Hastings, but we know that men like John Conolly, of London, and afterwards of Warwick, rendered most valuable services to the Association in its earlier days. Conolly's name is well known as one of the pioneers in the non-restraint method of treating lunatics. He was at one time lecturer on Medicine at University College, London, but afterwards removed to Warwick. It was while he was resident in that city, that he expressed at the second Anniversary Meeting, in 1834, those lofty aspirations and that forecast of the future of the Association which are quoted in the preface to this volume.

Dr. (afterwards Sir) John Rose Cormack had had much experience in medical journalism when in 1852

206

he was appointed Editor of the *Journal* of the Provincial Medical and Surgical Association, which then became the Association's Medical Journal, as recorded in the Section of this History on the *Journal*. In 1841 he had established the Edinburgh Monthly Journal of Medical Science, long after known and referred to as *Cormack's Journal*, which afterwards became amalgamated with *The Edinburgh Medical Journal*. After leaving Edinburgh and settling in practice at Putney, Cormack started another monthly periodical, *The London Journal of Medicine*, which had the names of most of the physicians and surgeons of distinction at that time in London on its list of contributors. This journal ceased to appear when the Association *Journal* began. Cormack's fame and his knighthood were the result of his devoted services to the distressed foreigners, and to the sick and wounded during the siege of Paris, in which city he had settled in 1869. Sending away most of his family, he deliberately chose to remain during the siege. An unselfish, public-spirited man, he died poor in 1882, and his family had to be helped by subscription among his former colleagues. Sir Richard Wallace provided for the medical education of his only surviving son. He seems to have been a man of great industry and fine character, highly respected by the British colony in Paris. He was the first Editor of the Association's *Journal* to have a name and reputation outside its ranks.

WILLIAM DALLA HUSBAND, F.R.C.S. Eng.
(1817-1892)
(See *B.M.J.*, 1892, Vol. II, p. 254).

Husband formed a link between Sir Charles Hastings and members still living.

He was unanimously elected President of Council, the highest honour which the Association could bestow, at the meeting in Leeds in 1869, and served for three years in that office, and as Treasurer 1875 to 1881. He was described by those who knew him as untiring and enthusiastic, never losing faith in the future of the Association. He retired owing to ill-health in 1881, dying in 1892. As a surgeon he was highly esteemed in and around the City of York. He had been Lord

Mayor of York and was a Deputy Lieutenant of the
West Riding of Yorkshire.

THE MIDDLE AGE.

" The Middle Age," to use the term chosen by Sir
Dawson Williams as title for a brilliant paper contributed to *The Glasgow Medical Journal* in 1922, was
critical for the Association. We cannot deal with its
personalities better than by quoting the greater part of
that paper. When in 1858 Parliament passed the first
medical Act, " the Association resolved not to relax
its efforts, and re-appointed its Medical Reform Committee. Of this Committee, Dr. Edward Waters was
the moving spirit. He was a physician in Chester, a
man of distinguished presence, persuasive speech, and
great tenacity of purpose ; the members of the Association, recognising how thoroughly he understood the
ins and outs of every question that could arise, were
content to leave the negotiations in his hands ; in the
consultations held between the Association and the
Government he acted as spokesman, and, through his
clearness of vision and urbanity of address, was able
so well to commend the medical cause to successive
Ministers that eventually the amending Act of 1886
was passed." In 1881 Mr. C. G. Wheelhouse, surgeon
to the Leeds Infirmary, became Chairman of Council.
He was well known as a general surgeon, and introduced a method of performing external urethrotomy by
opening the urethra in front of the stricture which found
its way under his name into all the text-books of the
period. He was a thorough-going believer in the
Association. He did an immense amount of work for it
as a member of the Council, and eventually as its
Chairman. Finally he became President of the Association when it held its Annual Meeting in Leeds in 1889.
A short, sturdy man of olive complexion, his genial
smile and gentle address truly expressed the kindliness
of his heart and his determination to see the best in
all men. His influence—and in his time it was great—
was due to these qualities, and to a simple persuasive
speech, more effective than eloquent. However much
one differed from Wheelhouse, it was impossible to be
angry with him.

208

His immediate successor as President of the Council, Sir Walter Foster, of Birmingham (afterwards Lord Ilkeston), was a different type. He entered the House of Commons early as a Member for Chester, and though he lost his seat there, soon found another, for he stood high in the counsels of the Liberal Party during the middle Gladstonian period ; after most efficient service to that Party as an organiser, he became Parliamentary Secretary to the Local Government Board in the Liberal Government of 1892. In the cold shade of opposition which followed in 1894 he maintained—without perhaps extending—his reputation, and when the Party to which he belonged returned to power his name was not in the list of new Ministers. Not long afterwards he resigned his seat and received a peerage. Early in his political career he gave an address on the political power-lessness of the profession, but was unduly disappointed that it produced so little apparent effect, forgetting, as so many able men do, that a single speech or pamphlet, however strong and well-marshalled its arguments, is seldom or never followed by immediate action. It is like throwing a big stone into a stagnant river ; there is a certain commotion, but no movement forward ; for that, patient spade-work to clear away obstructions must be continued over a long period.

Sir Walter Foster was a masterful chairman. When in 1887 he was succeeded by Dr. Thomas Bridgwater, it was whispered that King Log had replaced King Stork. Bridgwater was medical officer to Harrow School, and a highly successful general practitioner in that neighbourhood. He had long given much time and energy to the business of the Association. A genial, hospitable man, he was willing, after he had realised it, to admit that his ambition through all his years of unceasing work at Harrow had been to retire and live the life of a country gentleman while still capable of enjoying it. Like most members of the Council at that time, he had considerable experience in local administration, and made an excellent presiding officer. He was not much of a public speaker, and probably derived little pleasure from those ceremonies of the Association's year, in which the Chairman of the Council is expected to take a leading part. Any shortcomings in this respect were more than met by the qualities possessed by his intimate friend, Dr. Constantine Holman, who was elected Treasurer of the Association at Glasgow in 1888, at the beginning of Bridgwater's second year of office. Holman was at the head of a large practice at Reigate in Surrey; he held a commanding position in that district, was one of the best recruiters the Association ever had, and was known far and wide on account of his work for medical charities—especially Epsom College, of which he was Treasurer from 1887 to 1906. It was in recognition of this work that after he had retired to live in London, he received the honour of Knighthood. Constantine Holman was a conspicuous figure in any assembly; tall and broad-shouldered, his presence was imposing, and some of us, who loved the man, called him the Emperor. He was a ready, fluent and forcible speaker, and if smitten, not much disposed to turn the other cheek. After his three years as Treasurer he did not at all relax his interest in the Association, but remained one of its most conspicuous and courageous champions. Of his successor, Mr. (afterwards Sir) Henry Butlin, it is unnecessary to say more than that the willingness of a surgeon of so much scientific distinction, and so respected and beloved, to hold an administrative office for six years was a great help to the Association in London, where it has never been so strong as it desires or deserves. No account of the lions of our period could pretend to be complete, even as a sketch, without some mention of the two officials—the Editor of *The British Medical Journal* and the General Secretary. Ernest (Abraham) Hart, who held the first of these offices for some thirty years, was the son of a dentist in London. He was a boy prodigy at the City of London School, took the diploma of M.R.C.S. at the earliest possible age, and joined a famous practice in the business centre of London. He was a Jew by birth, and the leaders of this great community were prepared to second his desire to specialise in ophthalmology. Brilliant as his abilities were, they were perhaps not of the kind to command success in practice; at any rate, he did not persevere in this line. He had joined the staff of *The Lancet* at a very early age, but he was never disposed to play second fiddle, and saw his opportunity

210

in *The British Medical Journal,* then very little known beyond the small body of members of the Association. In 1864 the Metropolitan Counties Branch had appointed a Parliamentary Bills Committee to look after the political interests of the profession. It was allowed to lapse in 1870, but was revived as an Association Committee in the following year, when Hart was appointed chairman, and so continued until his death early in 1898.

This office gave him a very distinct place at the Annual Meetings when, during the discussion of public health matters, he made a striking and picturesque appearance. He was a small, very handsome man with a big head and a great mop of hair, which had gone prematurely white. He had made himself an excellent platform speaker, and his speeches at the Annual Meetings were eagerly awaited. He was well known in artistic as well as medical circles in London, and entertained freely in his large house in Wimpole Street ; it was beautifully furnished and adorned with a choice collection of Japanese curios which he was constantly weeding out. The emoluments he derived from his office as Editor were small, and his active spirit found many other outlets. His ambition to enter the House of Commons was never realised, but for a quarter of a century the policy of the Association in public health matters was largely determined by his influence. He held fast by the view that if the profession was to maintain and improve its place in the public estimation it must constantly strive to increase the efficiency of its services to the public, when other things would be added to it. He was greatly impressed by the discoveries of the new science of bacteriology, and like many, perhaps most, people of that day, expected from it immediate triumphs over disease, which have not yet been fully achieved. The subjects in which he was personally most interested were water-borne disease (typhoid fever and cholera) and vaccination, and upon both he was a voluminous writer. While still a very young man he had vigorously championed the cause of the Poor Law Medical Officers, and later on gave very valuable help to the movement for making the Army Medical Department an integral part of the Army.

211

Francis Fowke, the other officer of the Association at this time, was a character in his own way. Slight and erect, with curling hair and a grey beard, square-cut, in sixteenth-century fashion, always dapper in dress and rather prim in manner, he became well known to all who attended the Annual Meetings, and eventually earned the unbounded confidence of the Council and of the Association. He was the son of a surgeon at Wolverhampton, and began life as a hospital administrator ; when appointed General Secretary of the Association in 1872, he was Secretary of the General Hospital, Birmingham, where the meeting was held that year. That city was then the chief stronghold of the Association, and it was no doubt the influence of Birmingham members that led to his selection. Save for the belief in its future, firmly held by a few influential members, such as Mr. Husband, of York, Mr. Southam, of Manchester, Mr. Wheelhouse, of Leeds, and Sir Willoughby Wade and Sir Walter Foster, of Birmingham, the outlook was not very encouraging. After forty years of existence, the members numbered under 5,000, and the financial position was shaky. It was during Fowke's tenure of office, and largely owing to his business abilities and financial acumen, that a large reserve fund was formed, and (as he used with the driest of dry smiles, in rare moments of confidence, to say) securely locked up in buildings and a freehold site certain to appreciate in value. He was paid an absurdly small salary, but was in very truth a whole-time officer, giving every moment and every thought of a long working-day to the Association. In the evenings and in summer weekends he indulged his hobbies—photography, including micro-photography and astronomy, and sailing a canoe on the Upper Thames. As he was quite reckless, not very skilled, and never learned to swim, it is a little surprising that he lived to die in his bed.

Another masterly sketch of Hart and Fowke was drawn by Sir Henry Butlin in his Presidential Address at the Annual Meeting in London in 1910 on Past History and Great Officials (*B.M.J.*, 1910, Vol. II, p. 245), which cannot be omitted from any full appreciation of the characters of these two makers of the Association, and which will be found on a later page.

But besides such notable officials there have been, as Sir Dawson Williams pointed out, men who, though they did no active work on the machinery of the Association, " applauded the result, and by the active encouragement they gave to the Association in its endeavours to promote scientific and clinical medicine, rendered it invaluable help. No more typical instance could be named than the President who came into office at Glasgow in 1888. Sir William Gairdner never, I believe, took any part in the business of the Association, but it was his habit to attend the Annual Meetings, and he could usually be counted upon either to open a discussion or to express some opinion which would set men talking for an hour and thinking for months. For the same reason the debt of the Association to Sir Clifford Allbutt is great ; many times he chose an Annual Meeting as the occasion most suitable for inviting the profession to consider some wide-reaching principle in comparative pathology, medicine, or medical education, which was ripening for decision. The Association expressed to him its gratitude for his great services as President in the troublous years from 1915 to 1920 by presenting to him in 1922 its Gold Medal for Distinguished Merit. With these two eminent physicians I will couple three distinguished surgeons. The first is Lord Lister, who brought much of his most important work to the meetings of the British Medical Association ; mention need be made only of his Address on Surgery at the Annual Meeting at Plymouth in 1871, and of the series of demonstrations on antiseptic surgery which he gave at the Annual Meeting in Edinburgh in 1875 ; the second is Sir Henry Butlin, for thirty years or more a steady friend of the Association and its President in 1910, and the third is Sir William Macewen, who took an active share in the scientific work of the Annual Meeting in 1888." He was President in 1922.

HART AND FOWKE.

Sir Henry Butlin, President's Address. Annual Meeting in London. " Past History and Great Officials."
(*B.M.J.*, 1910, Vol. II, p. 245.)

" It was just about thirty-eight years ago that it (the Association) began distinctly to advance, and, as usual, it

213

was not measures, but men, that caused the advancement. Indeed, there has never been any question in my mind on this point. Nor have I ever had the least doubt of the particular men to whom the Association owes more than to any other men, dead or living. They were both officials of the Association, and each of them remained in its service for more than thirty years.

" The first was a little sallow-faced Jew, with clean-cut features and piercing eyes, active in mind and body and as keen as men are made. The reputation of our *Journal* when Mr. Ernest Hart became its Editor in 1866 was none too good, and only in the previous year a proposal had been made to the Annual Meeting to replace it by a less expensive journal. . . . I *know* that the library owed its actual origin to him, although it had been considered at the very first meeting of the Association. . . . The other official was Mr. Francis Fowke, not known to the members as the Editor was, and really only understood and esteemed by those persons who were closely associated with him in business affairs. He was our General Secretary and Manager, and to him fell the charge of all matters connected with the printing and publishing of the *Journal*, the advertisements, the collection of subscriptions, the arrangements for the Annual Meetings and I know not what else.

" He it was who advised the removal of the offices of the Association to that great artery of traffic, the Strand ; who gradually took over the printing of the *Journal*, the provision of the paper on which the *Journal* is printed ; who studied various methods of improving the illustrations in the *Journal* ; who devoted his attention to every little business detail with such success that the surplus income of the Association, which was £38 when he became its Manager in 1871, was nearly £5,000 when he resigned his post in 1902. No wonder that successive Treasurers placed their confidence in Mr. Fowke, and supported him one after another in the schemes which, with great caution and after long pondering, he put forward for some improvement in one or other of our business methods.

" It would be difficult to find two men less like each other than the Editor and the General Secretary and

214

SIR DAWSON WILLIAMS, M.D., F.R.C.P.,
Editor of British Medical Journal, 1898–1928.

R. WALLACE HENRY, M.D.,
CHAIRMAN OF
REPRESENTATIVE BODY,
1922–1925.

SIR HENRY BRACKENBURY,
M.R.C.S., L.R.C.P.,
CHAIRMAN OF
REPRESENTATIVE BODY,
1925–1928; CHAIRMAN OF
COUNCIL, 1928–(STILL IN
OFFICE).

Manager. Mr. Fowke was gouty and asthmatical, nervous and apprehensive, constantly apologetic, slow of speech and slow to form a judgment, particularly in matters relating to finance. No wonder his brilliant colleague looked upon him with a feeling almost of contempt. But there is no use denying it. In spite of what was said in some of the obituary notices of the Editor's financial abilities, and in spite of his nationality, he was really a very indifferent financier. And this was appreciated fully by the Manager, who repaid the feeling of contempt for himself by the strongest expression of distrust of the financial schemes of the Editor. It may easily be imagined that there were no feelings of cordial friendship between two such men. This was quite well known to many persons interested in the Association, and during the years that I was Treasurer it was several times suggested to me to do my best to heal up the dissensions between the two great officials. But I would not listen to such suggestions. No lasting peace was possible between them ; and my own opinion was that the safety of the Association was better secured by their hostility to one another than it would have been by their friendship. Each kept a watch upon the other useful in the interests of the Association. Had they combined there might possibly have been mischief. Had there been two Harts the Association would probably have been swiftly borne to that great personage to whom the beggar on horseback is said to ride. Had there been two Fowkes it might have gone to sleep."

Hart is commemorated by the Ernest Hart Memorial Scholarship, and Fowke by the Francis Fowke Bequest intended for the benefit or relief of the clerical staff of the Association.

(For Fowke Bequest see *Handbook*, 1929-30, p. 277.)

Butlin and Andrew Clark.

Besides those officers of the Association who were commemorated in " the Middle Age " others have since rendered notable service. Among them were Treasurers like Sir Henry Butlin, who from 1890 to 1895 rendered loyal service. The services of a distinguished metropolitan hospital surgeon have not so often been placed at the disposal of the Association that the circumstance should be passed over. In the careful hands of Sir Henry Butlin the finances of the Association prospered, so that it was able to afford the handsome premises in the Strand, which were only given up for the more spacious ones now occupied. Butlin became President in 1910, on which occasion he delivered the historical address from which quotations have already been made. Another hospital surgeon who long and faithfully served the Association was Mr. Andrew Clark, of the Middlesex Hospital, who was Treasurer from 1899 to 1901 and Chairman of Council from 1901 to 1905. In the latter year he retired on the score of ill-health when he was awarded the Gold Medal of the Association. He was an enthusiastic Volunteer and Territorial officer, being the first such to be appointed Hon. Surgeon to the King. He died in 1913. (The subject of this notice must not be confused with Sir Andrew Clark, Bart., Physician to the London Hospital, who died in 1893.)

EDWARD MARKHAM SKERRITT, M.D.
(1848-1907).
(*B.M.J.*, 1907, Vol. I, p. 1157.)

Andrew Clark was succeeded as Treasurer by Skerritt, who held that office from 1902 to 1904. He was a brilliant student at University College, London, and took all three Gold Medals in the M.B. and B.S. Examinations of London University. He won the Atkinson-Morley Surgical Scholarship at University College Hospital and graduated M.D. in 1874. In the next year a vacancy for a physician occurring at the Bristol General Hospital, he applied for and obtained it, serving on its staff for thirty-four years. In the same year he joined the Bath and Bristol Branch of the British Medical Association. He became a member of Council in 1884. He was a Vice-President of the Section of Medicine at the meeting in Bristol in 1894, and held similar office at the London Meeting in 1895. He died at the age of fifty-nine. He was of a reserved nature and rather stiff in manner but warm-hearted, and he had many close friends. His hobbies were hunting and gardening, for he loved an open-air life.

216

HENRY RADCLIFFE CROCKER, M.D., F.R.C.P.
(1845-1909).
(*B.M.J.*, 1909, Vol. II, p. 1729.)

Markham Skerritt was succeeded as Treasurer by Radcliffe Crocker, who from an apprenticeship in the provinces had made his way to University College Hospital, and by sheer merit and hard work had won a leading position in the profession and had become an acknowledged leader among dermatologists.

He joined the Metropolitan Counties Branch and was its Honorary Secretary in 1889, was elected a member of Council the next year and Treasurer of the Association in 1905. He had been previously a member of the *Journal* and Finance Committees. The need of more space at the office in the Strand had then become pressing, but there was considerable difference of opinion as to how this want should be satisfied. Dr. Crocker's energy and acumen bore a great part in the final decision to enlarge the Strand site and rebuild. The building, with its once notorious but now overlooked figures by Epstein, owed much to him. The now flourishing Medical Insurance Agency was founded through the efforts of a committee with which he cordially co-operated, as did the Editor of the *Journal*, Sir Dawson Williams. His health failed and he died suddenly in Switzerland. Sir Henry Butlin had paid an eloquent tribute to his merits (*B.M.J.*).

DR. EDWARD RAYNER, M.D.

Dr. Edward Rayner, Surgeon to the Stockport Infirmary, succeeded Radcliffe Crocker as Treasurer, and held the post for eight years from 1907 till 1916. Like so many of those whose names appear in this chapter, he was a student of University College. He took the Gold Medal for Forensic Medicine in the M.B. Examination of London University in 1869, and the M.D. degree in the following year. Rayner was an enthusiastic member of the Association and supporter of the new constitution. In 1914 he was awarded the Gold Medal of the Association, and the Chairman of Council in presenting it told the meeting what an anxious post that of Treasurer had been for the past few years, and described as "distinguished bravery" his action in administering the finances during a critical period. Dr. Alfred Cox, who as Medical Secretary knew him well and worked with him in the Central Office, wrote *inter alia* the following tribute at the time of Rayner's death :—

"His faith in the future of the Association was unassailable. The most striking evidence of this was the occasion on which when the funds of the Association were heavily overdrawn by the demands made on us by the Insurance Act fight, and the bankers were getting restive, he offered to place (and I believe did place) his own private account at the service of the Association. He was a very hospitable man. . . . Another thing which could not fail to strike anyone brought closely into contact with him, was his pride in his profession, in his own practice and in his own town. I never knew a man who was prouder of his position as a general practitioner than Rayner was."

His scientific education began at Owen's College, Manchester, and was continued at University College, London, and in Paris. He graduated B.A. London in 1863, but his time in Paris was something more than a passing visit, for he took there the degrees of B.L. and B.Sc. in 1864. He always retained a strong interest in French politics ; the capacious pockets of the rather old-fashioned coat he affected were seldom without one or two copies of the Paris newspaper to which at the time he happened to be subscribing. He was British juror in the class of medicine and surgery at the International Exhibitions held at Brussels in 1910 and at Turin in 1911.

TREASURERS
(1864-1924).

(*B.M.J.*, 1924, Vol. II, p. 976.)

George Ernest Haslip, M.D., was born and bred at Gravesend, Kent, and received his medical education at the London Hospital. He had a large private practice at the West end of London. He was elected Treasurer of the B.M.A. in 1916. He had been President of the Metropolitan Counties Branch in 1913 and Vice-President of the Section of Medical Sociology in the same year, but he was not at that time at all widely known to members of the Association. He had, however, been Chairman of the Medical Insurance Agency since 1909, and in that office had shown his capacity as a financier. No one knew better than he that in becoming Treasurer of the Association at the beginning of the third year of the War he was undertaking onerous duties, to which were to be added the anxieties necessarily connected with the purchase of the new House in Tavistock Square. As Sir Robert Bolam wrote in the *Journal* :—" One of his last official acts was the signing of perhaps the largest cheque so far drawn on our account—for the purchase of the House, in the negotiations for which his personal influence and acumen were conspicuous." The general financial position of the country was, of course, far from satisfactory, and the British Medical Association was suffering like other undertakings which had a commercial side. He gave much time and thought to the questions which came before him, and was in very frequent consultation with the then Financial Secretary Mr. Guy Elliston. The unexpected death of Mr. Elliston in April, 1918, very greatly increased Dr. Haslip's responsibilities and anxieties ; he did not shrink from giving his time very freely, and visited the office practically every day for many months preceding and following the Armistice. Through all this trying time he never lost his contagious courage and high spirits, and he came to be regarded with the greatest admiration and affection by all with whom he worked in the Central Office. The Association was never more fortunate in the choice of an officer than when it elected Dr. Haslip as Treasurer in 1916.

GUY ELLISTON.

(*B.M.J.*, 1918, Vol. I, p. 468.)

The British Medical Association was fortunate in obtaining the devoted services of such a man as Francis Fowke. Perhaps it was due to Mr. Fowke's judgment of personality and ability that his retirement found an Assistant Secretary in office so well fitted to succeed him as Mr. Guy Elliston.

Mr. Elliston had had a varied experience when he became Assistant Secretary to the Association in 1899, at the age of twenty-seven. He was the third son of

Dr. W. A. Elliston, who was President of the Association in 1900, when it held its Annual Meeting at Ipswich. He succeeded Mr. Fowke as General Secretary in 1902. The re-constitution of the Association in that year, and the great expansion of its medico-political work led to the creation of the office of Medical Secretary, and Mr. Elliston's sphere of duty was defined as that of Financial Secretary and Business Manager. His interest in everything concerning the welfare of the Association never flagged. He was always diligent in supplying information required by the Council or its committees, and did not spare himself in procuring and setting it out.

The financial position of the Association in 1902 was very satisfactory ; it owned the freehold of the house in the Strand, and possessed a considerable sum in investments, and as stated in the chapter upon " The Houses of the Association," it was decided to rebuild the premises in the Strand, which task was accomplished in 1908. The financial situation was seriously altered for the worse by the introduction of the Insurance Act in 1911, entailing on the Association a large expenditure in its struggle to maintain the just claims of the profession. For some years the position caused anxiety to those responsible for financial affairs and especially to the Treasurer, Dr. Rayner, and his executive officer, Mr. Elliston. The wise and prudent policy followed was rewarded by steady improvement until the outbreak of war, which very seriously upset the course of all business affairs, including those in any way concerned with printing and publishing. The increased cost of producing and despatching the *Journal* every week to twenty-four thousand members raised very serious questions, but the foresight and prompt decision displayed by Mr. Elliston as each fresh difficulty arose were of the greatest value in enabling the Association to maintain its work while safeguarding its funds. His action again and again received marks of appreciation from the Council, and his services should never be forgotten. The preliminary arrangements for Annual Meetings and for the exhibitions held during their sessions were in the hands of Mr. Elliston, and the smooth working of these meetings was largely due to his work.

The foundation of the Medical Insurance Agency, in which *The Lancet* and *The British Medical Journal* co-operated, has been described in another place. On the occasion of Mr. Elliston's death Dr. Haslip, who in 1909 succeeded Dr. Radcliffe Crocker as Chairman of the Committee of the Agency, placed on record his belief that the success of the Agency had been in a large measure due to the judicious and energetic manner in which Mr. Elliston conducted its affairs. Dr. Rayner, who was Treasurer from 1907 to 1915, also recorded his high opinion of the value of Mr. Elliston's services in the financial management of the affairs of the Association.

Mr. Elliston died of pneumonia on April 13th, 1918, after a few days' illness, at the early age of forty-six.

ROBERT LAWSON TAIT, F.R.C.S. Eng. & Ed.
(1845-1899).

President, Birmingham and Midland Counties Branch and of the Worcestershire and Herefordshire Branch. Member of Council, B.M.A. Hastings Gold Medallist.

Tait was one of the greatest surgeons of the nineteenth century. As Sir James Simpson's pupil, if not a nearer relation,* he was early familiar with gynaecology, which he almost revolutionised by his bold and successful surgical innovations. Owing largely to him the first hospital for diseases of women in Birmingham was established in 1871, and he was elected on the honorary staff at the early age of twenty-six, having already distinguished himself as a gynaecological operator.

Tait took an active part in the proceedings of the Council during his membership of it, and especially identified himself with the cause of medical reform. He delighted in controversey either viva voce or on paper, and in Birmingham was actively occupied as a lay journalist. His energy was unbounded, but he did not combine *sauviter* with *fortiter*, and his statistics were not always to be accepted without investigation. Nevertheless, to him are chiefly due the advances which have made abdominal surgery what it is to-day. A masterly

---

* *See* " Lawson Tait, his Life and Works," by Stewart MacKay, 1922.

account of his career will be found in *The British Medical Journal* for 1899, Vol. I, p. 1561.

Edmund Owen.

(*B.M.J.*, 1915, Vol. II, p. 200.)

Edmund Owen was one of the small number of Metropolitan Hospital surgeons who took an active part in the affairs and administration of the Association from 1883, when he was Secretary of the Section of Surgery at the Annual Meeting in Liverpool, till 1910, when his term of office as Chairman of Council ended. Undoubtedly his greatest service was rendered during the controversies which attended the re-organisation in 1900 and the following years. There is no doubt that his work as Chairman of the Constitution Committee, and his presentation of its report, went far to convince many members that the new constitution ought to have a trial.

In 1902 he was elected Chairman of the Colonial Committee, and in 1907 Chairman of the Council.

During the War, as representative of the St. John Ambulance Association, he arranged with Sir Frederick Treves the working union of that society with the Royal Red Cross. But the strain of war work was too much for him. He was attacked by apoplexy in the street, and died without recovering consciousness in 1915.

Owen held various honorary degrees, and was made a Chevalier of the Legion of Honour for his services to the French Hospital in London.

His breezy bonhomie and keen enthusiasm made him generally popular, and if, as in the case of Listerism, he condemned too hastily, he was open to conviction and not afraid to recant and to advocate what he had before condemned. At St. Mary's Hospital, where his public professional life was spent, he was highly popular with his students, for he was an excellent clinical teacher.

Sir Victor Horsley, C.B., F.R.S., First Chairman of the Representative Body 1903-6.

Victor Horsley was an enthusiast. He was incapable of lukewarmness in any cause. He held all his opinions very strongly. Those who remember his personality

222

cannot forget the effect made by his rather deep-set piercing eyes and his alert manner, which conveyed the impression that he was always ready to attack an opponent's view or defend his own with vigour.

He was one of those people who show to more advantage in office than in opposition, despite his undoubted powers of criticism. This, we think, was seen in the days of the agitation for reform of the Association when at the meeting called by the Medical Guild at Birmingham there was imminent danger of disruption of the Association. On that occasion his criticisms of the British Medical Association and the General Medical Council were effective enough, and his desire for amendment of the Medical Acts was shared by most of his hearers, but these things were not all " practical politics " at the moment. It was left to less fiery advocates to steer the meeting on a safe course and avoid disruption.

But when Horsley became the first Chairman of the Representative Body, he thoroughly appreciated the responsibility of his office and showed a combination of radicalism and respect for constitutional practice that was of the very greatest value to the reformed Association in the four critical years during which he presided over the Representative Meetings.

During the discussions over the introduction of the Insurance Act, when, to the lasting disgrace of the meeting at the Queen's Hall, he was refused a hearing, his indignation seemed to have obscured his vision of the facts, for it led him to make accusations against the Editor of the *Journal* which were unwarranted.

In the controversy over the forcible feeding of suffragettes he allowed his partisanship to overbalance his judgment, and many pages of the *Journal* were occupied with the expression of his views.

But these were but the foibles of an essentially noble nature. It can never be forgotten that he, who had achieved world-wide fame as a physiologist, neurologist and surgeon, and might well have been content with the laurels he had won, chose rather to plunge into the struggle for the reorganisation of the Association and to champion the rights of the General Practitioner as a member of the General Medical Council. The Association may be proud of the fact that during the

223

most active and distinguished part of his career as a surgeon and a scientist it always had the first claim on his time.

Although age might have prevented him from taking the field in a torrid climate, his patriotism led him to Mesopotamia, where he died in 1916. In his letters he exposed the scandalous neglect of the financial side of the Government of India, which was responsible for great suffering and loss.

His last letter to the Editor of the *Journal* was dated July 5th, 1916—that is to say, some ten days before his death. The information which it contained was commented on in a leading article aptly headed " A Voice from the Dead."

JOHN ROBERTS THOMSON, M.D., F.R.C.P.
(1844-1917).
(*B.M.J.*, 1917, Vol. II, p. 405.)

Formerly President, and afterwards Chairman of Council, of the British Medical Association ; Consulting Physician, Royal Victoria Hospital, Bournemouth.

Dr. Thomson was a Lowland Scot who settled in Bournemouth as a resident at the Royal National Sanatorium, when the place was little more than a village. There he spent the rest of his life, seeing it grow up to a County Borough. In the municipal as well as the medical life of the place he took a great part. He was a member of the county and borough bench and an original member of the Hants County Council, and for many years president of the School of Science, Arts and Technology, besides taking active part in other local educational work. He was also an enthusiastic Volunteer.

When the highly successful Annual Meeting of the Association took place at Bournemouth in 1891 he was President. In 1899 he was elected Chairman of the Council of the Association. He held this office in the troublous times of the agitation for reform of the constitution and during the great changes effected in 1900.

In that year he was appointed a member of the Constitution Committee. Dr. J. C. McVail wrote in the *Journal* on the occasion of his death that he was generally opposed to changes in the constitution, but that his membership was useful, as he put before the Committee the objections which he saw to the proposed changes.

He was a model of courtesy and urbanity. His favourite recreation was mountain climbing, but his activities in this line were restricted by lameness due to a serious bicycle accident at Bournemouth in the early 'nineties.

He died at the age of seventy-three years.

ROBERT SAUNDBY, M.D. Ed., F.R.C.P. Lond., 1887.
(*B.M.J.*, 1918, Vol. II, p. 271.)

Emeritus Professor of Medicine, University of Birmingham ; President of the Association 1911-12. He was born in London in 1849 and started life as a tea planter in India, but soon returned and entered as a medical student at Edinburgh University, graduating in 1874. There he held the offices of House Physician to the Royal Infirmary and to the Royal Hospital for Diseases of the Chest. In 1876 his long connection with Birmingham began, where he was appointed pathologist to the General Hospital in that city. He became physician to it in 1885, and held the office for twenty-seven years. He was long Professor of Medicine in the University of Birmingham. He was a member of the Midland Medical Society, and from 1895 to 1899 President of the Midland Medical Institution. In 1890 he gave the Bradshaw Lecture of the Royal College of Physicians, on the morbid anatomy of diabetes mellitus, a subject that always interested him. The year before his death he delivered the Harveyian oration. He died in 1918.

His book on the treatment of diseases of the digestive system reached a second edition in 1914, and his lectures on renal and urinary diseases a fourth edition in 1900. He also wrote a volume on the care and treatment of old age and a short book on urgent symptoms in medical practice in 1915.

The position he attained in Birmingham and in the British Medical Association led him to take particular interest in the subject of medical ethics, upon which subject he wrote a volume, which reached a second edition in 1907. This may be said to have laid the foundation for the medico-ethical work of the Association. He became a member of it in 1875, and from the first took a keen interest in the local work. He was one of the General Secretaries at the Annual Meeting in Birmingham in 1890, and when the Association next met in that city in 1911 he was President. He was Chairman of the Council from 1896 to 1899, Vice-Chairman of the Constitution Committee which sat at that time. He represented the University of Birmingham on the General Medical Council from 1905 to 1917. He was Middlemore Lecturer in 1892. He was Lieut.-Colonel, R.A.M.C.(T.). Soon after his death Sir H. Gilbert Barling, C.B., C.B.E., F.R.C.S., Vice-Chairman of the University of Birmingham and long Dr. Saundby's colleague at the General Hospital, wrote of him as follows :—

" He was a handsome, intellectual looking man, full of enthusiasm for the scientific side of medicine, and a prodigiously hard worker ; his enthusiasm and his industry remained to the end of his life.

" It would be ungrateful to forget the services he rendered as Editor of *The Birmingham Medical Review* which would have died of inanition but for his endeavours. Equally or even more valuable was the interest he showed in the Medical Institute of which he was for many years the Librarian, and for a long period the President. The provision of this excellent meeting-place for all the medical societies, and the extension of its library, owe more to Saundby than to any other person. Some four years ago the early indications of cardiac insufficiency began to show themselves, and perhaps it would have been better if our friend had recognised the wisdom of lessening his work, but this was foreign to his nature, and when he was mobilised as Lieutenant-Colonel, *à la suite*, in the Territorial Service he threw himself with his usual ardour into the new duties which undoubtedly strained and over-tried him gravely, and in my opinion they shortened his days. Those who only knew Saundby slightly will perhaps recall occasional offence arising out of temperamental irritability. It would be idle to deny this defect, but it did not represent the real man, and when the moment of irritability was over no one had deeper regret

226

for the incidents than he himself. The dignity and courage with which he bore his prolonged illness and his later great suffering a thousand times redeemed what was in truth a surface fault which was never associated with malice or ill-will."

THE RIGHT HON. ROBERT FARQUHARSON, P.C., M.D., LL.D., EDINBURGH, 1858.

The Right Honourable Robert Farquharson, P.C., M.D., LL.D., graduated at Edinburgh in 1858. His medical life was spent in the Army Medical Service, as medical officer to Rugby School and as dermatologist to St. Mary's Hospital, London. On succeeding to his father's estates in Scotland he ceased to practice, and two years later, in 1880, entered Parliament as the Liberal member for West Aberdeenshire. He held the seat till his retirement in 1906, doing very useful work in the House of Commons, where he was accepted as an authority on medical and scientific subjects, and was recognised as an unofficial spokesman for the medical profession.

Farquharson succeeded Hart as Chairman of the Parliamentary Bills Commission of the Association, and held that office till 1900. In this capacity he introduced many deputations to Parliament, and rendered valuable service. He published his " Reminiscences."

CHARLES LOUIS TAYLOR (1850-1920), ASSISTANT EDITOR OF *The British Medical Journal*.

Taylor had an unusual upbringing and an unusual career. Trained for the priesthood of the Roman Church in the Scots College at Valladolid, he found after four or five years that he had no vocation. Trained later at University College Hospital for the medical profession, he could not be induced to sit for a qualifying examination, although he served as house surgeon, and obviously could easily have passed. He was an accomplished linguist, speaking or at least reading seven languages, including colloquial Latin. He became Secretary to Sir Morell Mackenzie, and helped him much to bring out the second volume of his " Manual of the Diseases of the Nose and Throat." In 1886 he joined the staff of the *B.M.J.*, became Assistant Editor in 1897 and served until 1917, when ill-health compelled his resignation. Thus he served the *Journal* for thirty years, during four or five months of which he acted as Editor, while Dawson Williams was laid up by an accident. His memory was retentive and accurate of all that had appeared in the *Journal* in his day, and he made himself a master of certain subjects which were recurring subjects of public controversy, such as vaccination, anti-vivisection and Christian Science.

The interest shown in his casual notes on historical subjects led him to suggest a series of articles in the *Journal* which, under the headings of " Archæologica Medica " and " Nova et Vetera," have appeared from time to time. Many of the earlier of these were written by him.

He was a man of genial and kindly temperament, which endeared him to all those with whom he worked. He was a loyal colleague, and his fund of knowledge of the past and present of medicine, on which he was ever ready to draw in conversation, made him an interesting and stimulating companion.

JOHN CHRISTIE McVAIL, M.D.
(1849-1926).
(*B.M.J.*, 1926, Vol. II, p. 279.)

John Christie McVail was for many years well known for his work in the study of Small-Pox and Vaccination and in Public Health. He also took a prominent part in the organisation of the National Health Insurance system in Scotland.

He was appointed the first Medical Officer of Health for the counties of Stirling and Dumbarton in 1891. His annual reports of the health of those counties were admirable examples of what such reports should be. When the National Insurance Act came into force he was appointed Deputy Chairman of the Commission for Scotland, a whole-time Government post. He was also a member of the Scottish Board of Health. For many years he was an active member of the Association. In 1904 he became Chairman of the Glasgow North Western Division, and in 1905 he was elected President of the Glasgow and West of Scotland Branch. He was a member of Council for many years and a member of the

Constitution Committee in 1900-1901. The excellent historical sketch by him (reprinted in pamphlet form) entitled " Changes in the Constitution " has been freely drawn upon in the section of this work upon that subject.

McVail published a book, " Vaccination Vindicated," in 1887, and his Milroy Lectures on " Half a Century of Small-Pox and Vaccination," delivered in 1919, were republished in book form. In 1902 he had written for the Association a pamphlet entitled " Facts about Small-Pox and Vaccination," of which a second edition was called for in 1905. A revised edition appeared in 1924. He was a frequent contributor to the editorial columns of the *Journal*.

McVail was for many years a Crown representative on the General Medical Council.

Among the many distinctions bestowed upon McVail should be mentioned the degree of LL.D., conferred upon him by the University of Glasgow in 1908, and his appointment in 1912 to be Crown Member for Scotland on the General Medical Council in succession to his brother, Sir D. C. McVail, a distinguished Glasgow physician. He was a Fellow of the Royal Society of Edinburgh, and had been President of the Society of Medical Officers of Health of Great Britain and of the Incorporated Sanitary Association of Scotland. In 1906 he was presented with the Jenner Medal of the Royal Society of Medicine, and at the time of his death he was President of its Epidemiological Section. During the years when titular honours were somewhat freely distributed among the ranks of the profession it was remarkable that McVail, whose merits were so out-standing, was distinguished by remaining plain " Dr."

ELIZABETH GARRETT ANDERSON, M.D.
(*B.M.J.*, 1927, Vol. II, p. 844.)

The story of the opening of membership of the Association to women has been told in the section on Changes in the Constitution. A full account of the difficulties over which Miss Garrett triumphed in the end appeared in the *Journal* for December 22nd, 1927, p. 844, on the occasion of her death. The Society of Apothecaries being bound by their Charter to examine candidates, without discrimination as to sex, Miss Garrett, who had managed to obtain the necessary training in various places and under many difficulties, presented herself and passed the final examination in 1865. In 1866 she became medical officer to the St. Mary's Dispensary for Women and Children, which afterwards developed into the new Hospital for Women in the Euston Road, and is now called in her honour the Elizabeth Garrett Anderson Hospital for Women.

Miss Garrett obtained the M.D. Paris by examination in 1870. The next year she married with Mr. J. G. S. Anderson. When the London School of Medicine was founded by Miss Jex Blake, who was at that time unqualified, Mrs. Garrett Anderson became Lecturer on Midwifery. She became Lecturer on Medicine in 1876. In 1877 the practice of the Royal Free Hospital was opened to women students. In 1883 she succeeded Mr. A. T. Norton as Dean of the School, and held the post till 1903. During these years she was busy in private practice, in which she attained considerable success.

The decisive event in the medical women's struggle was the passing of Mr. Russell Gurney's Act in 1876, which empowered corporations and universities to grant them medical degrees, of which Act the London and Dublin Universities first availed themselves. Gradually the barriers were thrown down, until in 1909 the last gave way, when the qualifying examination of the conjoint board of the London Colleges was opened to women.

In this agitation for admission to membership of the Association, Mrs. Garrett Anderson took a large part. She was elected, in 1897, President of the East Anglian Branch and Vice-President of the Section of Medicine at the Ipswich meeting in 1900. She retired to Aldeburgh in Suffolk, where her family had long resided and where she was born. She was elected in 1908 Mayor of that Borough—the first woman to hold such a post in England. She died at the age of 81 in 1927, having been for some years in failing health. The Medical Women's Federation, an organisation which holds her memory in reverence, is presenting to the Association a replica of a portrait in oils of her by J. S. Sargent, R.A. This will hang in the Association's gallery to commemorate the first woman member of the Association.

230

Sir Robert Bolam, M.D., F.R.C.P., Chairman of Council, 1920–1928.

Sir Humphry Rolleston, Bt., G.C.V.O., K.C.B., M.D., F.R.C.P., Regius Professor of Physic, Cambridge.

ALFRED COX, M.B.,
Medical Secretary, 1912–1932.

Sir Dawson Williams, C.B.E., M.D., F.R.C.P.
(1854-1928).

Dawson Williams was a Yorkshireman who came up to London as a student at University College, where in due course he became House Physician. In 1884 he was elected Assistant Physician to the East London Hospital for Children, becoming Physician in 1894 and Consulting Physician on his retirement in 1902, consequent on his promotion to the Editorial chair of the *B.M.J.* His interest in pediatrics was lasting, and what he considered as his best work was a report to the Committee of the Clinical Society on the periods of incubation and contagiousness of certain infectious diseases, which necessarily dealt chiefly with children. This represented four years' work. He also contributed articles to Allbutt's " System of Medicine " and wrote an important book on the Diseases of Infancy and Childhood. But work such as the above naturally ceased on his appointment as Editor. His connection with the *Journal* began in 1881, only three years after he took his first qualification. He was appointed hospital reporter in 1884, principal sub-editor in 1886 and Assistant Editor in 1895. On the death of Ernest Hart in January, 1898, he was appointed Editor. The position of hospital reporter, which involved visits to the principal hospitals in London, had brought him into personal relations with the leaders of the profession, and so made him known to many distinguished physicians and surgeons, to his subsequent advantage as Editor.

The next thirty years were momentous for the British Medical Association, its *Journal* and the profession. How eventful they were to be was little foreseen by Ernest Hart when, in his last illness, he said to his probable successor, " I am leaving you a nice quiet time." As Sir Dawson Williams said, in reply to the toast of his health at the Council Dinner in 1923, this forecast was very quickly discredited. The reconstitution of the Association with all the turmoil and excitement which it caused, followed by the troublous and critical times of the introduction of the Insurance Act, and then the Great War, made sure that the Editor's office should be by no means a sinecure, or a bed of roses. In all these three trials he kept his head and gave wise counsel to the Association in particular and the profession in general. His advice and his influence were always cast on the side of caution and moderation, while he was firm in maintaining the rights and privileges of the profession.

Under his direction the *Journal* was improved in every way, and earned a reputation to which *The Times* bore testimony in a leading article on his retirement. The War, which threw heavy additional burdens on him, left him with a damaged heart, but despite the remonstrances of friends he persisted in his hard and constant work as Editor. The end came as he wished it should come, suddenly, and soon after his retirement. The numerous tributes to his fame in the lay, as well as the medical, press showed in what estimation he was held.

For his services to the medical department of the Army he received the honour of C.B.E. in 1919, and he was Knighted in 1921. In the same year the Gold Medal of the Association was conferred upon him. He held the honorary degrees of D.Litt. Durham, of LL.D. Glasgow, and D.Sc. Sheffield.

The Dawson Williams Presentation Scholarship at Epsom College was established in his memory by the Medical Insurance Agency, of which he was an active member. (See *B.M.J.*, 1928, Vol. I, pp. 416, etc.)

The Dawson Williams Memorial Fund was formed by subscriptions not long after his death. The proceeds are held by Trustees. The interest on the Fund is devoted to a prize to be awarded every two years, or at longer intervals, for the best work which had appeared on pediatrics since the previous award. An award was made in 1930, and a second is to be made this year.

J. A. MacDONALD, M.D., ETC.
(1853-1928).
(*B.M.J.*, 1928, Vol. I, p. 781.)

Dr. J. A. MacDonald succeeded Sir Victor Horsley as Chairman of the Representative Body of the Association in 1907.

He was an Ulsterman who had been a schoolmaster in the Methodist College, Belfast. Of fine physique, he played Rugby football for Ireland. He came to England

and settled at Taunton, where he soon became notable in all public activities and in politics. He was physician to the Taunton and Somerset Hospital.

In 1906 he was elected a member of Council. On the termination of his Chairmanship of the Representative Body he was elected to succeed Mr. Owen as Chairman of Council. He retired from that position in 1920 after serving ten arduous years which included the Insurance Act crisis and the whole of the War. He was elected a Vice-President of the Association at the Belfast meeting in 1909. He received the honorary degree of LL.D. from the University of Birmingham. The Association's Gold Medal of Merit was awarded to him in 1913. Moreover, a testimonial was presented to him during the Newcastle meeting in recognition of his services. For the seventeen years before his death he had been a direct representative on the General Medical Council.

When he died many pages of the *Journal* were occupied by personal tributes to his good qualities. It is impossible here to summarise them. Perhaps it will suffice to quote Dr. C. O. Hawthorne as representative. He wrote : " To differ from him was, of course, possible, but not to misunderstand him. Never hurried in his conclusions, and not unduly impatient of opposing arguments, he had a large capacity for decision and an ability to stand fast where he had chosen his ground. . . . His mind, like his physique, was of the robust order, and though circumstances sometimes compelled him to compromise he had no love for this form of strategy ; what appealed to him was the rigour of the game." He was devoted to the interests of the Association and spared no time or effort in its service.

SIR JENNER VERRALL, LL.D., M.R.C.S., CHAIRMAN OF REPRESENTATIVE BODY, CONSULTING SURGEON, SUSSEX COUNTY HOSPITAL
(1852-1929).
(*B.M.J.*, 1929, Vol. II, October 12th.)

Thomas Jenner Verrall had long-reaching connections with Sussex and with Brighton in particular. His father was Clerk to the Magistrates in Brighton, and he himself was sent to school there before proceeding to

Marlborough. On qualification in 1876, he began practice in Brighton and became surgeon to the Royal Sussex Hospital.

His record of service to the Association is long and perhaps unique. It opens with his appointment more than forty years ago as Honorary Secretary for East Sussex in the South-Eastern Branch. It would be tedious to recount the provincial offices which he held. His great work was done at headquarters. At one or other time he was a member of thirty committees or sub-committees. He had been Chairman of the Central Medical War Committee (for his work on which he was knighted), the Dominions, the Organisation, the Medico-Political and the State Sickness Insurance Committees, and he served on the Council from 1893 till his death. He was Deputy Chairman and afterwards Chairman of the Representative Body during the troublous days of the National Insurance Bill. So well did he guide the Representative Meetings that that body by unanimous vote made him a Vice-President of the Association. The Council had previously awarded him in 1914 the Gold Medal of Merit. In 1924 he was chosen to visit Canada with Dr. Alfred Cox, with the happy result that the Canadian Medical Association became affiliated to the B.M.A. in 1925.

The University of Aberdeen conferred on him the honorary degree of LL.D. in 1914. He served as a direct representative on the General Medical Council for eighteen years. His lifelong services to the profession, the Association and the public are inestimable.

W. E. HEMPSON

(1850-1930).

(*B.M.J.*, 1930, Vol. I, February 15th.)

William Ernest Hempson, Solicitor to the Association, was admitted a Solicitor in 1880, and started the firm of Hempsons, of which he was senior partner at the time of his death. In 1893 he was appointed Solicitor to the Medical Defence Union, and in 1900 to the British Medical Association. In the first-named office he obtained a wide knowledge of medical affairs, which was valuable to him and to the Association. His advice in legal matters was always sound, and he rendered great

234

services to the Association, which were acknowledged in the rare honour of honorary membership on his retirement. His health gave way, largely as a result of overwork during the War and post-War period, and he retired to the country in 1928, relinquishing his appointment, which was transferred to his firm, of which his son is senior partner. He died in 1930. Three years before his death he placed at the disposal of the Council, as a mark of esteem for the Association and appreciation of his happy relations with it, a sum of money to be awarded as a prize for the best essay on some phase or branch of public health.

EDWARD BEADON TURNER, F.R.C.S.
(1854-1931).

A familiar figure at all medical assemblies in London was removed when E. B. Turner died in 1931. A fine athlete, and a man whose mind was as active as his limbs, he was distinguished on the running track and football ground. A strong individualist, an outspoken debater, he was nevertheless able to work admirably with others. He believed intensely in private practice, disliked all movements towards the nationalisation of medicine, and never quite reconciled himself to National Health Insurance.

He held various Branch and Divisional offices, and became a member of Council in 1912 and Chairman of the Representative Body in 1915. He was a member of many committees and Chairman of the Medico-Political Committee for seven years. Notwithstanding the claims of a large private practice, and the great call on his time of his many Association committees, he found time to travel all over the country speaking at some 2,000 meetings on Venereal Disease and Social Hygiene.

For five years he was a direct representative on the General Medical Council.

DR. WALTER ERNEST DIXON, F.R.S.
(1871-1931).
(*B.M.J.*, 1931, Vol. II, p. 361.)

Dr. Walter Ernest Dixon, F.R.S., was one of the few pharmacologists in this country, as well as being

235

a distinguished physiologist, whose researches were not confined to the action of drugs. He qualified in London in 1895, having previously taken the degree of B.Sc. at the age of twenty. Subsequently he became M.D. Lond. and D.P.H. Cantab. He became Professor of pharmacology at King's College, London ; in 1899 he became assistant to the Downing Professor of Medicine ; in 1902 received the honorary degree of M.A. Cantab. In 1909 he was appointed University Lecturer in Pharmacology, and ten years later Reader in that subject.

His valuable and numerous services on Government Committees and on the League of Nations' Committee on Morphine were freely rendered, as well as his work in teaching students at Cambridge and carrying out original investigations.

His literary and editorial energy was remarkable. His "Manual of Pharmacology" went through seven editions and he contributed to several well-known text-books. His published papers on physiology amounted to twenty-eight before 1924. His work on the nature of Asthma, with the late T. G. Brodie, will always be remarkable. He assisted in the editorship of four pharmacological publications. As a remarkably attractive lecturer, and especially as an inspiration to those undertaking original investigation, he built up a School of Pharmacology at Cambridge and set an example of high ideals in this science, which, with A. R. Cushny, of Edinburgh, he had done so much to initiate in this country. He was elected F.R.S. in 1911 and Honorary Fellow of the Royal College of Physicians in 1930. For his services in the War as Temporary Surgeon-Lieutenant, R.N., the nature of which was not advertised, he received the O.B.E. He held various honorary foreign degrees, including the LL.D. from the University of Manitoba, conferred when the Association met at Winnipeg.

He held no office in the Association, but gave to it much help and advice as one of its chief advisers in regard to scholarships and scientific grants. His memory was perpetuated by the inauguration of the Walter Dixon Scholarship of the Association, in the present year. He was, as the Medical Secretary wrote, " a good B.M.A. man."

236

R. WALLACE HENRY, B.A., M.D.
(1867-1931).
(*B.M.J.*, 1931, Vol. II, p. 727.)

R. Wallace Henry, B.A., M.D., Past-Chairman of Representative Body ; Consulting Ophthalmic Surgeon, Wycliffe Society, and to the Leicester School for Myopes.

Wallace Henry took a great part in the medical life of Leicester, and an equally great part in the affairs of the B.M.A. generally, and specially in relation to the National Insurance Act.

His greatest achievement in Leicester, besides the organisation of the profession through his secretaryship of the Division, was the institution of what is generally allowed to be the most successful example of a public medical service in this country. This was the Leicester Union of Medical Practitioners, which was originally a large provident dispensary under lay control. But he made his mark when the Insurance Bill was introduced by his masterly grasp of the important points, and his power of making problems clear to his audience. Another local interest was Leicester University College. He was President of the Leicester Literary and Philosophical Society and of the Leicester Personal Health Association. As Chairman of the Representative Body he was very successful. He had an extraordinary facility of mastering voluminous documents and picking out the salient points, while a fine memory enabled him to retain the facts in question.

In later years his interest in Association affairs was mainly centred in his own speciality of Ophthalmic Surgery, the Ophthalmic Committee and the Building Committee of the Association. He was the prime mover in the formation and the first Chairman of the Ophthalmic Committee.

He was a good and persuasive public speaker, for he took pains to consider what he said, and he was particularly happy and humorous as an after-dinner speaker.

THE ASSOCIATION AND THE GREAT WAR

THE services of medicine are equally essential in war and in peace, for the fighting forces and for the civil population ; and the Great War imposed a heavy burden upon the profession, which had to undertake new activities without relaxing the old and without any possibility of increasing its effective personnel. Its success in the task was in no small degree due to the work of the Association, which supplied the machinery necessary for effective co-operation. A few figures will suffice to show the nature and extent of the problem. At the outbreak of war there were roughly 1,600 medical officers actually serving in the Royal Army Medical Corps and Royal Navy. The mobilisation of August 2nd involved the immediate withdrawal from civil practice of over 2,000 additional members of the Reserves and the Territorial Force, while the recruiting campaign opened two days later effectually depleted the reserve from which the vacancies in civil practice might otherwise have been filled, and diverted to combatant service a number of those who qualified during the next four years. In 1919 the total commissioned strength of the medical services of the armed forces, excluding the oversea contingents and the Indian Medical Service, numbered 14,701, whilst the names of 574 officers of those services who had been killed or died on service stood on the Roll of Honour. Yet there had been no substantial breakdown in essential medical services at home, notwithstanding the additional difficulties involved in abnormal movements of population due to the War.

The work to be described falls into four periods. The first, covering roughly the first twelve months of hostilities, was for the profession as for the nation a time of volunteer effort and of experiment in adapting existing machinery to new work. The second, which ended with

238

the appointment of Sir Auckland Geddes as Director-General of National Service in November, 1917, was marked by the transition to a compulsory system of recruiting, followed by recognition of the necessity to distribute the whole manpower of the nation with due regard to the maintenance of essential civilian as well as fighting services. During this period the Association secured public recognition, statutory as well as administrative, of the adequacy of its machinery for dealing with the medical side of the problem. During the third phase, from November, 1917, to the termination of hostilities, the Association, on behalf of the profession, accepted statutory obligations under the Military Service Acts of 1918 more extensive than those imposed on the general population. The period of resettlement which followed the Armistice saw the collapse of the Ministry of National Service in March, 1919, and a speedy and vigorous return of the Association to its normal activities.

On the declaration of War, the most pressing need of the profession was to provide for the work of the men who had already left or were due to leave shortly. Local action was immediate and spontaneous. In Southampton, where about half of the doctors in active practice were liable for service in one capacity or another, the remainder undertook on August 4th to safeguard the interests of their absent colleagues and maintain the local medical services throughout the War. The Exeter Division of the Association and the London Panel Committee also took early action, while in Scotland the Chairman of the Scottish Committee, Dr. J. R. Hamilton, called a conference of the whole profession, which met at Edinburgh on August 12th and appointed a body which, as the Scottish War Emergency Committee, carried out with conspicuous success the organisation of the profession in Scotland. This Committee based its organisation on the divisional machinery of the Association in Scotland, was financed by the Association and co-operated with the central organisation soon to be created for England and Wales. Its activities are described in detail in Dr. Currie's excellent *Mustering of the Medical Services in Scotland,* and therefore require no further reference here. Its convener was Dr., now Sir, Norman Walker, and its Secretary, Mr. T. H. Graham. The response of the Association centrally was equally prompt. On August 4th the Chairman of Council, Dr. J. A. Macdonald, placed the machinery of the Association at the disposal of the Government for the transmission of appeals to the medical profession and for any other object of national importance. On August 7th the need of immediate provision for the work of those proceeding on service was urged upon the Divisions by circular, and on August 8th the *Journal*, in its leading article on " The War : Some Immediate Duties," discussed the progress of recruiting, and the central and local collective action already described.

Thereafter the existing machinery of the Association was utilised locally and centrally to meet any special needs which arose, such as the organisation during the first few months of the War, in co-operation with the Pharmaceutical Society, of free medical attendance upon the dependents of men on service and assistance to the members of the Belgian medical profession. A member of the Association's clerical staff was at this time lent to the Prince of Wales' Relief Fund to help in the first stages of its organisation. In January, 1915, a Committee of Chairmen of Standing Committees was appointed to deal with the work arising from war conditions in England and Wales, and one of its first tasks was to assist in the creation of the Irish Medical War Committee. This was installed at the Dublin office of the Association, under the chairmanship of Dr. MacDowel Cosgrave, and, with Mr. J. Hayes as Honorary Secretary and the Irish Medical Secretary, Dr. T. Hennessy, as Assistant Secretary, it did good work for the profession and the community in Ireland throughout the War. A War Emergency Committee appointed by the Metropolitan Counties Branch of the Association now began to classify the practitioners in its area with a view to ascertaining the war work which each had undertaken or was prepared to undertake, and when Sir Alfred Keogh, Director-General of the Army Medical Service, asked for similar particulars for the whole country, the Committee of Chairmen immediately started work upon a War Register which eventually embodied all information bearing on the availability of individual practitioners throughout England and Wales for any form of service, and proved an indispensable instrument in the work soon to be begun.

Meanwhile the position of the Association had received official recognition. Until April, 1915, the authorities had had free access to the columns of the *Journal* for recruiting appeals. In that month, after a conference with Sir Alfred Keogh, the Chairmen's Committee took up the new responsibility of itself urging upon the profession the duty of responding to such appeals, both by volunteering and by undertaking such additional duties as would enable others to volunteer. This departure gave the Association a claim to satisfy itself that the men asked for were really needed, that those obtained would be utilised to the best advantage, and that reasonably equitable conditions of service would be guaranteed. From this point onwards, therefore, the Committee was admitted to the counsels of the D.G., A.M.S., who met its representatives in conference at regular intervals and heard such criticism of military demands and methods as it felt bound to offer.

By the summer of 1915 it was clear that the national emergency called for something more than enthusiastic individual effort on the one hand and adaptation of normal organisation to the requirements of war on the other. The transition to the second phase of the work was marked for the profession by the decision of the Committee of Chairmen to distribute the demands of the military authorities throughout England and Wales in such a way as to ensure that each district should furnish its fair share of the total number required. The complexity of this work necessitated more elaborate machinery than any yet existing, and in July the Representative Meeting created a War Emergency Committee " to organise the medical profession in England, Wales and Ireland, in such a way as will enable the Government to use every medical practitioner fit to serve the country in such a manner as to turn his qualifications to the best possible use ; to deal with all matters affecting the medical profession arising in connection with the War and to report to the Council." The Committee, which early adopted the name of Central Medical War Committee, consisted at the outset of sixteen members including the officers of the

Association. It was empowered to co-opt not more than six additional members, not necessarily members of the Association, to represent universities, the Colleges and other medical bodies. This inclusion of non-members, which marks the assumption of full responsibility for the organisation not only of the Association but of the profession at large, was a determining factor in the subsequent work of the Committee. The Chairman of the new body was Mr. Jenner Verrall, who later received the honour of knighthood in recognition of his services, and the Vice-Chairman, Mr. E. B. Turner. Important parts of its reference were carried out by an Executive Sub-Committee under the chairmanship of Dr. Charles Buttar, and later by a Local Arrangements Sub-Committee under the chairmanship of Dr. T. W. Shore. Its Secretaries throughout its existence were Mr. N. Bishop Harman, later to become Treasurer of the Association, and the Medical Secretary, Dr. Alfred Cox.

The first care of the Central Medical War Committee was to improve the local machinery. At its instance 179 Local Medical War Committees were instituted, representative of the whole profession, irrespective of membership of the Association, with areas based generally though not exclusively upon existing divisional areas. These bodies kept the Central Committee fully advised of local conditions, were responsible for the extremely delicate task of selecting individuals to undertake military service, for arranging for the work of men absent on service, and generally for all local activities in connection with the War. Later, at the request of the Central Committee, the Royal Colleges appointed a Committee of Reference to advise on all points arising in connection with the metropolitan hospitals and their staffs. This body, under the chairmanship of Dr. (afterwards Sir) Frederick Taylor, President of the Royal College of Physicians, with Mr. (now Sir) Frederick Hallett as Secretary, worked in close co-operation with the Central Committee from 1916 until the end of the War. On Dr. Taylor's retirement in March, 1918, Dr. Sidney Martin became Chairman, and continued to hold office until the dissolution of the Committee in March, 1919. Sir Rickman Godlee acted as Chairman for two months during Dr. Taylor's illness in 1916, and took a very

242

active part throughout. The creation of competent bodies for Scotland and Ireland has already been mentioned.

Since the best machinery is useless without power, the efficiency of the new organisation depended ultimately upon the driving force of individual co-operation. This was supplied in a measure of which one illustration must suffice. The Central Committee instituted in 1915 a voluntary system of enrolment under which all male members of the profession up to the age of 45 were asked to undertake to accept commissions if and when called upon to do so. The scheme was in essence voluntary, for the sanctions of the Military Service Acts by which it was reinforced in 1916 did not apply after the age of 41 ; yet the final number of enrolments stood at 5,233 out of a possible 5,662. But the support of the profession, however essential, was not all that was needed. If the Committee was to discharge its reference efficiently it required also the fullest possible support from the military authorities. Not only must the whole business of recruiting remain in its hands but it must have sufficient notice of the demands of the War Office. So far as the Army Medical Department was concerned this position was conceded in principle at the very outset. The Admiralty was less complaisant, but the demands of the Navy were not sufficiently extensive to involve the breakdown of the system. The understanding with the Army Medical Department was confirmed when Lord Derby, who became Director-General of Recruiting in 1915, recognised the enrolment scheme as taking the place for the medical profession of the general national scheme of attestation. It was reinforced by Army Council Instructions on the introduction of compulsion by the first Military Service Act of 1916, and given statutory support by Section 7 of the second Military Service Act. The essential feature of the system established under this Section was that appeals against military service made on grounds other than that of conscientious objection were, in the case of medical practitioners, decided by professional committees as opposed to the lay tribunals competent for the remainder of the community. This meant that whereas for the general population the direct demands of the military authorities were made subject to the adjudication of a civil body, for the medical profession all demands upon individuals were made in the first instance through the medium of a professional body, and the equity of those demands was finally determined by the same body; an anomalous arrangement justified by its notable success.

The co-operation of the civil departments administering statutory medical services was hardly less necessary. Their jurisdiction covered at the outset some 11,000 practitioners under contract with insurance committees and a considerable number of whole-time and part-time public health, poor law, school and asylum medical officers. Any conflict between the claims of the responsible departments and those of the fighting forces upon given individuals must in the last resort have been a matter for the War Cabinet, while the bare possibility of such a conflict tended to friction and delay. The Committee, therefore, undertook to obtain the consent of any Department interested before recommending an individual for military service, while the Departments agreed not to withhold their consent in any case where the Central Committee could report adequate arrangements for carrying on the work of the man to be released. Representatives of the Departments attended meetings of the Committee when cases in which they were interested were under consideration, while the special needs of the hospitals were safeguarded by the Committee of Reference. Unfortunately, there was ground for the suspicion that with one exception the co-operation of the civil departments was not so full as was desirable. That exception was the National Health Insurance Commission, and no account of the Association's war organisation would be complete which did not pay tribute to the manner in which Sir Robert Morant, then Chairman of the Commission, helped the Committee at departmental conferences, by supplying clerical assistance at a time when practically all efficient clerks not absent on military service had been absorbed by Government Departments, by assiduous attendance at its meetings and by every possible means. The Committee was also indebted for much valuable help to Dr. (now Sir) James Smith Whitaker, sometime

Medical Secretary of the British Medical Association, but then a member of the Insurance Commission, and to Mr. E. J. Maude, of the Commission's staff, who later became Solicitor to the Ministry of Health.

For some twelve months it was possible to meet the demands of the War Office through volunteers, who only awaited the Committee's approval of their release to take up their commissions ; but in July, 1916, it became necessary to call upon men of military age to implement their enrolment pledge, and the Committee was bound to give individual consideration to the personal circumstances of any who found difficulty in doing so. As the Central Professional Committee under the Military Service Acts it had also to consider the small number of appeals, mostly lodged under a misapprehension, referred to it by local lay tribunals. The hearing of appeals, therefore, became an important part of the Committee's work.

From the latter part of 1916 the Committee distributed the successive demands of the War Office amongst Local Medical War Committees on the basis of the ratio of doctors to population in each area, the allowance considered adequate being roughly from 1 to 5,000 in urban industrial areas to 1 in 2,500 in scattered rural districts. This was later reduced, under pressure of necessity and with many misgivings, to 1 to 6,000 or less in the former case. The quota required was modified to meet special difficulties on cause being shown by the local committee. The local committee selected the requisite number of doctors and made arrangements for their work, the men so selected being given an opportunity to appeal to both the local and central committees against their decisions. The system worked well, but local difficulties were enhanced by the approach of winter ; and in October, when meeting a sudden emergency demand from the War Office, the Committee pointed out that such departures from plan might cause local breakdown and necessitate a demand for the return to civil practice of certain individuals. Later it was, in fact, necessary to secure the demobilisation of a small number of doctors for work in areas where an unforeseen reduction of the medical personnel by death or sickness threatened disaster.

245

The difficulty of meeting the calls of the War Office was enhanced by the fact that the remaining personnel of the profession was so distributed as to prevent its full utilisation for the maintenance of civil services. In December, 1916, therefore, the Committee began to seek power to transfer redundant senior practitioners from well-supplied residential districts to the areas where the remaining men of military age were located, and with this object approved " the general principle of mobilisation of the medical profession apart from any question of the general mobilisation of the whole community." On the basis of this manifesto a scheme of professional mobilisation was drawn up in consultation with Mr. Neville Chamberlain, Director-General of the new Ministry of National Service ; but the Government was not yet prepared to apply the principle of compulsion to civil as opposed to military services, and no further action was taken for the moment.

In 1917 an incident occurred which threatened to terminate the activities of the Committee. The Government's decision to meet the attacks upon hospital ships by creating a number of additional hospitals oversea necessitated an increase of the medical staff, and the sinking of the hospital ships " Donegal " and " Lanfranc " on April 17th emphasised the need for speedy action. On April 18th the Army Council, in defiance of the standing agreement not to accept the services of any doctor other than the newly qualified without the consent of the Central Committee, and ignoring its statutory power, as the Central Professional Committee under the Military Service Acts, to cut off the supply of officers for the Royal Army Medical Corps by wholesale exemption of individuals from military service, ordered local recruiting officers to summon the remaining medical men of military age to report immediately for ordinary combatant service in the ranks. It will be understood that, although it was intended to use the men concerned for medical service, the Army Council had no power to vary the form of these orders, for compulsory military service imposed no obligation to accept a commission. The Central Committee, summoned as soon as the news was received, at once informed the War Cabinet, the Secretary of State for War and the D.G., A.M.S.,

246

that it would be unable to " continue to bear the responsibility in the eyes of the medical profession and of the community for protecting the medical needs of the civil community while meeting the requirements of the Army," unless it retained the power to decide on the actual distribution of the calls made by the military authorities. On the same day, in a letter subsequently communicated to the lay and medical press, Lord Derby agreed to restore the procedure so rudely interrupted. The Committee resumed its duties and the episode was closed ; but its effects were seen in a delay of about three months in securing the release for military service of the men covered by a call which the Committee had been on the point of issuing when interrupted by the action of the Army Council, and in a growing suspicion of War Office demands and methods throughout the profession, and even within the ranks of the Committee itself, as well as amongst the lay public. Up to this point the efforts of the Committee had been directed primarily to recruiting. The emphasis now began to shift to maintenance of the essential civil services.

The heavy demands now made by the War Office entailed a further reduction in the standards of civil medical service and a corresponding modification of the Committee's methods and machinery. The task of securing arrangements for the release of the remaining men of military age was therefore remitted to a new sub-committee, the Local Arrangements Sub-Committee, which forthwith undertook a detailed review of the whole country, dealing from day to day with such information about each area as its staff could collect from any available source and tabulate between sessions, while the full Committee increased its personnel and sat in three sections once or twice weekly to deal with the numerous appeals resulting from the intervention of the Army Council on the one hand, and the more drastic assessment on the other. Representatives of local committees now attended the central meetings as much to plead against the demands made on their areas as to recommend individuals for service. The work of the Local Arrangements Sub-Committee soon showed that without power to transfer doctors from one area to another for civil work it must shortly become impossible to release more men of military age, and the Committee informed the Government of the position.

Meanwhile distrust of War Office demands and methods gained ground. An official committee was appointed by the Government to inquire into current accusations of waste of medical personnel, after which certain minor improvements were effected, presumably on its recommendation ; but its report was not published, a fact which caused much adverse criticism. Nor was dissatisfaction confined to the medical profession. The application by military medical boards of new standards of physical fitness under the Review of Exceptions Act gave rise to much resentment and a demand that the Boards should be placed under civilian control. This general unrest was the prelude to the drastic change in the organisation of national resources with which the third phase of the work began. On November 1st, 1917, the whole question of the utilisation of manpower, including both the medical aspects of general recruiting and recruiting for the medical services, was remitted to the Ministry of National Service under the direction of Sir Auckland Geddes. The Ministry thus superseded the Central Committee as the authority responsible for holding the balance between the civil and military demands, and the Committee, relieved of ultimate responsibility, both to the military authorities and the civil community, and under no obligation to endorse the policy of the Ministry, naturally grew freer in its criticism and more emphatic in its protests. Direct communications between the Committee and the various Government Departments were now replaced by frequent discussions with the Ministry of National Service which, under no obligation to accept its recommendations, could not, in fact, deal with the profession without its help. Fresh channels of service were soon opened by the formation of the new medical boards and a Medical Advisory Council to the Ministry, and by additional statutory obligations under the Military Service Acts of 1918. Cordial relations were early established with the Medical Department of the Ministry under the Chief Commissioner of Medical Service, Sir James Galloway, who, as an active member of the Metropolitan

Counties Branch, had previously taken a leading part in the creation of the Association's war organisation. Co-ordination under the new regime was ensured by the appointment of Mr. C. P. Vivian, now Registrar-General, as liaison officer between the Ministry of National Service, the older Government Departments and the Central Committee, all of which owed much throughout the year to the tact and ability with which he filled a position of great delicacy.

The profession was now called upon to implement the undertaking given on its behalf by the Committee more than twelve months earlier. The Military Service Acts of 1918 extended the maximum age of general liability for compulsory service to 50, with the proviso that for any particular section of the community it might be increased at the discretion of the Director-General of National Service by another five years. The Committee had, however, already signified its approval of the extension of the maximum age for the profession beyond the general level, and accordingly the Act itself raised the maximum age for medical practitioners to 55. At the same time the principle of compulsion was applied for the maintenance of essential civil services, as well as for those of the armed forces, by the Military Service (Medical Practitioners) Regulations. These gave the Central Committee, acting in concert with the Director-General of National Service, control of all members of the profession not found physically unfit for military service up to the age of 55. The older men, not required for commissioned service, could be offered the alternative of military service in the ranks or employment in civil practice in whatever place and capacity seemed good to the Committee. An appeal lay from the professional to a central tribunal, but only by permission of the former and on personal grounds, and the one appeal so preferred was unsuccessful. Interference with private practice by compulsory transfers under the new powers was no easy matter to deal with. The sanctions provided were sufficient, but no scheme could be applied without meticulous provision for financial and other practical details in each case, and it was fortunate that the cessation of hostilities in November made the contemplated action unnecessary.

R 2

Much attention was given about this time to a number of expedients for economising professional resources, notably by the pooling of private and insurance practice through various systems of central clinics or surgeries, attended on a definite plan by a rota of local practitioners. Central surgeries had already been voluntarily established in various places ; the question now arose whether, under the new compulsory powers, any steps should be taken to extend such methods of organisation. Local conditions, however, varied so greatly that it was not thought expedient to try to impose any standardised scheme of the kind, though the attention of local committees was drawn to the success of the experiments referred to.

While the Ministry and the central and local committees were occupied with these matters the medical position throughout the country gave increasing cause for anxiety, and the release of practitioners from military service to deal with emergencies in civil practice became more frequent. The breaking point was not reached, however, until the appearance of influenza in the autumn of 1918, and here also the Armistice brought a timely measure of relief. Lists of practitioners for demobilisation were promptly submitted by the Central Medical War Committee, and although it was not possible to secure the immediate return of all the men named, some 900 were soon released from military service at the instance of the Ministry on grounds of urgent public need. These, together with a number of temporary officers seconded from the R.A.M.C. for civil service in the most dangerously depleted areas, with a promise of priority of demobilisation thereafter, enabled the Committee to tide over the most dangerous period without widespread catastrophe. A number of officers of the R.A.M.C. on home service also obtained emergency leave and did their share, while the Board of Education released certain school medical officers from the work of inspection to help in the emergency.

The fourth and last phase began with the Armistice. The Committee at once drew up a scheme of general medical demobilisation in which practitioners on service were grouped for return, first according to the urgency of the public need for their services and then, subject to this, according to their personal circumstances. It was expected that the Ministry of National Service would be able to enforce demands based upon such a scheme upon the military authorities, but the Ministry retired from the field at the end of March and the War Office, with which direct communications were now resumed, proved unwilling or unable to enforce on the Commands any scheme for demobilisation by classes. The work of the Central Committee during the period of demobilisation was therefore in the main restricted to assistance in individual cases of hardship.

The work of the Central and Local Medical War Committees was financed throughout by the Association at an estimated cost of £14,000. Towards this the Government subsequently made a retrospective grant of £5,000. In reckoning the total expenditure under this head allowance should also be made for the loss of revenue caused by the Council's refusal, during the voluntary period of recruiting, of all advertisements offering civil work to men of military age, a loss estimated at the time as in the neighbourhood of £2,500 a year. The ordinary activities of the Association were of course considerably curtailed during the War period, but its normal staff, depleted by the absence on service of the male members of military age, was not sufficient, even with the personnel lent first by the National Health Insurance Commissioners and later by the Ministry of National Service, to deal with the work of the Central Medical War Committee, and had to be supplemented by a number of temporary clerks. From 1917 to 1919 the Committee also secured the services, as temporary chief of staff, of Mr. J. A. Cumming, a retired Indian civilian, who was able to relieve the Medical Secretary of some of the work of internal administration, and Miss A. L. Lawrence (who afterwards became the first Intelligence Officer of the Association), who early joined the staff, gave invaluable service for which she was awarded the M.B.E.

Considerations of public policy, necessarily predominant during the War years, were not allowed to obscure the claims of the individual to the services of the Association. Indeed, for the time being those services were extended to non-members on equal terms with members over a wide field of action. The relatively small number of appeals against military service during the period when central and local medical committees were free to select individuals for service suggest some measure of success in pursuit of the elusive principle of equality of sacrifice. In the more material matter of protection of practices also, all that was possible was done. Generally speaking, those who remained at home did the work of their absent colleagues, on a basis approved by the central body, varying with the character of the district and the nature of the work done, but approximating to half fees for ordinary services, two-thirds for special and the full fee for midwifery. It was also agreed that those who remained at home should not, on the cessation of hostilities, countenance the permanent transfer to themselves of patients attended by them during the War. While it would be absurd to suggest that the individual practice did not suffer to a greater or less degree in every case by the absence of the principal, the fact remains that the great majority of those who remained at home loyally and laboriously shared, not only in the service of the public but in protecting the interests of their absent colleagues. In individual cases the burden imposed by this work was even heavier than that of military service, and some at least of the older practitioners on whom it fell gave their lives in national service as surely as did those whose names appear in the Roll of Honour. Effective action was taken by the Association in yet another direction. From the first the Central Committee warmly espoused the cause of the Territorial medical officer, who found himself at a grave disadvantage as compared with the Temporary Lieutenant, R.A.M.C., and it succeeded in securing concessions which greatly reduced this disparity. Finally, during the period of demobilisation the Association gave such help as it might in resettlement by methods described in detail in a memorandum on Medical Resettlement published in the Supplement to *The British Medical Journal* for March 1st, 1919.

Throughout the period of war and demobilisation individual cases of hardship were also taken up by the Committee and pressed to the limits set by consideration of the national need, and not a few officers obtained

252

redress of personal grievances through representations made on their behalf to the military and naval authorities. Memory of wrongs unremedied sometimes outlives that of substantial benefits received. It is, therefore, not out of place to remark here that the profession was enabled by the Association to do for its members what probably no other profession could have attempted; that in the case of men who served, the Association recognised no distinction between members and non-members, and that the true measure of its success lies in the tale of practical achievement rather than in any imaginary standard of perfection.

From July, 1914, to July, 1920, when Sir Clifford Allbutt, in his fifth year of office as President, welcomed the Association to Cambridge, no Annual Scientific Meetings were held; but the Association's primary object of promotion of the medical sciences was not forgotten. Throughout those years, in the face of every difficulty, *The British Medical Journal* maintained unbroken its record of experience and achievement, jealous lest any fragment of constructive knowledge should be lost in preoccupation with the destructive activities of war. The series of articles, republished in 1917 as a review of British Medicine in the War, may serve as an example of this work. Mainly through the initiative of Sir Dawson Williams, Editor of the *Journal*, a Special Clinical and Scientific Meeting was held in London in April, 1919, in order to afford the leaders in the medical and scientific work of the Forces, including the American contingent, an opportunity to discuss their experience before dispersing to resume civil duties in different parts of the world. Three days of discussion in Sections of Medicine, Surgery, and Preventive Medicine and Pathology were supplemented by numerous demonstrations. A full account of the meeting, together with a short review of the medical war services, and an address on the New Birth of Medicine by Sir Clifford Allbutt, was published in a special volume of *Proceedings*.

MEDICAL BENEVOLENCE

NO history of the British Medical Association, however brief, can altogether pass over its contribution to the work of medical benevolence. The need for provident and charitable organisations was discussed by Charles Hastings and William Conolly even earlier than 1832, and at the second Anniversary Meeting of the Provincial Medical and Surgical Association at Birmingham in 1834 a committee was appointed to explore the whole question, on the motion of Dr. John Baron. This committee rejected a comprehensive scheme embracing life assurance, annuities and a benevolent fund on the ground that the infant Association could not hope to compete with existing assurance societies, and confined its recommendations to the creation of a benevolent fund for the relief of distress among contributors and their dependents by means of grants, annuities and temporary loans. This plan was approved next year. The committee was reappointed to give effect to the scheme, with unlimited power to form local sub-committees, and a new clause was added to the laws of the Association providing that "a medical benevolent society under the restrictions proposed in the report of the committee presented to the Anniversary Meeting at Oxford be connected with the Association." This modest law was the first charter of the Royal Medical Benevolent Fund of to-day, though it will be noted that so far the scheme was for a provident society with benefits limited to subscribers, rather than a charity. The following year, 1835, the provident basis was discarded and the Benevolent Fund of the Provincial Medical and Surgical Association took definitive form as a purely charitable organisation, accepting contributions from "all persons friendly to the objects of the society, though belonging neither to the Association nor the profession," and extending relief not only to subscribers but to all medical men and their dependents. This decision was doubtless dictated by necessity, for the task of relieving existing distress in the profession at large was clearly beyond the financial resources of an Association then numbering some 600 all told. But it was coupled with two further decisions which paved the way to the ultimate separation of the fund from the parent body. On the one hand, the power to alter and amend the rules of the fund was vested in the contributing members, without reserving the exercise of any form of control to the Association. On the other, the meeting rejected a proposal to make a grant to the benevolent fund from the surplus of the general fund of the Association.

However slight the constitutional tie thus established between the Provincial Medical and Surgical Association and its Benevolent Fund, there is evidence that its existence was recognised by both parties up to the final separation in 1870. Of this three examples must suffice. William Newnham, of Farnham, who for some time combined the offices of chairman, secretary and treasurer of the fund, and who so identified himself with its fortunes that it was popularly termed " Newnham's Fund " in contemporary discussion, writing in 1849, stated explicitly that he worked " not as an individual, but in execution of a trust reposed in me by the Association, in obedience to the laws of that Association, and with the sanction of its authority." The important changes in the administration of the fund made the following year were not only reported to the Anniversary Meeting at Hull, but discussed and approved by it, and even so late as 1869 Dr. C. J. Hare, in moving the adoption of the report of the fund at the Leeds meeting of the Association, referred to it as " a great and integral part of the Association."

The headquarters of the fund were originally fixed at Cheltenham, the home of Baron and Conolly, who were respectively its first president and secretary and treasurer. A few of the more important stages in its development as a department of the Association deserve notice. The first grants were made in the year 1836-7. By 1845 sufficient funds had accumulated to necessitate the appointment of trustees, and Hastings, Baron and Newnham were appointed. It is no small tribute to the excellence of the organisation that its rules and regulations were adopted verbatim by Dr. Kingsley when he established the Irish Medical Benevolent Fund about this time. In 1850 the accumulated capital justified the grant of the first annuities. In that year also an attempt was made to widen the effective appeal of the fund by removing its headquarters from Cheltenham to London (an essential change made easier by the withdrawal of Baron through illness, and the fact that Conolly had moved elsewhere) and by changing its name to the Medical Benevolent Fund. These changes were not intentionally separatist in character, for in the same year the honorary officers of the Association, central and local, were co-opted to the managing committee of the fund. In 1853-4 a whole-time collector, the first paid officer of the fund, was appointed. The relation between the two bodies may be illustrated by the fact that in 1856, when the membership of the Association was 2,000, the fund had 900 subscribers, of whom 400 only were members of the Association.

The final separation came in 1870, when the accumulated resources of the fund were considerable and there was some doubt as to the financial stability of the Association. In that year the fund assumed the title of British Medical Benevolent Fund, and from then on ceased to report to the Annual Meetings of the Association, without, however, losing its good will and support. Indeed, five years later we find the fund congratulating itself on " a closer alliance " with the " great and influential British Medical Association."

It is not difficult to account for the slow growth of the fund by reference to the economic conditions of the time, but three additional causes deserve mention. Apart from personal considerations, the location of its headquarters at Cheltenham was unfortunate. It did not ensure vital contact with the Association, and it deprived the fund of the support of London. Again, the benevolent fund suffered from the preoccupation of the Association and the profession with attempts to create provident funds, and finally the association of charitable objects with Mr. Propert's scheme for an educational foundation undoubtedly diverted support upon which the fund naturally relied.

256

The idea of attaching a provident scheme to the Association was not finally relinquished when the benevolent fund was given its exclusively charitable basis. A committee was appointed in 1845, on the motion of Dr. Edward Daniell, of Newport Pagnell, to discuss and arrange the preliminary steps for the establishment of " an annuity fund for decayed members of the Association and widows and orphans of members." This committee seems to have exceeded its authority by actually inaugurating a scheme and obtaining subscriptions, and the meeting at Norwich next year decided " that the annuity fund be not considered an object of this Association." Thus deprived of support from the parent body the fund collapsed in 1849, giving place to an independent scheme inaugurated by Dr. Daniell and Dr. John Forbes, both staunch champions of the provident principle and prominent members of the Association, under the style of the British Medical Fund. This was a more ambitious and comprehensive project, including sickness insurance, but despite extensive advertising and expert actuarial advice, it had no better fortune than its predecessor and was wound up in 1851. A last attempt was made by the Association in 1863, when the Bristol meeting appointed a committee to consider and report on the establishment of a provident relief fund for members and their dependents. After taking expert actuarial advice the committee recommended a society to provide sickness insurance only. Its report was approved and a provident society for the purpose was actually registered as a friendly society in April, 1865, with Dr. B. W. Richardson as president of the board of directors. By 1866, however, only 32 subscribing and 41 honorary members had been secured, although the membership of the Association had reached 2,300 and the scheme had been well advertised. The total sum collected from the two sources amounted to about £900. The society was dissolved that October. The fate of these schemes, stillborn after difficult labour, seems to justify the original verdict of 1836 as to the impracticability of connecting a provident scheme with the Association.

While the Association took no active part in the foundation of Epsom College with its associated charities, it can claim priority in publishing a scheme for a similar institution. A committee was appointed by the Anniversary Meeting at Nottingham in 1844 on the proposal of Dr. Martin, of Reigate, to consider and report on " the best means of establishing a school for the comprehensive and liberal education of the sons of medical men." So great was its enthusiasm that it issued an interim report on the same day, and elaborated a working scheme and began to take subscriptions in the ensuing year. This fine outburst of energy proved ephemeral, and in 1846 the £1,610 which had been collected was returned to the donors and the project abandoned. It is hardly possible, however, that John Propert, himself a member of the Council of the Association, was ignorant of the details of this scheme when, early in 1851, he conceived the idea of devoting his unique abilities as a propagandist to the task of founding Epsom College. As President of the Metropolitan Counties Branch of the Association three years later, he described the progress of his foundation to a sympathetic audience at the conversazione held during the Anniversary Meeting.

In 1907 a new source of support for medical charities was created in the Medical Insurance Agency, established on the initiative of the Editors of *The British Medical Journal* and *The Lancet* to meet the need of the profession for special facilities for insurance. This need had been enhanced by the new liabilities created by the Workmen's Compensation Act of 1906, which pressed heavily upon medical employers of assistants, *locum tenens* and dispensers. The Medical Insurance Agency gives free advice to practitioners, secures for them the most favourable terms available for all classes of insurance, allowing considerable rebates to the insurer, and, after meeting working expenses, distributes the balance of the commission received from insurance companies among the medical charities. In this way over £42,500 has already been saved to the profession by way of rebate, and over £25,500 distributed to the charities. In memory of the late Editor of *The British Medical Journal*, one of its founders, the Agency has recently established, in conjunction with the Council of Epsom College, the Dawson Williams Presentation Scholarship. The Association, precluded by its constitution from undertaking such work directly, has from the outset been closely concerned in the activities of the Agency, and has always been represented on the managing committee by its Treasurer and by other members conversant with insurance problems.

After the separation of the Medical Benevolent Fund from the British Medical Association, the direct activity of the latter in assisting medical charities was confined to receiving from its members subscriptions for transmission to the charities named by them, and keeping the claims of the several funds before its members through the columns of the *Journal*; but soon after the War the pitiful inadequacy of the amount available for the relief of distress within the profession began to attract increasing attention. In 1924 a committee was appointed to explore the position, and in 1925 the Representative Body agreed unanimously that the Association should throw its full weight into an effort to put the existing medical charities on a sound basis. It was decided to use the local organisation of the Association for the purpose in a way very similar to that adopted in 1850. Each Division was urged to appoint a charities secretary to take the matter in hand. To ensure continuity a new feature was added to the organisation by the creation of a central Charities Committee, charged with the duty of urging the claims of the charities upon the Association at large, and the institution of a special Charities Fund vested in the members of Council in office for the time being. Into this fund the contributions collected by the Association are passed, to be distributed to the medical charities in accordance with the wishes of the donors or, failing the expression of such wishes, at the discretion of the trustees. By these means increasing sums have been distributed annually to the charities since 1925. But the amount raised is still far from satisfactory; indeed, in the words of the report of the original benevolent fund of the Provincial Medical and Surgical Association in 1845, " the fund . . . has been found to work admirably well ; . . . the only difficulty the committee have ever had to contend with has been a want of funds."

In the new organisation the Association has been careful to avoid competition with the established funds ;

it works solely for their better support. The same principle was observed in 1925 when a new fund, known as the Sir Charles Hastings Fund, was created through the generosity of the late Lieut.-Col. J. W. F. Rait, I.M.S., then a member of Council, and Mrs. Rait. The trustees of the fund are the Chairman of the Representative Body, the Chairman of Council and the Medical Secretary. The fund is used at their discretion and with a minimum of formality, to help urgent cases which fall outside the sphere of action of the other funds.

THE ASSOCIATION AND
THE LAW

FOR centuries the medical art has been practised in Great Britain under the regulation, more or less strict, of the law which expressed in Royal Charters and Acts of Parliament an intention to protect the public against malpractice, and to defend the privileges of members of certain professional corporations. As did the Medical Acts of the last century, so the ordinances of previous centuries gave more heed to the protection of the public than of the practitioner.

In a recently published work, " The Law Relating to Medical, Dental and Veterinary Practice," Mr. Frederick Bullock, LL.D., has put the position very clearly, and his exposition, coming from a non-medical source, is so much the more impartial. He says :—

" At least four centuries of experimental legislation in regard to the practice of medicine and surgery in this country have brought us to a stage at which the practice of certain parts of the healing art is prohibited to all but legally qualified persons, while the rest of the field is open to be exploited by all who will.

" At the present day no uncertificated person may practise as an apothecary, no unregistered person may practise dentistry, no unqualified person may treat venereal diseases. Moreover, no unregistered person may hold an appointment as medical officer of any public institution or sign certain certificates ; no uncertificated woman may habitually and for gain attend women in childbirth otherwise than under the direction of a qualified medical practitioner ; no unregistered or unlicensed person may use certain dangerous drugs in his practice. . . . In the professions of law and medicine a prolonged course of study is essential before practice in either can safely be entered upon. Neither in law nor medicine does knowledge come by intuition. But in

261

medicine less even than in law can the knowledge acquired for practice be gained solely from books. A knowledge of the anatomy and physiology necessary to an understanding of the principles of surgery and medicine can only be attained by attendance at a recognised course of study at a medical school, for the State prohibits the use of the human cadaver for the study of anatomy except at such institutions. . . . The calling of the doctor is one which exacts from him far more than the mere exercise of professional knowledge and skill. He must be ever at the call of the public. No trades-union fixes his hours of labour ; public opinion looks upon his refusal from sheer fatigue to accept the last of many night calls as a wilful neglect of duty—the same public opinion which holds the refusal of the workman to do more than his day's allotted work to be loyalty to his class. . . . But more than this, the doctor loyally submits to a corporate discipline imposed in the public interest which restricts his liberties and interferes very often with his own material prosperity.

" In 1908 a Committee of the General Medical Council reported . . . that the practice of medicine by unqualified persons was prohibited in 43 British Colonies and in 33 foreign countries."

The present position of prohibition to unqualified persons of certain branches of practice only has its ridiculous aspect. As Mr. Bullock has written :—" Is Cancer more easily curable than venereal disease ? Is paralysis less important than an aching tooth ? " To which we would add another question :—Is more training needed to fit a practitioner to conduct a labour than to reduce a dislocation or set a Potts' or Colles' fracture ?

Medicine and the law have for many years had certain points of contact quite apart from Forensic Medicine, and the most important of these of late years, as far as the practitioner is concerned, have had to do with the care and certification of lunatics, while as far as the Association as a body has been concerned it has been the fearless denunciation of quackery and of unethical behaviour which has caused serious anxiety and financial loss on more than one occasion.

An action for damages on a charge of libel or slander is a formidable thing to face ; more particularly so if

J. C. McVail, M.D., F.R.F.P.S. Historian of Constitution and Government of the Association, 1924.

W. E. Dixon, M.D., F.R.S., Member of Arrangements and Scientific Grants and Science Committees.

THE RIGHT HONOURABLE SIR CLIFFORD ALLBUTT,
K.C.B., M.D., F.R.S.,
President of Association, 1916–1921.

the subject is a technical one, which a jury and even a judge may not fully understand. Juries seem to enjoy awarding swingeing damages which are to come out of somebody else's pockets. As an instance, we may quote the case of Kitson v. Playfair, in which a distinguished obstetric physician was ordered to pay £12,000 and costs for libel and slander involving a breach of professional confidence committed in a misguided attempt to protect the honour of a family.

In 1909 a case occurred which shows the necessity for the most extreme care in commenting on actions at law. In a short editorial paragraph headed " Medical Men and Legacies from Patients," a certain doctor was congratulated on the result of an action brought by relatives of the deceased patient to upset a will. The result had been a compromise. No name was mentioned in the *Journal* of any person except that of the doctor above-mentioned. Nevertheless, one of the parties, who happened to be also a medical man, complained of the editorial paragraph. What appears to have been an ample apology was inserted in the *Journal*, but it was not accepted as sufficient reparation. In January, 1910, an action for libel was tried, which the Association did not defend, but, acting on legal advice, paid £100 into Court. The jury, however, returned a verdict giving damages of £750 against the Association. It appears that the Editor was misinformed about this case, and acted upon a newspaper report and advice which he believed he could trust, but which turned out to be untrustworthy. The case affords a striking instance of the lurking libel which may be read into an entirely innocent comment, made without any malicious intent, and even without mention of the plaintiff's name.

In 1912 (Bell v. Bashford and B.M.A.) the Association was cast in damages of £2,000 for a libel adjudged to be contained in an article on " Quacks and Quackery " in the *Journal* of May, 1911, in which a qualified medical man was characterised as a cancer quack, his methods being compared to those of many notorious quacks of past times, such as were exposed by Sir Spencer Wells in a well-known pamphlet.

In the same year the proprietor of a remedy for tuberculosis brought an action for libel against the *Journal* for its exposure of his pretensions in an article which was reprinted in "Secret Remedies" (a publication by the Association dealing with secret remedies and patent medicines). The jury disagreed. The action was tried again by the same judge before another jury two years later, when a verdict for the defendants with costs was returned. As often happens in such cases, no costs could be recovered from the plaintiff.

What has become known as the "Coventry Case" is of such importance that a somewhat full note of its principal features seems to be called for. The trouble arose from a deep-seated feeling of dissatisfaction among the members of the Division with the conditions of service of the medical staff of the Coventry Provident Dispensary.

In February, 1906, the Coventry Division applied for a "Warning Notice" in *The British Medical Journal* concerning the Dispensary, in the following circumstances. Owing to the refusal of the management of the Dispensary to accept reforms suggested by the Division on the lines of the report on the general subject by the Medico-Political Committee, the Division declared that no member should associate himself with any Provident Dispensary run on such lines as that of Coventry.

The question became acute in 1907, when at the request of the Division, five practitioners resigned their appointments at the Dispensary on the following grounds :— (i) Absence of wage limit ; (ii) administration entirely under lay control ; (iii) acceptance of members at unnecessarily low rates of subscription ; and (iv) the feeling that the existence of the Dispensary stood in the way of any betterment of local contract practice conditions. Practitioners had, from time to time, taken the place of the five members so resigning their appointments under the Dispensary, and had consequently been rigidly ostracised both professionally and socially. The 1907 staff was four in number.

As *The British Medical Journal* commented at the time :—

" This open rupture of the Coventry Dispensary staff with the Committee of Management is, so far as we are aware, the first instance in which a Division and the medical officers concerned have taken definite action to carry into operation the principles as regards provident dispensaries approved by the Annual Representative Meeting in July last." (*British Medical Journal*, 1907, Vol. I, p. 646.)

The profession in Coventry thereupon organised a Dispensary of its own, on the lines approved by the Association, and those practitioners who continued to serve or who took service under the Coventry Provident Dispensary were ostracised not only by the local practitioners in the Division, but also by consultants in Birmingham and other large towns.

The struggle went on from year to year, the five medical officers who had resigned continuing to conduct their own institution with considerable success and consequent damage to the receipts of the Provident Dispensary. The " Warning Notice " continued to appear in the *Journal*. In 1910 a conference was held in London between the members of the Committee of the Provident Dispensary and the Contract Practice Sub-Committee of the Association, to consider the possibility of so modifying the constitution of the Dispensary that it should be acceptable to the Coventry Division and the Association generally. The conference was a friendly one, but agreement could not be reached on some fundamental points. At length in January, 1915, the Council of the Association had to instruct its solicitor to accept service of a writ in an action for conspiracy, libel and slander brought by some of the ostracised practitioners against some members of the Coventry Division personally, and against the Association in its corporate capacity. The trial of the action was in March, 1916, postponed until " more peaceful times " by common agreement between the parties, but actually the case was heard in July, 1918, when the most deadly and decisive phases of the War were imminent, and judgment was delivered in October.

This case of Pratt and Others *v.* the B.M.A. and Others was heard by Mr. Justice McCardie without a jury. He decided against the Association on all points, and awarded damages which in the aggregate amounted to £3,810. The judgement, the delivery of which occupied some four hours, showed little appreciation of the Association's position or point of view. The Council at first decided to appeal, but this decision was subsequently rescinded and the damages and costs were paid.

It was at once realised that the importance of the judgement in this action upon the present and future work of the Association could not be over-stated or over-estimated, seeing that with it standing against them, the good work which the Association had done in the past would, it seemed, in the future in great measure be restricted and its activities paralysed. The fact must not be overlooked that, despite the use of a drastic boycott and, during a number of years, the employment of means that were declared by the Judge to be illegal, neither the Provident Dispensary nor its medical officers were defeated, and that therefore the loss of a weapon which had been proved ineffective was the less to be deplored.

It was decided to lay a case before counsel and seek their advice as to future courses of action, and as to any change in constitution which might be desirable as a means of protection.

The result of this advice was a complete overhaul of the actual machinery of the Association, which since that time has not been impugned.

Various medico-legal questions interested the Association in its early days. In 1841 a resolution passed at the Annual Meeting stated that the Association " desires to record its strong feeling of repugnance to a statute which permits the woman (criminal) who has quickened to plead pregnancy as a bar of execution, while the same individual [sic], though equally the mother of a living child, but not having quickened, must suffer the extreme penalty of the Law, thus making a distinction where there is no difference, and fatally though ignorantly sacrificing an innocent life with that of its guilty parent." The statute which postponed the execution of the death sentence on a pregnant woman is so seldom invoked nowadays, that its existence is almost forgotten by the general public. In former days when death was the penalty for many offences, it was often appealed to. It will be remembered that Shakespeare made the Maid of Orleans invoke its protection, as though it had been valid in Normandy.

In 1849 the sale of poisons required regulation. Dr. Sibson called attention to the prevalence of secret poisoning with arsenic and a petition was agreed upon calling for regulation of the sale of that drug. Apparently as a result of this and a subsequent petition, a Bill founded on the report of a committee of the Association was introduced and became an Act in 1851.

The Association has on more than one occasion and in the most emphatic language asserted its belief that the practice of experiments upon living animals was essential to the progress of physiology and of the sciences of medicine and surgery. In the Jubilee summary for the year 1874 (*British Medical Journal*, 1882, Vol. I, p. 874) the following account will be found of an early attempt to restrict inquiry :—

" During the Meeting at Norwich, M. Magnan, of Paris, performed experiments on two dogs, for the purpose of bringing before the profession in England the results at which he had arrived from his researches on the action of alcohol and absinthe. In consequence, proceedings were instituted at Norwich by the Royal Society for the Prevention of Cruelty to Animals against M. Magnan and Messrs. H. S. Robinson, J. B. Pitt, R. W. White and H. Turner, members of the local Committee, for that they ' did unlawfully ill-treat, abuse and torture certain animals—to wit, two dogs—contrary to the Statute.' The magistrates dismissed the case, as it was not proved that the English defendants took any part in the experiments ; but they considered the case a proper one for the Society to prosecute. The matter was subsequently brought by the local Executive Committee at Norwich before the Committee of Council, by whom the following resolution was passed at a meeting on January 14th, 1875 :—

That the Committee of Council sympathises with the honorary secretaries of the Norwich Meeting and approves the action they have taken with respect to the recent discussion on Vivisection ; that it desires to congratulate these gentlemen on the result of the trial arising out of that discussion, and recommends that the expense to which they have been put in defending themselves be paid out of the funds of the Association."

It has never been demonstrated that in this country any cruelty has attended physiological investigations. The Act restricting painful experiments on living animals,

267

known as the Anti-Vivisection Act, was passed without any valid evidence of the need of it being produced. Because certain continental observers had published accounts of proceedings which appeared to show callousness and a lack of feeling, physiologists in this country are placed under the stigma of cruelty, and their efforts to find out the secrets of nature hampered in a way unknown in any other country. France, Germany, the various States of the American Union and the Dominions, trust their men of science not to inflict unnecessary pain. It is only in Great Britain that the laws against cruelty were thought to be insufficient, and an Act passed to secure that the British searcher after the causes of disease in man and other animals should strive with one hand tied behind him ; for it amounts to this when experiments may only be undertaken in certain licensed places, and under conditions and restrictions which must and do act as deterrents of would-be investigators.

The Association has never ceased to forward the legitimate claims of physiological investigators, and has frequently taken action in Parliament to frustrate the efforts of those who would further impede their invaluable work. In 1927 the Science Committee of the Association, in opposition to a Dogs Protection Bill then before Parliament, convened a conference which was attended by nearly 100 representatives of universities, medical schools, medical and scientific bodies and professional organisations interested in research. The conference passed a strong protest against the imposition of further restrictions upon experimental work on dogs or other animals, and expressed an opinion in favour of an alteration of existing law to permit the use, for purposes of research and under proper safeguards, of some of the stray and unowned dogs now destroyed by the police. The Dogs Bill, together with many predecessors and successors, has always been defeated, largely owing to the action of the Association.

In the early years of this century the non-medical coroner for South-West London took the unusual course of neglecting to call the practitioner who had last attended the deceased, or to entrust the pathological examination to him. Instead of so doing, he made a practice of calling in a pathologist of his own selection.

268

Had this pathologist been one of known reputation, this course would have been less objectionable, but there was no obvious evidence that the gentleman in question was better qualified to ascertain the cause of death than the average practitioner in South-West London. Moreover, the exclusion of the evidence of the practitioner who had treated the deceased in life, might well result in a miscarriage of justice.

The Medico-Political Committee conferred with the South-West London Medical Society, the Medical Defence Union and the London and Counties Medical Protection Society, and these bodies conjointly represented to the Lord Chancellor that the coroner in question was not fulfilling his duties under the Medical Act. But the Lord Chancellor was not to be moved, nor was an application made by the Association as freeholders and ratepayers in the Strand before the Auditor of the Local Government Board more successful. A coroner when once appointed is only answerable to the Lord Chancellor, and if, as in this case, that dignitary declines to act, it appears that nothing can be done. The grievance ceased only with the life of the coroner in question. Lord Halsbury remained impervious to the severe criticism of *The British Medical Journal* and the comments of *The Times*.

The Association long interested itself in attempts to abolish the insanitary practice of kissing the book in the taking of oaths. The Oaths Act of 1888 was the first fruit of such efforts, but it only made it optional for a person to whom an oath is administered to swear with uplifted hand, as in Scotland. The Oaths Act, 1909, enacted that the person taking the oath shall hold the New (or in the case of a Jew the Old) Testament in his uplifted hand, and shall say or repeat after the officer administering the oath the words "I swear by Almighty God that," followed by the words of the oath prescribed by law. Provided that in the case of a person who is neither a Christian nor a Jew, the oath shall be administered in any manner which is now lawful. "This Act shall not apply to Scotland."

In recording the passage of this Act the *Journal* remarked :—"So passes, it may be hoped, the antiquated and insanitary form of kissing the book."

The medical certification of lunatics has been a frequent source of trouble to members of the Association. An older generation remembered the litigation which ensued on the certification of that gifted but litigious lady, Mrs. Georgina Weldon, who at one time dwelt in a house on the site of part of the Association's Headquarters Building. The present generation is still very uneasily aware of the cases of Harnett v. Bond and Adam (1925) and v. Fisher (1927), which, among others, have shown how dangerous to themselves are attempts of medical men to do their duty to their mentally afflicted patients. The Association has made repeated attempts to get the law altered so as to protect practitioners in the execution of their duty to the public.

In 1885 the Parliamentary Bills Committee exerted its influence in favour of a Lunacy Acts Amendment Bill, reporting that " it was felt that the absence of fair and reasonable protection in the performance of duties in connection with persons of unsound mind would greatly aggravate the already increasing difficulty of getting medical men to certify in cases of insanity. This Bill was, unfortunately, dropped owing to a change of Government, but five years later another Bill was introduced and became an Act.

As Mr. Bullock, in the book referred to earlier, says :—

" The Lunacy Act of 1890 was passed for the purpose *inter alia* of protecting medical men and others against vexatious actions where they have acted in good faith, and in order to give security against any possible abuse of the discretion given to medical men, a judicial inquiry was provided for and a judicial decision required before a person could be permanently confined as a lunatic."

Unfortunately, the protection afforded under this Act has proved to be far from adequate, and new legislation has of late years been urgently called for. The several actions brought by Mr. Harnett, that of De Freville v. Dill and Hume-Spry v. Smith and Watson, have shown that the protection afforded by the Act is woefully incomplete, and will be so, as long as judges and juries are to be found ready to decide upon what was the state of mind of a plaintiff years before he or she came before them, and on the *bona fides* of a Lunacy Commissioner in circumstances which they cannot appreciate.

270

The Association submitted evidence in writing and orally to a Royal Commission on Lunacy Law and Mental Disorder in January, 1925, which was approved by the Annual Representative Meeting in that year.

The Royal Commission on this subject reported in 1927, as stated in a Memorandum by the Lunacy Committee of the British Medical Association (Supplement, *B.M.J.*, 1927, Vol. II, p. 84).

The British Medical Association witnesses before the Commission had urged two desiderata : one, the protection of the practitioner by conferring on him when certifying the status and immunity of a witness ; the other, the enactment of legislation which would make it possible to treat a patient temporarily and under restraint without certification.

The Commission declined for various reasons to recommend the first, but proposed to put the onus of proof of want of reasonable care upon the plaintiff instead of on the doctor. The Committee was of opinion that the Association should press for the introduction into the form of any detention order of words indicating that before signing the order the judicial authority has satisfied himself that the medical practitioner concerned has exercised reasonable care.

To some extent the recommendations of the Commission met the demands of the Association as regards the second desideratum. The Annual Representative Meeting, after considering the above Memorandum (Supplement, *B.M.J.*, 1927, Vol. II, p. 66), passed the following resolution :—

" That the Representatives thank the Lunacy Law and Mental Disorder Committee for the Memorandum on the Report of the Royal Commission on Lunacy Law and Mental Disorder, refer it to the Council and request the Council to reappoint the Committee with instructions to take whatever steps are possible to secure what the Report of the Royal Commission declares to be ' fair,' namely, that the medical profession should not be asked ' to perform their essential part under the menace of litigation which, even if unsuccessful, may spell financial or professional ruin.' "

In 1929 the Annual Representative Meeting approved a further Memorandum on a " Report of the Royal Commission."

The work of Dr. R. Langdon-Down stands out as specially notable in connection with this branch of the Association's activities during the past twenty years.

It is noteworthy that the Mental Treatment Act of 1930 follows the lines of the Association's recommendations as to the provision for treatment of certain cases of mental disorder without certification, rather than those laid down by the Royal Commission. The claim to complete immunity from civil action for practitioners performing duties under the Acts was not conceded, but the additional protection recommended by the Royal Commission is considerably strengthened in the relevant Section 16 (2) of the Act of 1930, which provides that no proceedings, civil or criminal, shall be brought in any court against any person who has discharged such duties " without the leave of the High Court, and leave shall not be given unless the Court is satisfied that there is substantial ground for the contention that the person, against whom it is sought to bring the proceedings, has acted in bad faith or without reasonable care."

QUACKERY

IN its early days the Provincial Medical and Surgical Association advocated the prohibition of all medical and surgical practice except by legally qualified persons, but, as related in the chapter on Medical Reform, it very soon became evident that this was an object impossible of attainment. Since the year 1840 the numerous Bills proposed or supported by the Association have not contained clauses designed to forbid unqualified practice. It is, however, worthy of remark that of late years without much notice or resistance the legislature has passed measures absolutely forbidding the practice of midwifery, of dentistry, or the treatment of venereal diseases by unqualified persons, and no one may now call him or herself a veterinary surgeon without legal qualification. All other departments of medicine and surgery are freely open to every man, woman or child in Great Britain, provided that the unqualified practitioner does not attempt to prescribe or administer drugs included in the operation of the Dangerous Drugs Acts or infringe the provisions of the Medical Act by representing himself to be a Registered Medical Practitioner. As may well be imagined, the ingenuity of the unqualified practitioner is frequently and successfully exercised with the view of infringing the spirit of the latter restriction while keeping inside the letter of the law.

The discussion which took place at the Annual Representative Meeting in 1930 on the report of the action of the Association's representative (Dr. Alfred Cox) at the previous conference of the Association Professionelle Internationale des Médecins showed that there is no change in the public attitude on this matter, and no likelihood of any legislation on it in this country. Moreover, it was stated at the conference that in those countries where unqualified practice was forbidden by law, it nevertheless flourished, and quackery was quite as rife as in countries which, like Great Britain, made little or no attempt to restrain it. The subject must be considered as outside practical politics. Dr. Cox said : " Personally he did not believe it was possible to suppress the desire of human nature for quackery." As Lowell wrote in the " Biglow Papers " :—

> " The right to be a cussed fool
> Is safe from all devices human,
> It's common (ez a gin'l rule)
> To every critter born o' woman."

Almost unanimously the Representative Meeting approved the opinion expressed by Dr. Cox at the Paris meeting as to the impracticability of any attempt to put down unqualified practice by means of legislation.

Before the passing of the Medical Act a Committee on Quackery was appointed which in 1851 presented a report condemning the practice of homœopathy. In more recent years a wider view has been taken, and it has been realised that in medicine there is no orthodox doctrine, but that when once a man has obtained a registrable qualification in the usual way, he is entitled to hold his own opinions on therapeutics. Homœopathy, therefore, is no longer stigmatised as quackery, whatever opinion the majority of the profession may hold of the judgement of its professors. The question of consultation with homœopaths and their admission to membership of the Association is a matter of ethics, and is considered in this book under that heading.

But the sale of remedies of secret composition and their apparent legitimisation by the imposition of a Government tax and stamp has been denounced by the Association from its very early years. In 1839 a Committee of the Provincial Medical and Surgical Association on Quackery pointed out that the Revenue derived by the Government from this source amounted to £50,000 per annum. It recommended the delivery of lectures on empiricism and the circulation of tracts. In 1841 the Committee on Empiricism recommended the abolition of patents for *secret* remedies and of the tax upon them. In 1840 the report had run :—" Your Committee would suggest the propriety of appropriating a part of the funds of the Association in obtaining trustworthy analyses of many of the more popular and injurious quack medicines." Sixty-nine years later this suggestion and subsequent ones were acted upon, when a series of

274

articles on the composition and cost of secret remedies appeared in the *Journal*, and these articles were republished in book form in 1909 under the title "Secret Remedies, What they Contain and What they Cost." This volume had a very considerable sale, and no doubt had a good effect in opening the eyes of the more sensible of the lay public, so that they realised how slight were the grounds upon which the proprietors of so-called patent medicines based their claims to therapeutic success. That volume was followed by another, "More Secret Remedies," which was published in 1912.

The Association has more than once urged upon the Government of the day the desirability in the interests, and for the protection, of the public of making the publication of the composition of every secret remedy compulsory by an enactment that the names of the ingredients and their quantities should be printed on the labels of all so-called "Patent" medicines. The analyses made for the Association in the investigations which led up to "Secret Remedies" showed how widely the composition of the same nostrum often varied at different times. In the frequent cases where their components were practically inert, this did not much matter, but in the case of others containing active drugs such as opium and acetanilide it constituted a grave danger to the public. This glaring defect was, however, used by some proprietors of the remedies as an argument to discredit the analyses published by the Association, for they were able to show that these analyses in some cases differed from those made of specimens of preparations purchased at another time, or perhaps in another place. "Secret Remedies" and its sequel, however, showed conclusively with how little care and regard to accuracy many preparations had been made up. In the case of pills and powders variations in strength could be and were clearly demonstrated.

Only one action was brought against the Association on account of these publications with the result, as mentioned in the chapter on Medicine and the Law, of a verdict for the defendants.

Nevertheless, the trade still goes on and flourishes, and no administration seems likely to forgo the income derived from that source, although it may be hoped that publication of the formula of composition on the label may some day be insisted upon as a condition before the Government stamp is affixed. In that case, Secret Remedies would cease to be secret and would lose most of their power to impose on the credulous.

SELECT COMMITTEE ON PATENT MEDICINES.

In 1912 the Government appointed a Select Committee to consider and inquire into the question of the sale of patent and proprietary medicines and medical preparations and appliances and advertisements relating thereto, to which the Association forwarded a Memorandum of Evidence. In support of this evidence the following witnesses appeared before the Committee :— Sir Malcolm Morris, K.C.V.O., Professor W. E. Dixon, F.R.S., Mr. P. MacLeod Yearsley, Dr. Arthur Whitfield, Miss Mary Sturge, Dr. R. E. Crosse, Mr. Henry Sewill, Mr. E. F. Harrison, F.I.C. (responsible for the analyses in " Secret Remedies " and " More Secret Remedies "), and the Medical Secretary.

The Select Committee reported in August, 1914, and made certain recommendations, which the Council considered to be " of the most far-reaching and satisfactory kind." They included the registration of all proprietary remedies on the basis of confidential communication to a competent authority of the formula of every remedy, a full statement of the therapeutic claims made or to be made and, in the case of appliances, the deposit of a specimen : the administration of the law governing the sale and advertisement of proprietary remedies, including the new machinery, to be a function of the Ministry of Public Health, " when such a body is created," and in the meantime of the Local Government Board. Other recommendations of the Committee included the amendment of the Indecent Advertisements Act on the lines suggested by the Association, and the total prohibition of the advertisement and sale (except the sale by doctor's order) of medicines purporting to cure the following diseases :—Cancer, consumption, lupus, deafness, diabetes, paralysis, fits, epilepsy, locomotor ataxy, Bright's disease and rupture (without operation or appliance). The prohibition of all advertisements of

276

remedies for sexual diseases and of medicines which suggest that they might be used as abortifacients was also recommended, as well as measures for frustrating many well-known knavish tricks of the nostrum-mongers. The Select Committee expressed its strong desire that there should be early and effectual legislative measures taken to bring into operation the foregoing recommendations.

High hopes were then entertained that a Bill would soon be introduced and passed into law, giving effect to the recommendations, but the continuation of hostilities and the events which followed the Armistice and even the official end of the War in 1921 prevented the fulfilment of the hopes of the Committee and of the Association. The Government introduced and passed through the House of Lords in 1920 a Bill to regulate the manufacture and sale of certain medicines and surgical appliances, but it never got any further owing, it is understood, to the difficulty of reconciling the various vested interests concerned. It can, however, be safely said that the action of the Association, coupled with the new sense of responsibility which is actuating many educated advertising agents, has led to a considerable improvement as regards the grosser forms of quack advertisement.

277

THE HOUSES OF THE ASSOCIATION

(*This Section is based to a very great extent upon the article on pp.* 111-117 *of the Special Commemorative Number of* The British Medical Journal *of July* 18*th*, 1925.)

WHEN the Provincial Medical and Surgical Association was first founded it had no house of its own, and it appears that such was the case as long as the headquarters remained in Worcester. Long after the Association assumed its present title, its offices in London were little more than editorial and publishing offices of the *Journal*.

The first volume of *The Provincial Medical Journal*, that for 1840, had London on its title-page, and this volume and its successors till 1852 laid no claim to be the official organ of the Provincial Medical and Surgical Association. In that year the *Transactions* of the P.M.S.A. came to an end and the Association acquired a local habitation and the *Journal* was called "The Association Medical Journal: published for the Association by Thomas John Honeyman at the office, 37, Great Queen Street, Lincoln's Inn Fields," thus beginning the long connection with the Honeymans, father and son, and with Great Queen Street, well known to Freemasons through its Tavern and Hall. Here (on the North side of the street) the Association used two rooms as offices over the Printing Office of Mr. Richards. But this was not the office of the Association in the sense in which the term is now used, but only a printing and publishing office, and only intermittently so, for Volume II of 1867 was " Published for the Association by Robert Hardwicke, 192, Piccadilly," as were the succeeding five half-yearly volumes. The Association returned, however, to Great Queen Street at the end of 1870, and Thomas Richards printed the *Journal* at No. 37, as he had done the first volume for 1867, while No. 36 was taken as an office

278

N. Bishop Harman,
f.r.c.s., Treasurer, 1924–
(still in office).

R. H. Todd, Secretary
of Federal Committee
of B.M.A. in Australia.
First recipient of Gold
Medal of Australian
Federal Committee.

HOUSES OF THE ASSOCIATION

GREAT QUEEN STREET,
1853–1878.

161A, STRAND, 1878–1886

of the *Journal*.   In 1871 the Committee of Council,
of which Mr. W. D. Husband, of York, was Chairman,
Dr. R. W. Falconer, of Bath, being Treasurer, reported
to the Annual Meeting at Plymouth that the management of the Association was in an unsatisfactory state,
owing chiefly to defective organisation and supervision,
and they recommended that a business man should be
appointed Secretary, that his office should be in London,
that he should collect subscriptions, manage the *Journal*
and obtain advertisements for it, be responsible for all
the preliminary arrangements for the Annual Meeting
and act as Clerk to the Council and Committees and at
general business meetings.   The recommendation was
accepted by the Annual Meeting, and this decision
and the choice that was then made of a General
Secretary was one of the most momentous that the
Association has ever made.   It marked the turning
point in its finance and prosperity.   Of Mr. Francis
Fowke, who was elected to the office thus created, much
more is said in the chapter on Personalities.   It was
his business ability and prudence which led to the
Association acquiring in succession larger and more
valuable premises from time to time.

The first house occupied by the Association was
No. 161A, Strand, on the South side of that street facing
St. Mary's Church.   This was taken in 1878, when
Dr. Alfred Carpenter, of Croydon, was Chairman of
Council and Dr. W. D. Husband, of York, the Treasurer,
upon whom and Mr. Fowke the responsibility lay.   The
upper part of the new House was occupied by the printing department, but the Committee of Council had a room
for its meetings capable of seating thirty to forty persons,
and a small room stolen from a landing by the erection of
a glass screen was contrived for the use on publishing days
of the Assistant Editor, who was soon joined as Sub-
Editor by Mr. Alban Doran (died in 1927).

The progressive increase in the membership and the
prosperity of the Association made expansion justifiable
and necessary, and when in 1888 an opportunity offered
the Association bought the lease of 429, Strand at the
corner of Agar Street for £4,500.   The premises had
been occupied for some years by the Briton Life Insurance Company, of the Board of which the distinguished

Dr. Benjamin Ward Richardson had lately been Chairman. The house had also associations with medical journalism, for Thomas Wakley the second, editor and proprietor of *The Lancet*, was one of the Medical Examiners to the Briton Company. Rather more than £5,000 was expended on furniture and necessary alterations. In 1888 the Association was able to buy for the sum of £3,200 the lease of the two adjoining houses, Nos. 2 and 3, and in 1896 for £750 that of Nos. 4 & 5, Agar Street. In 1894 the Association acquired for £4,640 the freehold of two small houses in a court behind the front building, and ultimately, by an exchange with neighbouring leaseholders, it obtained an L-shaped site upon which its third house was erected. Eventually the Association acquired the freehold of the houses in the Strand and Agar Street. The total amount expended in acquiring the site and the buildings on it and putting them in order was £8,500.

The improvement of the accommodation provided in these various houses became an urgent consideration in 1904. Divers circumstances combined to bring this about. The reorganisation of the Association in 1902, leading to the formation of a number of Standing Committees and the creation of the office of Medical Secretary, who took up the full duties of his office in 1903, threw a great strain upon the accommodation in the old buildings. Such provision as was possible was made for the committees and the Medical Secretary and his staff, but it had become obvious that the space available was altogether inadequate for the proper conduct of the work. The Library had outgrown its accommodation, and the room in which it was housed, though finely proportioned and not ill-fitted for a reading room, was so unfit for the other purposes for which it was wanted, namely, the holding of meetings of the Council, of conferences or of large committees, that it was found desirable to accept the hospitality of the Metropolitan Asylums Board, which placed its spacious board room at the disposal of the Council for quarterly and other large meetings. Something had to be done. At first it was thought that it might be possible to obtain the needful accommodation by remodelling the house in the Strand and rebuilding those in Agar Street and behind it. However, after a very thorough investigation of the possibilities by the Premises and Library Committee under the chairmanship of Mr. Andrew Clark with the assistance of statements and estimates furnished by the General Secretary, Mr. Guy Elliston, the Committee recommended and the Council agreed that the most prudent and economical course would be to clear the whole site and erect a building specially designed to meet the requirements of the Association. As the result of a limited competition, and on the advice of Mr. William Henman, F.R.I.B.A., Mr. Percy Adams, F.R.I.B.A., was commissioned to plan the ground floor and basement for letting as business premises, reserving all the rest of the building for the Association's use. During the nineteen months between Easter, 1907, and November, 1908, the Association was lodged in temporary premises in Catherine Street, Strand.

The new premises contained the General Office on the first floor, the Medical Secretary's office on the second, the Editorial on the third, and the Printing Office on the fourth floor. The lofty Library gave opportunity for a mezzanine floor, which was used as an extension of the General Office ; and the Medical Secretary's department eventually overflowed on to the third floor. In this allotment of space committee rooms are included in the Medical Secretary's department.

The Association was made the victim of a newspaper " stunt " on the occasion of the completion of the new building. The second floor was adorned with a number of above-life-sized statues between the windows by a sculptor (Epstein) whose art at that time was not so non-representative as it has since become. Among other subjects certain pathological and physiological changes in the nude human form were decently and artistically represented ; an evening paper, however, chose to denounce them as outrages upon decency and good taste, and for a short time the faces of wayfarers in the Strand were upturned to a degree that was equally dangerous to their persons and the contents of their pockets. This nine-days' wonder was soon forgotten, and the statues have since been allowed to rest in peace, scarcely noticed by the passer-by, in their elevated position. Antiquarians of a later generation may, perhaps, have difficulty in discovering how the sculptures came there and what, if any, was their meaning.

When more committees were appointed the pressure on the space became greater and greater. This was one consideration which led to a search for a new and larger site, another was that the house in the Strand afforded no hall for large meetings, such as that of the Representative Body, nor for conferences between the Association and other bodies. It was thought also that the Association might be equally conveniently housed in some neighbourhood where the price of land was much less than in the Strand, and where there might be more elbow room. The fact that the membership had increased in round numbers from 20,000 to 30,000 between 1905 and 1925 may be taken as one proof of the need for more space.

A building partially completed was found close to St. Pancras Church, occupying the site endeared to all Dickensians as that of Tavistock House, which the " Inimitable " occupied for nine years. The building had been commenced before the War by Sir Edwin Lutyens, R.A., for a society which had given up possession of the site while the buildings were still in an unfinished state, and during the War the department of the Paymaster of the Forces made use of it. As it contained space for one of the finest halls in London, as well as two other large halls, it appeared peculiarly fitted for the purposes of the Association. It was acquired on advantageous terms from the Disposals Board, and a lease of two hundred years was obtained from the Duke of Bedford. The new House and the historical associations of its site were described fully in the Special Commemorative Number published on July 18th, 1925, after the House had been opened by His Majesty King George the Fifth five days earlier.

Among the many features of the House of the Association should be mentioned the beautiful gates at the entrance to the Court of Honour. These Gates of Remembrance, designed by Sir Edwin Lutyens and made by the Birmingham Guild, are a memorial to the 574 members of the Association who fell in the Great War. The gates are surmounted by a bronze shield bearing on either side in gold letters the words " Memory and

282

Praise," and " Faithful hath been your warfare." The names of these members are inscribed in the " Book of Honour," which is to be seen in the Hastings Hall, the illumination of which was a labour of love on the part of Sir Frederick Hallett, formerly Secretary of the Examination Board of the Royal Colleges of Physicians and Surgeons. The Great Hall is unique among the Halls of London, with its high vault supported by two rows of Corinthian columns of a brilliant peacock blue colour. In the Council Chamber will be found panels containing full lists of the officers and chief officials of the Association, together with a list of Benefactors and Gold Medallists. Among the treasures of the Association is the President's Chair, presented on the occasion of the opening of the House by the Australian Branches. It is constructed of Australian wood and leather. The back of the chair bears on its front aspect the Australian Federal coat of arms, and on the rear, stamped in gold lettering, the following inscription, which most aptly sums up not only the feelings of those who presented the chair, but the nature of the relations between the home Association and its oversea Branches :

BRITISH MEDICAL ASSOCIATION

PRESIDENT'S CHAIR

Presented by the Branches of the British Medical
Association in Australia

to

the Parent Association in England

in token of

kinship, loyalty and goodwill

to celebrate the Entry of the Association into its New
House, Tavistock Square, London

July, 1925.

" . . . ties which, though light as air, are as strong as
links of iron."

In the Common Room will be found two Kudu Heads presented in 1927 by the South African Federal Council on behalf of the South African Branches ; the head of a Rhinoceros presented by the Rhodesian Branches in 1930 ; and a very fine Bison Head presented by the Canadian Government on the occasion of the Annual

283

Meeting of the Association at Winnipeg in 1930. The New Zealand Branch presented in 1928 an Inkstand made of silver, greenstone and New Zealand woods ; the Tasmanian Branch in 1925 sent a Chairman's Hammer made of Tasmanian wood ; and the South Australian Branch in 1925 presented an inscribed Silver Jug of old French workmanship for the President's Table.

On the centre block of the right-hand pier of the extension of the House, facing the Gates of Remembrance, appears the following inscription :—

" This House of the British Medical Association was opened by His Majesty King George V. The Memorial Gates were dedicated by Randall Davidson, Archbishop of Canterbury, July 13th, 1925."

And on the corresponding block of the left-hand pier is the following :—

" In recognition of services rendered by the Building Committee, 1922-29 :

Sir Robert Bolam, M.D., F.R.C.P., LL.D., Chairman ; H. B. Brackenbury, LL.D., M.R.C.S., L.R.C.P. ; N. Bishop Harman, F.R.C.S. ; G. E. Haslip, M.D. ; C. O. Hawthorne, M.D., F.R.C.P., LL.D ; R. Wallace Henry, M.D. ; L. Ferris-Scott, F.C.A., Secretary.

Architects :
Great Court, Sir Edwin Lutyens, R.A.
Front Court, C. Wontner Smith, F.R.I.B.A.
Contractors :
Ford and Walton, Ltd."

Among these names there is one which stands out as pre-eminent in the work that had to be undertaken before the building was ready for occupation—that of Sir Robert Bolam, Chairman of the Committee. He it was who more than any other directed the work and inspired the members of Council and of the Representative Body with the great possibilities which the acquisition of such a home placed in the power of the Association.

The Great Hall, designed and proportioned by Sir Edwin Lutyens, has recently been completely redecorated by Mr. Leslie Bloom, an artist of much experience in large-scale decorative work.

The direct colour photographs which appear in this volume give some idea of the infinite graduations of tone used in the Great Hall.

284

The new headquarters building was not long to be left in its dignified retirement at the end of Tavistock Place North. The Association having acquired the valuable property lying between the new building and Tavistock Square, it was obvious that reconstruction was necessary in the interests of sound finance. Accordingly, all the old buildings on the site were pulled down and a new block built, thus converting the quadrangle into a closed Court containing the Gates of Honour and approached by an archway in the façade which now carries on continuous alignment of Tavistock Square and Upper Woburn Place. The new building forms a handsome block of offices, as may be seen in the illustrations published in the *Journal* of December 7th, 1929. At about the same time the Council Chamber was reconstructed and the Library greatly added to and reorganised.

THE SCOTTISH HOUSE.

Premises in Rutland Square, Edinburgh, were secured by the Association in 1919 when the new post of Scottish Medical Secretary was created and Dr. J. R. Drever appointed. A notable increase of membership and extension of the Association's activities in Scotland followed this step, and in December, 1924, the Council approved a recommendation of the Scottish Committee that " It is desirable that the Association should have its own House in Scotland." The choice fell upon No. 6, Drumsheugh Gardens, previously occupied by Dr. N. T. Brewis, who had died in 1924, and the new House of the Association in Scotland was formally opened at that address on Thursday, June 4th, 1925, by the Right Honourable Sir John Gilmour, M.P., Secretary for Scotland, Dr. C. E. Douglas, Chairman of the Scottish Committee, presiding at the ceremony.

The new House, though providing sufficient accommodation in some respects, did not allow of a hall large enough for conferences or for the meetings of kindred societies which are regularly held in the Edinburgh House of the Association. Accordingly, when (in 1927) the adjoining building No. 7 came into the market, the Council decided to buy it and to combine the two properties on the first floor. By this means a handsome Hall has been obtained with seating accommodation for 300, and, in addition, a large Committee Room, a Common Room and Cloakroom.

THE IRISH HOUSE.

The offices of the Irish Medical Secretary of the Association and his staff were at 16, South Frederick Street, Dublin, until March, 1932, when they were removed to 18, Kildare Street.

OTHER B.M.A. HOUSES.

In various parts of the world the Association has a local habitation and home of its own, but special mention should be made of the fine building of the New South Wales Branch opened in Sydney in 1930. The House of the Victorian Branch opened May 20th, 1925 ; the House of the South Australian Branch in Adelaide, opened June 28th, 1914 ; the House of the Queensland Branch at Brisbane ; and the building occupied for many years by the Cape Western Branch, South Africa. Full particulars, with illustrations of these buildings, will be found in the *Journal* of July 18th, 1925.

MEDICAL ETHICS

THE promotion of medical ethics was implied among the objects of the Association, as set forth in the fifth paragraph of the Prospectus under the title of " Maintenance of the Honour and Respectability of the Profession generally."

This included medical ethics in the stricter sense of the term, as regulating the conduct of members of the profession towards one another, as well as the relations of the profession to their patients and the non-medical public ; but for the first few years of the existence of the P.M.S.A. the subject did not attract much attention. At the Anniversary Meeting of 1840, however, the second report on Empiricism was presented. It referred to the evils resulting from empirical practices, and from the sale of patent medicines. The report stated that some of those evils could only be remedied by well-directed local restraints, while the removal of others must depend principally on the establishment of a more uniform standard of education and in the cultivation of a higher tone of morality among the members of the profession. It was recommended that defaulters from the accepted code should not be admitted to membership of the Association, or, if already admitted, that they should be expelled. " Strict moral integrity " was demanded.

In 1847, at the Annual Meeting at Derby, Sir Charles Hastings raised this question again, but without action following.

In 1849 the West Somerset Branch took action in a case of fraudulent diploma, and expelled the President Elect " on account of unprofessional conduct in consulting with an unqualified person." This incident led to the appointment of a Committee on Medical Ethics.

In 1851 a Committee on Quackery made a report in eight resolutions which were adopted by the Anniversary Meeting condemning Homœopathy and consultations with homœopaths. A copy of these resolutions will be found in the *Journal* of 1882, Vol. I, p. 859. A similar Committee was appointed in 1853 with instructions to frame a code of ethical laws. Again in 1858 a Committee was appointed " to prepare a well-considered expression of the duties of members of the medical profession towards society at large."

For a long time the ethical subject which most occupied the attention of the Association at Branch and Annual Meetings was the relationship between its members and practitioners professing homœopathic principles. This came up again and again, and many resolutions were passed from time to time.

The subject was reconsidered by the Central Ethical Committee, which reported in 1910 (Supplement, *B.M.J.*, 1910, Vol. I, p. 65).

This report sums up the question so thoroughly that it seems advisable to quote it *in extenso* as follows :—

" CENTRAL ETHICAL COMMITTEE.

Report of Council on the Relation of Homœopaths to the Association.

" The Annual Representative Meeting at Sheffield passed the following Resolution :—

That it be an instruction to the Council to consider the whole question of the relation of Homœopaths to the Association.

MEMORANDUM.

" The Reference entails consideration of the following matters :—

(i) Whether the persons in question may or should be elected Members of the Association ;

(ii) Whether or upon what terms those who are Members should be permitted so to remain ; and

(iii) What degree of professional recognition such persons should receive from Members of the Association.

" In regard to the first and second considerations, attention must be given to the past action of the Association and to the position created by the present Regulations, and by the practice of the Central Council and Branch Councils, upon which the Regulations confer a discretion in these matters.

" The older records bearing upon the subject are in some measure imperfect, but the following statement is believed to be accurate so far as it goes :—

" In 1851 Resolutions were passed by the Annual General Meeting to the effect that Homœopaths should not be elected as Members of the Association, and disapproval was expressed of any school of medicine retaining any teacher who upheld the teaching of Homœopathy.

" In 1852 a Resolution was passed that a clause be included in the By-laws, requiring candidates for election to the Association to state in writing that they neither were, nor intended to become, Homœopathists, but it appears doubtful whether this Resolution was actually given effect to by the necessary amendment of the By-laws being carried out.

" In 1858 and 1861 Resolutions were passed by General Meetings repeating and confirming the resolutions previously adopted on the subject.

" It is not clear what action was taken to make the above Resolutions effective and, before the next recorded act of the Association in connection with this subject, fundamental changes were introduced into its constitution, by the incorporation of the Association as a Limited Company in 1873, and by the adoption of certain By-laws in 1882. These changes would put out of operation any pre-existing Regulation which was not in terms incorporated in the new Regulations. In 1885 the Council remitted the subject to the Branches, and a plebiscite was taken in each Branch, the result being an expression of opinion that avowed Homœopaths should not be elected as Members, but that any Members professing Homœopathy should not be expelled. Again it appears that the expression of opinion was permitted to remain inoperative, the steps necessary to make it legally effective, namely, by an alteration of the By-laws, not being taken.

" In 1897 the Council replied to representations from a Branch that every effort was made to prevent the election of Homœopaths, ' although there was nothing in the existing By-laws making their election illegal.'

" Under the regulations at that time in force, the Central Council elected ' unattached ' Members, and it

289

was a rule that the Homœopathic Directory should be searched for the information of the Council.

" The above narrative shows that in the period of the history of the Association prior to the adoption of the new regulations in the year 1902, notwithstanding repeated expressions of opinion adverse to Homœopaths, the legal steps which it was always within the power of the Association to take to exclude such members absolutely from membership were not taken, the matter being left as at present to the discretion of the electing bodies. Moreover, the records have not disclosed any instance of a Member being expelled on the ground of his profession of Homœopathic doctrine or practice as a Homœopath."

The present policy of the Association, as set forth in the *Handbook,* is that the Association should not attempt to pronounce in connection with the question of homœopathy or in any other connection what constitutes sound doctrine in medicine or surgery, nor condemn individual practitioners on the ground that they hold peculiar views of pathology or treatment, or give effect to such views in the practice of the profession.

The eligibility of homœopaths to membership of Branches depends on the rules of the Branch concerned. Some Branches definitely disqualify homœopaths and others do not. As regards consultation with homœopaths the Report of the Central Ethical Committee on the Ethics of Consultation made in 1908, and approved by the Annual Representative Meeting, was to the effect that it is the duty of a practitioner to refuse to meet in consultation a practitioner whose exclusive profession of any peculiar system of treatment would render consultation futile.

In 1854 and 1865 the Council condemned the publication of biographies of living medical men.

In 1894 the Council decided (1) that all advertisements for unqualified assistants to conduct branch practices apart from the Principal should be excluded from the *Journal,* and (2) that the term " unqualified " should not appear in the advertisements in the *Journal.*

In 1897 the Association intervened in a dispute between the Government of South Australia and the medical staff of the Adelaide Hospital who had resigned.

Two gentlemen went out from England to fill vacancies. Their names were removed from the list of members under By-law 3 (*B.M.J.*, 1897, Vol. I, p. 1189).

The ethical action of the Association was called for and successfully exerted in rather curious circumstances in 1903 (Supplement, *B.M.J.*, May 2nd, 1903, p. xxxix).

By an order of the Court of Chancery of the County Palatine of Lancaster, a scheme was directed to be prepared on behalf of the Liverpool Throat, Nose and Ear Hospital with respect to the disposition of certain moneys standing to the credit of the action of Evans *v.* Jones in that Court, which consisted of an accumulation of royalties paid by Messrs. Evans on the sale by them of certain pastilles, known as antiseptic throat pastilles, and of which by the order of the Court they are permitted to be sole manufacturers and vendors. These accumulated royalties amounted to £1,400, and were expected to amount to £1,000 a year in future. These royalties were to be paid as a donation to, or for the benefit of, the hospital and the scheme was approved by all concerned except the General Medical Council, which warned the medical men appointed to the staff of the hospital against associating themselves in any way with the sale of a medicinal remedy, the composition of which they are pledged not to divulge. Thereupon the medical staff severed their connection with the hospital.

The Solicitor to the Duchy stated that the hospital scheme fell to the ground as it was presumed that the objection would apply to all other medical men.

He asked the General Secretary of the B.M.A. whether the Association would move the General Medical Council to take objections to any qualified medical practitioners taking the place of those resigned, and in the same circumstances, as if so, the Attorney-General would have to devise some other scheme not opposed to professional ethics.

The Council replied that the objections taken by the General Medical Council were shared by the British Medical Association.

In 1905 the Ethical Committee recommended and the Annual Representative Meeting approved the recommendation that all medical officers of Hydropathic

Establishments "should make it a condition of their engagement that their names should not be inserted in any advertisements except in the medical journals."

An important decision was taken in 1907 when the Annual Representative Meeting approved the recommendation of the Ethical Committee " that the Association should take all cases of a penal nature before the General Medical Council as Complainants." This decision had the drawback of making the resignation of membership of the Association, or withdrawal from the hearing of any case presented by the Association, necessary for all those members who hitherto were also members of the General Medical Council. This dilemma has led to very few cases being presented by the Association.

In 1908 a question was ventilated which had for many years caused discussion and sometimes bitterness in the profession. This concerned the relations between Consultants and General Practitioners. The founders of the Association were provincial consultants, but necessarily the great majority of members were in general practice, and then, as now, most of the best-known consultants were in London.

The Representative Meeting in this year instructed the Council to prepare, through the Central Ethical Committee, a report as to the desirability of the recognition of a special class of practitioners under the title of consultants, distinguished by the fact that they confine their practice to the treatment of patients in co-operation with other practitioners. Practitioners, however, who so confine their practice are few. The exigencies of medical practice render it practically impossible for a hospital physician or surgeon to refuse to see any patient unless the latter is introduced by another medical practitioner. Attempts have been made to draw an analogy between Barristers and Consultants and Solicitors and General Practitioners, but there is no true analogy. The status and powers of Barristers and Solicitors are strictly prescribed by law and their respective functions strictly limited, whereas the law recognises no difference between the senior members of a hospital staff and the latest qualified general practitioner. Suggestions for the regulation of the relations of general practitioners on the one hand and specialists and consultants on the other

292

based on the supposed analogy with the law have come to nothing, and are unlikely to be fruitful as long as patients are at liberty to consult whom they choose.

But the term Consultant is used in another sense, and it has been defined by the Annual Representative Body as meaning any practitioner who is called upon by the patient or by any person acting on behalf of the patient, to advise in special circumstances with regard to a patient who is already under the care of another practitioner, that other being referred to as the " attending practitioner."

A very complete code of rules bearing on the Ethics of Consultation was approved in 1908, and reported upon again by the Council and approved by the Annual Representative Meeting in 1923, and will be found in the *Annual Handbook*.

The Association has always taken up an attitude definitely discountenancing all forms of advertisement of any practitioner's peculiar merits, or supposed merits to the lay public, however veiled such advertisements might be. At the Annual Meeting in 1909 the Chairman of the Central Ethical Committee moved and the motion was adopted by the Annual Representative Body, " that it is the professional duty of Medical Authors of articles in Medical Journals to co-operate with the proprietors and editors of those journals in preventing any improper use of such articles for purposes of advertisement."

Indirect methods of advertising have been the subject of consideration on various occasions.

In 1925 the Central Ethical Committee's report was approved by the Representative Body. The main policy of the Association as formulated in that report is as follows :—

From time to time there are discussed in the lay papers, topics which have relation both to medical science and policy and to the health and welfare of the public, and it may be legitimate or even advisable that medical practitioners who can speak with authority on the question at issue should contribute to such discussions. But practitioners who take this action ought to make it a condition of publication that laudatory editorial comments or headlines relating either to the contributor's professional status or experience shall not be permitted ; that his address or photograph shall not be published ; and that there shall be no unnecessary display of his medical qualifications and appointments. There is a special claim that practitioners of established position and authority shall observe these conditions, for their example must necessarily influence the action of their less recognised colleagues. Discussions in the lay press on disputed points of pathology or treatment should be avoided by practitioners ; such issues find their appropriate opportunity in the professional societies and the medical journals (para. 12 of report).

As long as a practitioner does not infringe the rules of conduct enacted by the General Medical Council, he cannot be punished by the Association except by expulsion from the Association. This power has been very rarely used, and it is the moral suasion exerted by the known disapproval of his fellow practitioners which is the Association's chief disciplinary weapon. As stated in the section on Law, a threat of ostracism or other punishment may be found to be libellous and involve unpleasant consequences to those who utter it. The kind of case in which members have to be most often warned against certain actions is one in which for any reason it is decided by the Association that the conditions of certain appointments are unsatisfactory. In such cases " Important Notices " formerly called " Warning Notices," are published in the *Journal* advising intending applicants to consult the Medical Secretary before making application.

On this subject the following " Declaration of Policy " was made at the Annual Meeting of 1914 :—

" That the Representative Body rescinds all its previous decisions relating to the Warning Notices, and empowers the Council to approve and adopt Regulations which in the opinion of the Council are appropriate relative to the insertion in the *B.M.J.* of notices regarding appointments, and that the control of these notices be in future entirely in the hands of the Council."

The ethical machinery of the Association is the result of long experience and very careful and prolonged consideration. It has been developed gradually, and for the most part from small local beginnings, and is now so devised as to meet the actual needs of the profession.

294

Experience has shown the necessity of central control and co-ordination and of uniformity throughout the Association (*Handbook*, 1930-31, p. 119).

Differences between members of the profession arise from time to time, and when one or both of such members belong to the Association its advice is often sought. To deal with such cases the Central Ethical Committee has been set up. It deals on behalf of the Council with questions of professional conduct, and advises the Council as to cases of proposed expulsion of members.

There are also local Ethical Committees of Divisions and Branches for the guidance of which uniform Ethical Rules have been framed and approved by the Representative Body. It is the duty of the Honorary Secretary of a Division upon receipt of a complaint to refer the matter at once to headquarters for advice in order not only that he may be advised against any possibly illegal procedure, but also that he may have placed at his disposal the experience and " case law " accumulated at headquarters.

Another class of ethical cases are those owing to differences which have arisen between members of the profession and lay bodies or persons employing them, either in connection with fees or salaries or terms or conditions of service, which may seem inconsistent with the honour and interests of the profession or the self-respect and reasonable independence of its members. The services of the Association are not infrequently involved in such cases.

There are parts of the country where the maintenance of a united front by the profession is absolutely essential if the life of a medical practitioner is to be worth living, and where resistance to attempts of outside bodies to impose unfair conditions is one of the most important functions of the Association (*Handbook*, 1930-31, p. 124).

THE ASSOCIATION AND SCIENCE

ONE of the chief objects of the Association at its foundation in 1832 was the improvement of medical science. Consistently throughout its history the Association has devoted a considerable part of its energies and its income to the scientific side of its work, and it is noteworthy that the first of the principal objects of the Association at this day is " the promotion of the medical and allied sciences." It may fairly be said that the prestige which the Association enjoys is in no small measure due to its scientific activities.

In giving practical effect to this side of its work, the Association has promoted discussions upon scientific topics at its Annual Meetings ; disseminated information through *The British Medical Journal*, and special journals, such as *The Archives of Diseases in Childhood* and *The Journal of Neurology and Psycho-pathology*, all of which are published by it (see *Handbook*, Section VIII) ; appointed, from time to time, Special Committees to consider and report upon particular aspects of medical science ; conducted collective investigations throughout the general body of the profession ; awarded scholarships, grants and prizes ; and organised lectures both amongst members of the medical profession and of the lay public. In addition, it has established a Library, and the local units of the Association, of which there are several hundreds, devote the greater part of their energy to the consideration of scientific and clinical questions.

During a discussion at the Annual Representative Meeting in 1929 as to the expenditure involved on its scientific work, the Treasurer estimated that the Association spent at least £35,000 of its income every year directly or indirectly in the cause of the advancement of science.

296

THE WORK OF SPECIAL SCIENTIFIC COMMITTEES.

In 1877 the Association inaugurated its public-spirited policy of appointing and financing Special Committees for the investigation of scientific problems. The first such body was appointed to inquire (1) wherein lies the special danger of chloroform, and (2) to try and discover if any anæsthetic existed the use of which would avoid such dangers. The Association granted further money in 1888 for research on anæsthetics by Professor McWilliam, whose reports were published in 1890. In the next year the Council appointed another committee with a wide reference. Its report made in 1900 dealt with forty-five methods of using the usual anæsthetics. In its conclusions it is stated that " No method of administration of chloroform is free from danger, but an examination of the communicated cases appears to show that the occurrence of danger depends largely upon the administrator who employs any particular method."

This Committee did not deal with the question of percentage of chloroform vapour in the air inspired, but the Committee appointed by the Council in 1901 on the suggestion of Dr. A. D. Waller, F.R.S., went very thoroughly into that important aspect of the problem. The 1901 Committee was composed of a number of distinguished medical and scientific persons, and its main objects were to determine the minimal dose of chloroform necessary to secure adequate anæsthesia without endangering life, and to investigate methods of quantitatively determining the presence of chloroform in the air and in living bodies.

The work of the Committee extended over several years, and many important investigations were carried out by it. It was generally acknowledged that its report, which was published in 1911, threw valuable light upon the problems which the Committee was appointed to consider.

The Therapeutic Committee appointed in 1887 reported in 1890 on the action of various drugs. Its Chairman was Sir Lauder Brunton, who was succeeded by Professor Gairdner, of Glasgow. In 1907 this Committee undertook an inquiry into the relative value of local anæsthetics suggested as substitutes for cocaine, and in the following year a report was made by Dr. Le Brocq, who concluded, as a result of his investigations, that novocaine was the most satisfactory substitute for cocaine. This Committee also instituted investigations into new remedies, and it devoted much energy in making suggestions for revision of the British Pharmacopœia. From 1910 onwards the Committee became a Standing Sub-Committee of the Science Committee, with instructions to promote, supervise, or direct research in pharmacology and therapeutics, and in 1913 it investigated and reported on the action in rheumatic fever of salicylic acid and chemically allied bodies. The work of the Sub-Committee became no longer necessary in 1921 following on the appointment by the Association of a pharmacologist to advise the *Journal*.

The Section of Ophthalmology in 1907 urged the appointment of a Committee to consider the question of prevention of Ophthalmia Neonatorum. Thirteen members were appointed, with Mr. Sydney Stephenson as Chairman (including representatives of the Royal Society of Medicine, the Ophthalmological Society and the Society of Medical Officers of Health), and their report was published in 1909. The Committee urged compulsory notification of ophthalmia neonatorum, and this was adopted by the Government in 1914 with very considerable effect on the incidence and effects of the disease. The Central Midwives Board altered its Rules to conform with the recommendation of the Committee that purulent vaginal discharge requires medical assistance.

In 1907 also the Obstetric Section urged the Association to take steps to secure early recognition of Uterine Cancer, and a Special Committee was appointed to consider the matter. Two appeals, the object of which was to promote earlier recognition of the disease, were issued by the Committee (1) to medical practitioners and (2) to nurses and midwives. The report of the Committee was published in 1909.

As a result of a recommendation of the Section of Surgery in 1910, the Council appointed a Special Committee of twelve to inquire into and report on ultimate results obtained in the treatment of Simple Fractures. Surgeons and surgical registrars in large hospitals and others were requested to grant access to patients and records for 1906–1910, and 3,000 cases were investigated. The report of the Committee, the Chairman of which was Mr. W. J. Greer, was published in the *B.M.J.* of November 30th, 1912, and it tended to steady opinion in the profession, which seemed to be in some danger of being carried away by the brilliant advocates of new methods of which some, such as open operation, were quite impracticable in general practice. An appreciation of the work of the Fractures Committee was received from the American Surgical Association, which asked for advice and assistance in setting up a similar Committee.

The work of Special Committees had perforce to be suspended during the period of the War, but in 1919 a Special Committee was set up " to consider social and economic questions affecting the public welfare as to which the medical profession has special knowledge, and to take such steps as may be found necessary in order to create or develop public opinion thereon." The Committee, under the Chairmanship of Dr. E. R. Fothergill, selected for investigation the topic of " The Value of Maternity and Child Welfare Work in relation to the reduction of infant mortality." The Committee sought the help of representatives of bodies likely to have a practical experience and interest in the subject chosen ; it held an extensive inquiry, and received the evidence of a number of individuals and associations. Its efforts were directed to the determination of the relative value of the various methods adopted in dealing with this problem, and to the formulation of general rules for the guidance and development of this work in the future. The Committee's report was issued in 1921.

Arising out of a recommendation of the Section of Medicine, a special Sub-Committee of the Science Committee was appointed in 1924 to consider the question of rheumatic heart disease in children. Sir Humphry Rolleston was the Chairman of the Sub-Committee. The first report of the Sub-Committee was published in the *B.M.J.* Supplement of July 3rd, 1926, and dealt with the matter under the following headings :—

(i) The Environmental and Other Predisposing Causes of Rheumatic Infection.

(ii) Recent Investigations into the Bacteriology of the Rheumatic Infection.

(iii) The Effect of Tonsillectomy on Rheumatic Infection in Children.

(iv) The Organised After-Care of Rheumatic Children in Great Britain.

The second report was published in the *B.M.J.* Supplement of April 16th, 1927, and dealt with The Prevention and Control of Rheumatic Infection in Children. One of the results of the work of the Sub-Committee has been the establishment in various parts of the country of Rheumatic Treatment Centres for children, and two grants of £100 each were subsequently made by the Association in order to assist the work of the Paddington Green Children's Hospital Centre.

In 1925 a Committee was appointed " to consider and report on the present tests for ' drunkenness,' with recommendations as to their modifications or improvement." The Committee, whose Chairman was Sir William Macpherson, reported in 1927, and its conclusions and recommendations dealt *inter alia* with (i) the definition of the word " drunk " ; and (ii) considerations on which medical practitioners should base their conclusions as to the state of persons being examined.

Arising out of a report by Dame Janet Campbell, of the Ministry of Health on Maternal Mortality (in which allegations were made which the Association thought to be unfounded), a Special Committee was appointed in 1925 to investigate the question of causation of puerperal morbidity and mortality and any administrative action it considered necessary. This Committee, whose Chairman was Sir Ewen Maclean, also had under consideration the report of the Special Committee of Obstetrics and Gynæcology of the Royal Society of Medicine, the report of the Scottish Departmental Committee on Puerperal Morbidity and Mortality, and suggestions sent in by individual medical practitioners. An interim report of the Committee was issued in 1926, and this was remoulded in the light of the replies received from the local units of the Association. The final report of the Committee was approved by the Representative Body in July, 1928. It concluded with eight recommendations, chief among which were the need for the prosecution of further investigations, and the paramount importance of antenatal care. It became

300

evident in the course of the inquiry that the incidence of puerperal sepsis was due to factors some of which were not known, but the report may be said to have acquitted general practitioners throughout the country of the responsibility, which it had been attempted to lay upon them, for the mortality from this disease. As a result of the work of this Committee the Association has asked general practitioners to keep records of their midwifery cases, and it is hoped that an analysis of these records will throw a good deal of light upon the reason for the persistent high morbidity and mortality rates.

In 1926 the subject of Psycho-analysis was investigated. The Committee, of which Dr. R. Langdon-Down was Chairman, and which consisted of acknowledged experts in the field of psycho-therapy, and upon which general practitioners were also well represented, presented a balanced report on this difficult but interesting subject. The report of the Committee, published in the *B.M.J.* Supplement of June 29th, 1929, gives a historical survey of the analytic or exploratory work for medical purposes which led to the elaboration in 1895 by Prof. Freud, of Vienna, of psycho-analysis ; contains a brief summary of modern psycho-analytical methods and teaching, and of other analytical methods ; deals with certain misconceptions concerning psycho-analysis ; cites the conditions which are treated by psycho-therapeutic measures, and more particularly by psycho-analysis ; and contains criticisms advanced against the theory and practice of psycho-analysis, together with an authoritative reply to the criticisms.

At the present time, under the Chairmanship of Professor R. J. Berry, a Committee is investigating the subject of Mental Deficiency, more especially with regard to methods which have been suggested to reduce its incidence and to the facilities for medical education in this subject.

COLLECTIVE INVESTIGATIONS.*

As early as 1837 there appeared in *The Transactions of the Provincial Medical and Surgical Association* a report on Influenza based on the observations made by a number

---

* For other details of the history of this subject see Supplement to *The British Medical Journal* for December 31st, 1927, and January 7th, 1928.

of physicians and general practitioners. Ten years later a notice appeared in the *Transactions* signed by the President of the Association and the President of the Council as authorised by the Annual Meeting, inviting all members to send records of their experience and opinions on burns and scalds to Mr. Crompton, of Manchester, who had been appointed by the Association to draw up a report thereon. The 18th Volume of *Transactions* contained reports on Anæsthesia and on the Medicinal Action of Arsenic ; and in the *Journal* for 1849–50 there was one on Cholera.

From time to time more or less organised inquiries, such as that on Chloroform, were made and reported upon, but it was at the Annual Meeting of 1880 that Professor G. M. Humphry, of Cambridge, in his opening address, suggested that the Association should undertake the collection of facts relating to disease in a careful and systematic manner. He recommended the appointment of a medical investigation committee with a secretary and registrar. Accordingly, in the following October, the Committee of Council appointed a Sub-Committee of seven to consider the matter. In their report in 1881 this Sub-Committee brought forward a scheme which was adopted. The President of the Council (Mr. C. G. Wheelhouse), Dr. Carpenter, Mr. Husband, Dr. Sieveking, Dr. Clifford Allbutt, Dr. Balthasar Foster, Professor Humphry and Dr. Ransome were appointed as the Collective Investigation Committee. In the next year (1882) Dr. F. A. Mahomed was appointed Secretary, and work was at once begun on inquiries into several diseases, viz.: Acute Pneumonia, Chorea, Acute Rheumatism, Diphtheria and Syphilis. In July, 1883, was published the first number of the *Collective Investigation Record* containing a final report on the Phthisis question, and provisional reports on Pneumonia, Chorea, Rheumatism and Diphtheria. The Committee also drew up and Macmillan published for the Association a " Life History Album," which was to be for the general public at once a diary and a medical history, an anthropometric record and a photograph album. Each album was to belong to and describe one particular individual. It would be interesting to know whether any of these albums are still in

302

existence, and to what extent they were utilised. In October, 1883, Dr. Mahomed resigned the secretary-ship, and Dr. Wilmot Herringham was appointed to succeed him. A retrospective editorial article in the *B.M.J.* stated that the movement started by the Association had been taken up by other countries, such as the United States of America and Germany. " The year 1883 found the movement beginning amid a good deal of enthusiasm, a good deal of indifference and a good deal of distrust. But distrust was lessening, indifference was unaltered, and enthusiasm had become steady approval and acceptance of Collective Investigation." Dr. Herringham resigned his secretaryship in 1884, and Dr. Isambard Owen succeeded as Secretary.

The second volume of the *Collective Investigation Record* was issued in 1884, on Pneumonia and Puerperal Fever. It was then decided to cease publication of the *Record* and to print the reports in the columns of the *Journal*, where they would be available to all the members. Inquiries into Diphtheria, Old Age and Cancer of the Breast were still going on when the Committee reported in 1885.

In 1888 the Collective Investigation Committee issued its report. Dr. A. Carpenter said that " the fact was that they had been too ambitious, seeking to embrace too large an area and to obtain too much information at a time when members of the Association were not likely to adopt the suggestions made by the Committee." Of the Reports issued this year, that on Acute Rheumatism was by Dr. T. T. Whipman, of St. George's Hospital, that on the Maladies of Old People, and one on Aged Persons, by Professor G. M. Humphry, and one on the Connection of Disease with Habits of Intemperance by Dr. Isambard Owen. This last made quite a stir. As an editorial article put it :—" All over the country Dr. Owen has been represented as laying down that total abstainers do not live so long as moderate drinkers, or even as those who are actually intemperate. . . . The conclusion attributed to Dr. Owen is utterly unwarrantable, though it has been paraded in high-class journals of which better things might have been expected."

The Committee had also completed a report on the Geographical Distribution of Rickets, Acute Rheumatism,

Chorea, Cancer, and Urinary Calculus, which were shortly to be published, and had entered into a fresh inquiry into the origin and mode of propagation of epidemics of diphtheria. In 1889, however, the Committee wound up its inquiries with supplementary reports on Habits of Intemperance and on the Causes of Death in Gouty Men, which were published early in the year. Subsequently, collective investigation in this form was abandoned.

In 1927 the Representative Body authorised a revival of the system of collective investigation in a new form, this time use being made of the machinery of the local units of the Association. The preliminary work on the scheme was carried out by a joint Sub-Committee of the Science and Insurance Acts Committees of the Association, and in the first instance it was decided to conduct two inquiries simultaneously, one into the Treatment of Varicose Ulceration, the other into the After-History of Gastro-Enterostomies. The methods adopted in the investigations were varied with the nature of the problems to be considered. In the Varicose Ulceration inquiry every Division of the Association was asked to obtain the names of as many members as possible who would undertake to assist in the investigation. In the case of the Gastro-Enterostomy inquiry the questions were sent in the first instance to the surgeons of every hospital of over one hundred beds in the country, with, if necessary, later reference to the practitioner into whose charge the patient may have passed. Dr. Arthur P. Luff was appointed Honorary Director of the Researches and the inquiries had the cordial approval of the then Minister of Health, Mr. Neville Chamberlain.

The report upon the Varicose Ulceration inquiry appeared in the *B.M.J.* of Dec. 22nd, 1928. The main conclusions arrived at were that the injection treatment offered the best results in combination with the application of Unna's zinc gelatin. Where for any reason injection was impracticable, Unna's zinc gelatin treatment was shown to be valuable. According to the information supplied by those practitioners who took part in the inquiry, ultra-violet radiation was also recommended, when proper hospital appliances and technique were available. Sodium salicylate solution of a strength of

20 to 40 per cent. was recommended as an injection in preference to other substances. It was generally agreed that Dr. Luff's report upon the results of the investigation was a valuable contribution to the subject.

The first report on the Gastro-Enterostomy inquiry was published in the *B.M.J.* of Dec. 7th, 1929, and subsequent reports on Dec. 14th and 28th, 1929, and Feb. 22nd, 1930. The report dealt with the subject under five headings, duodenal ulcers, pyloric ulcers, gastric ulcers, perforated ulcers and growths. A summary of the results of the investigations under the first heading showed that duodenal ulceration was about five times more common in males than in females ; that the liability to duodenal ulceration rapidly diminished after 50 years of age ; that about three-fourths of the patients returned to full work within three months of the date of the operation, general improvement of health and well-being occurring in all but a few cases ; that the results of the operation were satisfactory in about 90 per cent. of the cases ; and that the post-operative mortality was five per cent., the mortality being highest in patients from 40 to 50 years of age.

It would unduly lengthen this section of the History to indicate a summary of the results under the other four headings. Suffice it to say that Lord Moynihan, P.R.C.S., commenting upon the result of the investigations, stated that it had " contributed something of real value to our knowledge ; and something of a kind which has, I think, no parallel in any other country."

At the present time there is being conducted a collective investigation into the Incidence of Cancer and its History after Treatment. The inquiry is limited to carcinoma of the breast, cervix, rectum, and tongue, and its primary object is to obtain information as to the previous history of patients suffering from these forms of carcinoma ; of the evolution of the disease ; of the result of the treatment ; and the duration of the disease, both when treated and untreated.

The Award of Scholarships, Grants, Medals and Prizes.

The Association may justly claim to have been one of the pioneer bodies to award scholarships and

305

grants for the furtherance of medical research; and indeed for nearly sixty years now it has allocated a definite portion of its income for the encouragement of direct scientific investigation. The number of such awards by various bodies is now very considerable, but it is a fact which stands greatly to the credit of the Association that its scholarships and grants were among the very first of their kind, and that this side of the work of the Association has been undertaken not in the pecuniary interests of its members, but in the pure interests of medical science and with the intention of benefiting mankind in general. As long ago as 1839 the first of the proposed sections " for the investigation of particular departments of medicine " reported on the subject of Vaccination to the Annual Meeting at Liverpool. We have already commented on the elaborate and costly illustrations of Dr. Ceely's paper on the same subject (*see* p. 38 of this History) in that year.

In 1869, in accordance with a recommendation of the Section of Physiology, it was resolved at the Annual Meeting " that it be remitted to the Committee of Council to decide on some subject of original investigation and to appoint a Committee to conduct such an investigation, and to report at the next Annual Meeting ; the Committee of Council to be also empowered to grant such sum as may be considered necessary for carrying on the investigation and the experiments connected therewith." In compliance with this resolution the Council appointed Dr. Hugh Bennett, Professor of Chemistry in the University of Edinburgh, to investigate the antidotes to the effects of Strychnine and Opium, and granted £50 as payment to his assistants. Later on (in December, 1869) the Therapeutic Investigation Committee approved the payment of £100 to the assistants. Professor Hugh Bennett's researches extended over five years, and included twelve pairs of poison and antidote. The report was published in full in the second volume of *The British Medical Journal* for 1874. In that same year this aspect of the Association's work was put upon a firm footing. The Committee of Council recommended to the Annual Meeting that £200 should be applied for the purpose of making grants-in-aid of researches in medical science and collateral subjects, and

306

that a committee should be appointed to advise as to the distribution of the proposed grants. This recommendation was approved and authority was given for the appointment of a Grant-in-Aid Committee. In subsequent years, as the Scientific Grants Committee, this Committee administered the sums of several hundreds of pounds annually voted for the furtherance of scientific investigation. This body is now represented by the Science Committee. In 1883 two research scholarships were awarded. Year after year in the Reports of the Council laid before Annual Meetings, and later before the Representative Meeting, there have appeared records of work done and of sums voted for the prosecution of further research. As will be seen from the list of scholars appearing on page 308, not a few of those who received such help have since made names famous in medicine, surgery and their allied sciences. In 1885 the grants were numerous and their recipients distinguished. The following list of names speaks for itself :—

> Dr. P. M. Chapman, London.
> Dr. V. D. Harris, London.
> Dr. D. Noel Paton, Edinburgh.
> Professor E. A. Schäfer, F.R.S., London.
> Mr. D. A. Gresswell,　　　　　　　　　,,
> Mr. Victor Horsley,　　　　　　　　　　,,
> Dr. G. Thin,　　　　　　　　　　　　　　,,
> Dr. Angel Money,　　　　　　　　　　　　,,
> Dr. F. Warner,　　　　　　　　　　　　　,,
> Dr. Dawson Williams,　　　　　　　　　　,,
> Mr. Alfred Lingard,　　　　　　　　　　　,,
> Mr. Sidney H. Martin,　　　　　　　　　　,,
> Dr. J. Barr, Liverpool.
> Dr. Sidney Ringer, London.
> Dr. J. Theodore Cash, Aberdeen.

The majority of the owners of these fifteen names have since attained European reputation in one or more branches of Medicine, Surgery, Biology or Pathology.

Again in 1888 two research scholarships were granted of £150 each in addition to £300 voted as annual grants-in-aid. Among the reports made was one by Dr. C. E. Beevor and Mr. Victor Horsley on the motor functions of the cranial nerves. The names of Messrs. Shattock,

Ballance, Berry Haycraft and J. S. Haldane also stand out in the records.

After the death of Mr. Ernest Hart in 1898 a Research Scholarship was founded in his name, and from that time onwards the Association has made an annual award of about £1,000 in scholarships and grants.

This year (1932) the Council has decided to name one of its scholarships the Walter Dixon Scholarship, in honour of the memory of Prof. W. E. Dixon, of Cambridge, who for many years gave yeoman service to the Association in many departments of its work, but particularly in connection with the award of scholarships and grants.

The scholarships are given to candidates qualified to undertake research in any subject (including State Medicine) relating to the causation, prevention, or treatment of disease.   In practice it is found that the scholarships are of particular value to those holding a junior appointment at a university, medical school, or hospital, as the scholar is thus enabled to keep in close touch with the practical side of clinical medicine.

The following is a list of the Association's Scholars :—

Date of Scholarship.	*Scholar.*
1883 ..	Sir William Watson Cheyne, F.R.C.S., F.R.S.
	Dr. J. Priestly.
1885 ..	Dr. Augustus Waller, F.R.S.
1887 ..	Dr. S. H. C. Martin, F.R.C.P., F.R.S.
1888 ..	Prof. Ralph Stockman, F.R.C.P.
1890 ..	Dr. S. Monckton Copeman, F.R.C.P., F.R.S.
1891 ..	Dr. T. J. Bokenham.
	Prof. E. H. Starling, F.R.C.P., F.R.S.
1892 ..	Prof. J. B. Haycraft.
1894 ..	Dr. W. S. Fenwick.
	Dr. E. Lloyd Jones.
	Dr. G. E. C. Wood.
1896 ..	Dr. J. S. Risien Russell, F.R.C.P.
	Prof. J. B. Leathes, F.R.C.S., F.R.C.P., F.R.S.
	Prof. T. Swale Vincent.
1897 ..	Sydney Rowland, M.A.
1898–9 ..	Dr. J. Le Mare Bunch.

Date of Scholarship.	*Scholar.*
1898–9 ..	Prof. G. Elliot Smith, F.R.C.P., F.R.S.
1899–00 ..	Prof. J. W. H. Eyre.
	Prof. J. S. Macdonald, F.R.S.
1900–01 ..	Prof. Stuart McDonald, F.R.C.P.
	Sir John H. Parsons, F.R.C.S., F.R.S.
1901 ..	Prof. A. S. F. Leyton, F.R.C.P.
	Sir Thomas Houston.
1902–3 ..	Prof. F. A. Banbridge, F.R.C.P., F.R.S.
	Dr. W. Jobson Horne.
	Dr. G. A. Watson.
1903–4 ..	Mr. J. O. W. Barratt, F.R.C.S., F.R.C.P.
1904 ..	Dr. Thomas Evans.
	Mr. John Thomas Hewetson, F.R.C.S.
	Dr. Janet E. Lane-Claypon.
1905 ..	John Anderson Craw.
	Prof. H. E. Roaf.
1905–6 ..	Prof. Major Greenwood, F.R.C.P., F.R.S.
	Dr. H. De Riemer Morgan.
1906–7–8..	Dr. W. Henwood Harvey.
1907 ..	Dr. A. E. Barnes, F.R.C.P.
1907 ..	Dr. T. Shirley Hele.
1907–8 ..	Dr. J. P. McGowan.
1908 ..	Dr. E. L. Kennaway.
	Dr. Otto May.
1909–10 ..	Dr. H. Ackroyd, V.C.
	Dr. W. J. Penfold.
	Dr. Charles Bolton, F.R.C.P., F.R.S.
1909–10–11	Dr. W. Nicoll.
1911–12 ..	Prof. A. J. Clark, F.R.C.P.
	Dr. R. T. St. J. Brooks.
1911–12–13	Mr. A. P. Mitchell, F.R.C.S.
1912–13 ..	Dr. Emily Helen Morris.
1913–14 ..	Dr. R. R. Armstrong, F.R.C.P.
1913–14 ..	Dr. S. P. Bedson.
1913–14 1919	Mr. E. G. Slesinger, M.S., F.R.C.S.
1914 1919	Dr. Orlando Inchley.
1919–20–21	Dr. Arthur Compton.
1920–21 ..	Prof. R. St. A. Heathcote.
1920–21–22	Dr. S. W. F. Underhill.

Date of Scholarship.	Scholar.
1921–22 ..	Dr. H. A. Harris.
1922 ..	Mr. Basil Graves, F.R.C.S.
	Dr. J. V. Walsh.
1923 ..	Dr. G. I. Strachan, F.R.C.S.
	Dr. Muriel J. Thomson.
1923–4 ..	Mr. Hugh W. B. Cairns, F.R.C.S.
	Dr. A. J. Copeland.
1924 ..	Mr. Norman McO. Dott, F.R.C.S.
1924–5 ..	Dr. Alice Bloomfield, F.R.C.S.
1925 ..	Dr. J. M. D. Scott.
1925–6 ..	Dr. Helen M. M. Mackay.
	Dr. P. C. Raiment.
1926–7 ..	Dr. C. H. Whittle.
	Mr. W. Combe Wilson, F.R.C.S.
1927 ..	Dr. G. R. Cameron.
1928 ..	Dr. A. A. F. Peel.
	Dr. J. M. Yoffey.
1928–9 ..	Dr. Dugald Baird.
	Dr. J. C. Hoyle.
1928 ..	Dr. N. L. Lloyd.
1929–30 ..	Dr. R. W. Brookfield.
	Mr. C. F. W. Illingworth, F.R.C.S.
1930–31 ..	Dr. E. C. Warner.
	Dr. E. S. J. King.
1931 ..	Dr. J. F. Brock.
	Dr. N. F. C. Burgess.
	Dr. D. E. Denny-Brown.
1932 ..	Dr. E. C. Warner.
	Dr. J. F. Brock
	Dr. N. F. C. Burgess.
	Dr. D. E. Denny-Brown.

MEDALS AND PRIZES.

The Hastings Medal.—The Hastings Medal was apparently founded in 1860, as a prize for an essay or a paper by a member of the Association on some subject connected with the practice of medicine, surgery, or midwifery, physiology, or public health. The prize, first given in 1864, took the form of a gold medal.

Further awards of the Medal were made in 1866, 1870 and 1873. In intervening years the Medal was not

429, STRAND, 1886–1908.

429, STRAND, 1908–1925.

B.M.A. House, Tavistock Square, Court of Honour.

B.M.A. House, Tavistock Square, Looking Westward.

awarded because of lack of competitors or insufficiency of merit in the essays submitted and the award of the Prize fell into abeyance in 1877 when the question of its continuance was referred to a sub-committee from which it apparently never emerged again.

The following awards of the Sir Charles Hastings Medal have been made :—

1864   To Dr. J. L. W. THUDICHUM for his essay on " Urochrome."

1866   To Mr. FURNEAUX JORDAN for his essay on " Shock after Surgical Operations and Injuries."

1870   To Dr. J. MILNER FOTHERGILL for his essay on " Digitalis, its mode of action and its use."

1873   To Mr. LAWSON TAIT.

It is interesting to note in connection with this question that the year when this prize was apparently discontinued was the year in which the Gold Medal of the Association was instituted.

The Gold Medal.—The Gold Medal of the Association, now recognised as the highest honour in the disposal of the Association, was instituted in 1877 for distinction of a more general kind. The original regulations passed at the General Meeting in Bath, August 9th, 1878, provide for gold, silver, or bronze medals, but the silver and bronze medals were only awarded on one occasion, namely, in 1877, when three doctors who were associated with H. N. Davies in the Pontypridd Colliery action received the silver medal and eight the bronze.

The Medal is given for " Distinguished Merit," and may be awarded by the Council of the Association to anyone " who shall have conspicuously raised the character of the Medical Profession by scientific work, by extraordinary professional services, or by special services rendered to the British Medical Association."

The Gold Medal has been given to the following :—

Year.   *Name and Service.*

1877   H. N. DAVIES, Pontypridd. Heroic conduct, self-denial and humanity at a colliery accident at Pontypridd.

1879   Surg.-Maj. JAS. REYNOLDS, V.C., Dublin. Extraordinary professional services rendered at Rorke's Drift, Zululand.

x   311

1880   WILLIAM FARR, London. Long, unwearied and successful work on behalf of statistical and sanitary science; light thrown upon many physiological and pathological problems; and advancement of the health of the nation.

1886   EDWARD WATERS, Chester. Long-continued, self-denying and able service in the cause of medical reform.

1888   FRAY ORMROD, Workington. Gallant rescue work in a colliery accident.

1888   Surg. T. H. PARKE. Highly distinguished service as surgeon to Emir Pasha Relief Force.

1896   Surg.-Capt. H. F. WHITCHURCH, V.C. Extraordinary gallantry in performance of professional duty on the field of battle.

1897   CLAUDIUS GALEN WHEELHOUSE, Leeds. Great and prolonged service to the Association and profession.

1897   Rt. Hon. Sir B. WALTER FOSTER, London. Great and prolonged service to the Association and profession.

1904   Sir CONSTANTINE HOLMAN, London. Great and prolonged service to the Association and to the Hospitals.

1905   ANDREW CLARK, D.Sc., London. Distinguished service to the Association.

1913   J. A. MACDONALD, Taunton. Great and prolonged service to the Association and profession.

1914   EDWIN RAYNER, Stockport. Great and prolonged service to the Association.

1914   Sir JENNER VERRALL, Leatherhead. Great and prolonged service to the Association and profession.

1915   Maj. ARTHUR MARTIN-LEAKE, V.C. and Bar. Extraordinary bravery and devotion to duty on the field of battle in South Africa and in Belgium.

1919   Capt. N. G. CHAVASSE, V.C. and Bar, Liverpool. Extraordinary bravery and devotion to duty on the field of battle, saving many lives. He died of his wounds.

1921   Sir DAWSON WILLIAMS, London. Distinguished service to the Association and profession.

1922   Rt. Hon. Sir T. CLIFFORD ALLBUTT, Cambridge. Distinguished services to the profession and the Association, and in commemoration of his five years' Presidency of the Association at the time of the Great War, 1915–21.

1924   HENRY BRITTEN BRACKENBURY, Hendon. Arduous and distinguished services to the Association and profession.

1925   Sir ROBERT BOLAM, M.D., Newcastle-on-Tyne. Distinguished services to the Association and the profession.

1926   Sir HUMPHRY ROLLESTON, Bt., Cambridge. In recognition of his scientific work and of his distinguished services to the profession and to the Association.

1931   N. BISHOP HARMAN, London. In recognition of distinguished work in ophthalmology, and of valuable service rendered to the Association.

1931   ALFRED COX, London. In recognition of valuable and devoted service to the profession and to the Association.

PRIZES.

At the first Anniversary Meeting in 1833, which was held at Bristol, Dr. W. M. Thackeray, of Chester, offered a prize for an essay on a medical subject. Dr. William Makepeace Thackeray (1769–1849), physician to the Chester Royal Infirmary, was one of four medical sons of Dr. Thomas Thackeray, of Cambridge, and was first cousin once removed of the novelist. In the first volume of *The Transactions of the Provincial Medical and Surgical Association* (1832) there appeared a biographical memoir of his younger brother, Dr. Joseph Thackeray, Physician to the Bedford Infirmary, which gives a good many details of the history of this family. William and Makepeace were Christian names favoured by the Thackerays. They were those of the grandfather of the novelist as well as of his cousin. (See *B.M.J.*, " Nova et Vetera," " The Thackerays," Vol. II, 1931, p. 396.)

No response seems to have been made to Dr. Thackeray's first offer, and in 1837 he increased the amount of the prize to £50, the subject to be " The sources of the common continued fevers of Great Britain and Ireland and the ascertaining of the circumstances which may have a tendency to render them communicable from one person to another," open to members of every accredited school for Medicine and Surgery in the United Kingdom. The Prize was awarded in 1840 to Dr. Davidson, of Glasgow.

After this award of the Thackeray Prize, there seems to have been no prize offered until 1852, when two prizes of twenty guineas each were offered by the Council for the best reports of medical and surgical cases. That for medical cases was awarded to Dr. Arthur Okes, and that for surgical cases to Mr. W. J. Moore. The offer of these prizes does not seem to have been repeated in subsequent years.

The Stewart Prize is awarded from funds placed in the Association's trust by the late Alexander Patrick Stewart, of London, for valuable researches in reference to the origin, spread and prevention of epidemic disease. When Dr. Stewart retired from the office of Honorary Secretary of the Metropolitan Counties Branch, after having held it for seventeen years, he was presented with a sum of £500 raised by subscription in recognition of his valuable services to the Association, as well as to his Branch, and he very generously presented £400 of the above sum to the Committee of Council. The Prize usually takes the form of a certificate and a cheque for from £30 to £50, and is awarded not oftener than every three years. Dr. Robert Cory, to whom it was awarded in 1886, sacrificed his health and shortened his life by acquiring cerebral syphilis in the course of his investigation into vaccino-syphilis. The following awards of the Prize have been made :—

Year.   *Name and Subject.*

1882   Surg.-Gen. VANDYKE CARTER. In acknowledgment of minute and extensive research in connection with relapsing fever.

1886   ROBERT CORY. For his scientific research into the communicability of syphilis in vaccination.

1889   E. KLEIN. For very valuable and prolonged researches on micro-organisms, and especially for work in connection with the etiology of scarlet fever.

314

Year.	Name and Subject.

1891 J. BURN RUSSELL. For his numerous researches and writings on the origin, spread and prevention of epidemic disease.

1893 Sir R. THORNE THORNE. For important work done on the subject of diphtheria.

1895 Brig.-Surg. Lt.-Col. D. D. CUNNINGHAM. For his bacteriological work in India, especially in the investigation of the bacillus of cholera.

1897 G. SIMS WOODHEAD. For eminent work done in connection with the study of tuberculosis, especially with regard to the Royal Commission on the subject.

1899 Surg. F. J. ABERCROMBIE DALTON. For his original investigations in Beri-Beri.

1901 Sir PATRICK MANSON. For his original researches and discoveries.

1903 F. W. MOTT. In recognition of important work already done, or of researches instituted and promising good results, regarding the origin, spread and prevention of epidemic disease.

1905 WILLIAM H. POWER. For his classical researches into the influence of smallpox hospitals upon the spread of the disease in surrounding populations.

1908 Col. Sir DAVID BRUCE. For his researches into the origin and prevention of Mediterranean Fever.

1910 Maj. GEORGE LAMB. In recognition not only of his own work, but also of the entire work of the Plague Commission and every member thereof.

1913 W. LEONARD BRADDON. For his researches into the epidemiology of Beri-Beri.

1916 Col. W. H. HORROCKS. For his work in preserving the British Army on the continent from epidemic disease.

1918 Lt.-Col. R. McCARRISON. For his researches into the physiology and pathology of the thyroid gland and the parathyroid glands, and especially for the light he has thrown on the epidemiology of goitre.

1920   Miss HARRIETTE CHICK. In recognition of her own work and that of the band of scientific women associated with her in the investigations into the means of preventing Scurvy and Beri-Beri in Armies and among populations suffering from privation.

1922   JOHN C. McVAIL. In recognition of his distinguished services to the community in the advancement of preventive medicine.

1924   Prof. EDWARD MELLANBY. For his important discoveries on the relation between rickets and dietetic deficiency.

1927   Sir MALCOLM WATSON. In recognition of the scientific and administrative work that has freed large tracts of tropical Malaya from malaria, and has proved of high service both to preventive medicine and to economic developments.

1932   Sir ALMROTH WRIGHT. In recognition of the work he has initiated and carried through in relation to the prevention of typhoid.

The Middlemore Prize was founded in 1880 by Mr. Richard Middlemore, F.R.C.S., Consulting Surgeon to the Birmingham Eye Hospital, for the best essay or work on any subject which the Council of the Association may from time to time select in any department of ophthalmic medicine or surgery. The Prize consists of a certificate and a cheque for £50. The following awards have been made :—

| Year. | Name and Subject. |

1882   W. ADAMS FROST. The scientific and practical value of improvements in ophthalmological medicine and surgery made or published during the past three years.

1886   GEORGE A. BERRY and W. ADAMS FROST. Discoveries in Ophthalmic Science.

1890   W. A. BRAILEY and PRIESTLEY SMITH. For their contributions to the science of ophthalmology.

1894   E. TREACHER COLLINS. Adjudged to have published the most important contribution to Ophthalmology during the past five years.

316

1897   HILL GRIFFITH. Errors of Accommodation and Refraction of the Eye.

1900   ERNEST E. MADDOX. For the best essay or work on any subject in the Department of Ophthalmic Medicine or Surgery.

1904   J. HERBERT PARSONS. Awarded on account of his work in connection with the Intra-ocular Circulation and Pressure and their relation to the Intracranial and General Circulation on the course of Fibres in the Optic Nerve and on the influence of the Cortex Cerebri on the movement of the Pupil.

1907   SYDNEY STEPHENSON. For his contributions to the Science of Ophthalmology.

1908   SIMEON SNELL. Ophthalmia Neonatorum.

1911   C. W. G. BRYAN. Serum and Vaccine Therapy in connection with Diseases of the Eye.

1915   R. FOSTER MOORE. The Pathology of the affections of the retina met with in connection with diseases of the Kidney.

1917   WM. CLARK SOUTER. Disorders of the eye and of its functions induced by war injuries not directly affecting the eye.

1920   HARRY MOSS TRAQUAIR. Perimetry (inclusive of Scotometry) ; its methods and its value to the Ophthalmic Surgeon.

1925   BASIL GRAVES, M.C. For his contribution to the knowledge of the microscopy of the living eye, especially in relation to the use of the Slit Lamp.

1929   WILLIAM STEWART DUKE-ELDER. The Clinical Study of the Vitreous Body, its swellings, contractions, opacities and reactions to Toxic invasion ; with special reference to Glaucoma and Detached Retina.

The Sir Charles Hastings Clinical Prize.—The Sir Charles Hastings Prize was instituted by the Council of the Association in 1924, to stimulate systematic observation, research and record in general practice. It is open to members of the British Medical Association engaged in general practice, is awarded annually, and takes the form of an illuminated certificate and a money award of fifty guineas. The first award was made in 1926, and the following is a list of the Prizemen :—

Year.   *Name and Subject.*
1926 NORMAN PORRITT. The Abdomen in Labour.
1927 JOHN SINCLAIR MANSON. Observations on Human Heredity.
1928 AMBROSE WILFRED OWEN. Some renal conditions met with in general practice.
1929 ARTHUR CROOK. Albumen in the Urine in Association with Pregnancy and Childbirth.
1930 WM. HENRY BRADLEY. Nasopharyngeal Epidemics in Public Schools.
1931 HUBERT OLIVER GUNEWARDINE. The Stroke in High Arterial Blood Pressure.
1932 LESLIE GEORGE HOUSDEN. Studies in Breast-feeding.

Katherine Bishop Harman Prize.—In April, 1926, Mrs. Katherine Bishop Harman, M.B., B.S. Lond., wife of the Treasurer of the Association, presented to the Association the sum of £1,000 for the establishment of a prize to be awarded by the Council for the encouragement of research into the disorders incident to maternity. The Prize is open to registered medical practitioners in the British Empire, consists of an illuminated certificate and a money award to the value of about £80, and is awarded biennially for the best essay or work on any subject solving the problem of the risks of serious loss of health and even death to which mothers are liable during childbirth, or in recognition of important; work on the above lines already done, or of researches instituted and promising good results. There have been three awards as follows :—

Year.   *Name and Subject.*
1928 RONALD HARE. Researches on Septicæmia, with special reference to puerperal septicæmia.
1930 R. R. ARMSTRONG and HAROLD BURT-WHITE. The Problems of Puerperal Sepsis.
1932 JOHN SMITH. Clinical Study: the Causes and Prevention of Death in Childbirth from Septicæmia.

The Hempson Prize.—Mr. W. E. Hempson placed at the disposal of the Council, upon his retirement in March,

318

1928, from the post held by him for thirty years of Solicitor of the Association, and as a mark of esteem for the Association and appreciation of his happy relations therewith, a sum of twenty-five guineas, to be awarded as a prize for the best essay or treatise on some phase or branch of public health. The subject was " A study of personal experiences in the inspection and treatment of school children under the auspices of any elementary education authority," and it was awarded in 1929 to Dr. A. C. T. Perkins (Bury St. Edmunds) for the study submitted by him on " The Problems presented by school preventive medicine in rural areas."

Prizes for Essays by Final-year Medical Students and Recently Qualified Medical Practitioners.—From 1922 onwards the Association has awarded sums not exceeding £150 annually in prizes for competition by final-year medical students in the medical schools of the United Kingdom for essays on clinical and pathological subjects to be chosen by the Association, the Schools being grouped for this purpose and an equal proportion of the £150 allocated to each group. In 1925 the competition was extended to include medical schools in the British Empire overseas, and in 1929 it was decided to include in the competition not only final-year medical students, but also newly qualified practitioners of not more than one year's standing.

Dawson Williams Memorial Prize.—The Dawson Williams Memorial Fund was established by a voluntary subscription among the friends and admirers of the late Editor of the *Journal*, in 1928. The administration of the Fund was placed in the hands of a body of Trustees composed as follows : The Presidents (for the time being) of the Royal College of Physicians of London, the Royal College of Surgeons of England, the British Medical Association, the Royal Society of Medicine and the Section for Disease in Children of the Royal Society of Medicine, and the Editor of *The British Medical Journal*.

The object of the Fund is the award of a prize, every two years, or at longer intervals at the discretion of the Trustees, in recognition of work done in connection with pediatrics. The first award was made in 1930 to Dr. F. J. Poynton, for his work on behalf of rheumatic children, particularly with regard to the establishment of special "rheumatic centres." The Trustees have decided to make the second award to Sir Robert Jones, Bart., for his work in connection with the pediatric side of orthopædics.

THE SCIENTIFIC SECTIONS OF THE ANNUAL MEETING.

An important aspect of the scientific work of the Association is the Scientific Sections which are held in connection with the Annual Meeting. The discussion of subjects connected with scientific medicine was first introduced as part of the business of the Annual Meeting in 1865; and two years later, at the Meeting at Dublin, in 1867, the Scientific Sections as at present known were inaugurated. There were at this Meeting four Sections—Medicine, Physiology, Surgery and Midwifery.

Since that time, with the exception of the period of the Great War, 1915-1919, the Sections have been held annually and have grown in number, till there are now some fourteen to twenty Sections each year, dealing with the various branches of medical science. The selection of the Sections is made in the first instance by the local Executive of the Meeting, subject to the approval of the Council of the Association. The programme for each Section is in the hands of the Officers of that Section, who are nominated by an Arrangements Committee of the Council composed partly of representatives of the local Executive of the Meeting and partly by representatives elected by the Council.

At the Sections, which are open freely to all members of the Association, medical topics of current interest or of a controversial nature are freely debated, the invited speakers being recognised authorities in the subject selected both from this country and abroad. The debate is open to all those present. The Sections also present an excellent opportunity, of which full advantage is taken, of bringing before members of the Association the latest discoveries in the field of medical science, and the attendances show that this branch of the scientific work of the Association is much appreciated by the members at large. One Section, that of Medical Sociology, is open to the lay public; the subject discussed is

320

invariably one of general sociological interest with a medical bearing, and among the speakers are included lay persons with expert knowledge.

For many years it was the practice to have, in addition to the Sections, addresses in medicine and surgery given by prominent members of the profession, but in 1921 this practice was discontinued, as it was felt that they detracted from the interest and usefulness of the Sections.

Mention must be made of the Popular Lecture, which since 1904 has formed a feature of the Annual Meeting. As its title denotes, this function is intended primarily for the lay public, and it has generally been very successful. The lecturer is not necessarily a medical man, but is chosen for his knowledge of some scientific or medico-sociological subject of topical interest.

SIR CHARLES HASTINGS LECTURE.

There is a second Popular Lecture given under the auspices of the Association, though this has no connection with the Annual Meeting. Realising the greater interest taken by the public generally in health questions, the demand that was arising for information on the subject, and the necessity for this information being given by properly qualified persons, the Association in 1927 arranged, as an experiment, for the delivery by a prominent member of the medical profession of a lecture to the lay public on a topic of general public health interest. The first lecture was given in the House of the Association, London, by Sir Berkeley (now Lord) Moynihan, who took for his subject " Cancer and how to fight it " ; and the success of the lecture was such that the Council decided to continue it, under the title of " The Sir Charles Hastings Lecture," as a yearly event. Except as regards 1929, when rebuilding operations were proceeding, the Lecture has been given annually in the House of the Association, as follows :—

1928 : " The Foundations of Health," by Sir George Newman, K.C.B.

1930 : " Health and Empire," by Sir Andrew Balfour, K.C.M.G., C.B.

1931 : " Diet and Health," by Professor Edward Mellanby, F.R.C.P.

THE LIBRARY.

The Library of the Association was originally started by Mr. Ernest Hart, who made a nucleus collection of books from those submitted to *The British Medical Journal* for the purpose of review. From this small beginning the Library was gradually developed, largely under the auspices of Mr. Spencer Honeyman, who served for a period of 41 years as the Association's Librarian and retired in 1929, and of Mr. Walter G. Spencer, M.S., who gave invaluable service to the Association by acting as its Honorary Librarian during 1923–9. On the retirement of Mr. Honeyman, Mr. T. J. Shields was appointed Librarian. For a considerable time the Library was only available for the use of members for reference purposes, but in 1918 it was decided to extend the scope of the Library and to provide members with lending facilities. This proved to be a most popular development. In 1922 the number of books lent to members was 3,700, but by 1931 this figure had increased to 14,690. The Library now contains about 40,000 volumes, including books in all branches of medicine, a collection of Thèses de Paris and Thèses de Lyon, believed to be unique in this country, also a collection of books which formed part of the Library of the Association's founder, Sir Charles Hastings.

THE SCIENTIFIC WORK OF THE LOCAL UNITS.

The local units of the Association have always devoted a considerable proportion of their energies to the discussion of scientific topics in the field of medicine and its allied sciences. The pages of *The British Medical Journal* through the years record a consistent activity in this direction, and there can be no doubt that the free exchange of thought at these meetings arising from the practical experience and difficulties of everyday professional work constitutes a valuable form of postgraduate education. Prior to the reconstitution in 1902, practically the whole of the meetings of the Branches was given over to discussions upon clinical and scientific problems, and with the formation of Divisions, which meant the establishment in a large number of areas of a medical society which was a unit of the Association, this aspect of the Association's work greatly extended. It needs to be noted, however, that at this time there was great need for the formulation of a medico-political policy and the moulding of that policy meant that, for a time at all events, the Divisions could not devote too much of their energies to scientific matters. Thus in 1913 it is recorded that 839 medico-political meetings were held by the local units as against 190 clinical and scientific, whereas in a recent year the clinical meetings had increased to nearly 700, with a corresponding decrease in the number of medico-political meetings. During recent years a system of " B.M.A." lectures has been established. The object of this arrangement is to enable the local units to secure the services at their scientific meetings of recognised experts who live at a distance, and with whom the members of the Division are not ordinarily in consultation. These arrangements have proved successful, and the most important meetings of many Divisions are those when a visit is paid by a " B.M.A." lecturer.

THE ASSOCIATION AND NATIONAL HEALTH INSURANCE

THIS is a very important chapter in the history of the Association, for the struggle which occurred on the introduction of the National Health Insurance Bill of 1911 not only tested severely the power of the Association to represent the interests of the medical profession of the country and the strength of its new constitution, but opened up a new field of medico-political action.

In 1910 the question of the better provision of medical attendance for the working classes was raised by the report of the Royal Commission on Poor Law, which, appointed in 1905, reported in 1909, making serious reflections on the medical provision for the poorer classes and suggesting various ways of dealing with the subject, all of them entailing an increase of the responsibility of the State or of local authorities for the provision of medical attendance, and any of which would, if adopted, seriously affect the medical profession. The Association at once got to work and the report of its special Poor Law Reform Committee can be found in the *B.M.J.*, Supplement, February 5th, 1910, p. 41 *et seq.* In a report to the Divisions dated February 2nd, 1910, the Council severely criticised the existing methods of poor law relief from both the public and the medical points of view. In this report were laid down certain principles which were to play a great part in the forthcoming struggle :—

(1) That medical services rendered on behalf of the State should be paid for by the State ;

(2) That the payment should be adequate and in accordance with the professional services required ;

(3) That there should be adequate medical representation on all Committees formed to control medical assistance.

Immediately after the adoption of the new Constitution the Association had recognised that the question of

324

the provision of medical attendance for the working classes was a matter needing inquiry and reform. The exhaustive inquiry and report on Contract Practice issued in 1905 (see Section, " Contract Practice and the Association ") was the result, and it proved invaluable in educating those who undertook the championship of the profession in the Insurance Act struggle. Its immediate effect on the Association was to make it decide to get into the hands of the profession itself the various means of giving medical attendance on contract terms, and the method suggested was the setting up in every working-class area of an organisation to be called a " Public Medical Service." These bodies were to be voluntary associations of medical practitioners who would settle on what terms and conditions contract medical practice should be offered in their locality, and would keep the whole management in their own hands. The Public Medical Service of Southampton, formed under the inspiration of Dr. A. A. MacKeith, in 1903, was of great service as giving a concrete example of such an institution in working order and entirely under professional control.

The Association at once turned its attention to the consideration of the National Health Insurance Bill, which was designed to give a medical service under insurance conditions to the class of the community for which the Association had itself proposed to cater. The Bill was introduced in May, 1911, became law in December, 1911, came into partial operation in July, 1912, and the medical benefit provisions commenced in January, 1913.

In March, 1911, the Association issued to Divisions a Report on the Organisation of Medical Attendance on the Provident or Insurance Principle. This was a very exhaustive exposition of the whole situation, and placed the profession in possession of information which it was essential it should have in anticipation of the Bill. The Bill raised political passions to a great height. Its promoter, Mr. Lloyd George, then Chancellor of the Exchequer, suggested that it might be regarded as a non-party measure, and there were many members of the Opposition who favoured its general principles, but it was not long before party feelings were involved. The proposed system depended for its successful operation very largely on the friendly societies who had had much experience in voluntary insurance for the working classes. To them were added the trade unions and the great collecting insurance companies, who quickly saw that unless they were allowed to take part in the administration they would be overshadowed. These bodies, afterwards known collectively as " Approved Societies," were soon in active consultation and co-operation with the Chancellor. But there was no such consultation with the medical profession as represented by its organisation until the main lines of the measure were laid down, and not then until pressure was brought to bear by the Association. The Bill in its first form placed the control of those members of the medical profession concerned in working the system under the "Approved Societies." It provided the sum of 6s. per annum for payment for medical attendance and drugs. It did not allow any freedom of choice of doctor, but left the Approved Societies to appoint doctors. There was no income limit applicable to the beneficiaries, and there was no mention of medical representation on any of the bodies concerned in the administration of the system.

On June 1st, 1911, exactly four weeks after the introduction of the Bill, the following demands were formulated by a Special Representative Meeting of the Association which Mr. Lloyd George attended, and where he both gave and received much useful information. These demands became known as the " Six Cardinal Points " :—

1. An income limit of £2 a week for those entitled to Medical Benefit.

2. Free choice of doctor by patient, subject to consent of doctor to act.

3. Medical and maternity benefits to be administered by insurance committees and not by Friendly Societies. In connection with the question of the method of administration of medical benefit, the Representative Meeting of the Association resolved that all questions of professional discipline should be decided exclusively by a body or bodies of medical practitioners, and that the power of considering all complaints against medical practitioners should be vested in a local Medical Committee, with a right of appeal to a central Medical Board to be appointed for that purpose.

326

TAVISTOCK HOUSE
(*from Tavistock Square*).

HOUSES OF THE ASSOCIATION

B.M.A. HOUSE,
EDINBURGH.

B.M.A. HOUSE, SYDNEY,
AUSTRALIA.

4. The method of remuneration of medical practitioners adopted by each insurance committee to be according to the preference of the majority of the medical profession of the district of that committee.

5. Medical remuneration to be what the profession considered adequate, having due regard to the duties to be performed and other conditions of service.

(The Representative Body later resolved that the claim of the Association should be for 8s. 6d. as a minimum capitation fee, not including extras and medicine.)

6. Adequate medical representation among the insurance commissioners, in the central advisory committee, and in the insurance committees, and statutory recognition of a local medical committee representative of the profession in the district of each insurance committee.

There ensued a long struggle in which much heat was generated. The medical profession had for the first time in its history been brought up against an acute political issue in which it was directly involved, and, like other citizens, doctors found it impossible entirely to dissociate their professional from their political views. But as time went on the Association's new machinery found itself. Large numbers of practitioners all over the country threw themselves into the fight with an ardour and a devotion which elicited admiration even from the Approved Societies and the Government, both of which recognised that the medical profession was now effectively organised and could not be ignored.

During the course of the struggle no less than nine Representative Meetings were held, at which the main and often the only subject of discussion was the Bill. In the summer of 1911 the Association obtained the signatures of 26,000 practitioners to the following Pledge : " I the undersigned hereby undertake that in the event of the N.H.I. Bill becoming law, I will not enter into any agreement for giving medical attendance and treatment insured under the Bill, excepting such as shall be satisfactory to the medical profession and in accordance with the declared policy of the B.M.A. : and that I will enter into such agreement only through a local Medical Committee representative of the medical profession in the district in which I practice, and will not enter into any individual or separate agreement with

Y

any approved society or other body for the treatment of such persons." At the same time, in order to safeguard the position, the Association organised the formal resignation of all Friendly Society and similar contract medical appointments, and held in its hands some 33,000 resignations which covered the great majority of the whole.

A fund called the Central Insurance Defence Fund was raised during the campaign and had a list of 13,472 guarantors, the total guarantees amounting to £134,397. It was calculated that a sum of £53,000 was spent during the campaign, of which more than half came from the ordinary funds of the Association, the rest coming from this Fund.

During the protracted negotiations which took place, the Association gained many of its points and vastly improved the position of the profession. Free choice by doctor and by patients was conceded ; the administration of the system was taken away from the Approved Societies and given to new bodies called Insurance Committees on which the medical profession was represented ; local bodies representative of the profession were set up in every Insurance area and given very considerable powers and duties as regards the medical side of administration of the system ; the discipline of the insurance doctor was left very largely in the hands of bodies of his peers ; the *method* of remuneration was left to be settled by the local committees of doctors ; and the special claim of the rural practitioner was acknowledged by the institution of a " Special Drug Fund " of £30,000, and a Special Mileage Fund of £50,000.

Thus, of the six Cardinal Points, four had been gained practically completely. On one of the remainder—amount of remuneration—the amount (though never accepted formally by the Association as satisfactory) was raised from the originally offered 6s., including the provision of drugs, to 9s. On one point only did the Association fail to get any concession of substance. The Government absolutely refused to fix an income limit, declaring it to be administratively impossible, and by large majorities Parliament decided that every manual worker, whatever his income, should be compulsorily insured,

328

and therefore entitled to medical benefit. True, the Insurance Committees were empowered to fix a *local* income limit, but nobody believed they would do so and the provision has been a dead letter.

At the Special Representative Meeting held in December, 1912, just before Medical Benefit came into operation, the following resolution was carried by a very large majority :—

" That this Representative Body, having carefully considered the replies of the Chancellor of the Exchequer to the Deputation appointed at the recent Representative Meeting to confer with him, is of opinion that they do not remove the strong objections to the Regulations and conditions of service determined on by the last Representative Meeting, but confirm the then expressed opinion that such are, in the best interests of the public and profession, unworkable and derogatory."

This was done in spite of the knowledge that the headquarters staff had in its hands evidence that all over the country considerable numbers of practitioners were breaking away from their pledge—partly no doubt because many had come to the conclusion that the terms now gained were good enough to justify them in accepting service, and largely because the word had gone round that the Government had secured a considerable number of men who were willing to be employed directly by the Government as " strike breakers," and that in certain (or rather uncertain) selected areas a service would be forthcoming in January, 1913. There was a rush all over the country to " get on to the panel " before it was too late, and on January 17th and 18th, 1913, a Special Representative Meeting was held which carried the following resolution, and the fight was over :—

" That this Representative Meeting, recognising the force of present circumstances, and consulting the best interests of the Association and the unity of the profession, now releases all practitioners from their Undertakings and Pledges."

In retrospect the achievement of the Association must be regarded as of the first importance. It was able to secure the acquiescence of the great majority of the medical profession of the country to its acting as the voice of the profession, no serious attempts being made during the fight to dispute its authority. Its action radically altered the original nature of a system which provides medical attendance for a third of the population, and the alterations were all of a nature which brought the system more into line with the wishes of the profession. The position thus secured by the Association has never been lost—on the contrary, each successive Government has acknowledged the Association as the representative organisation of the whole profession, a gain which in itself would justify all the energy and money expended during the struggle. But there is no doubt that the end of the fight left behind it much ill-feeling and heartburning in the profession, and for a time the influence of the Association was shaken. Its membership, which rose rapidly during 1910–12, dropped from 1913 to 1918 (partly due to the War but also largely due to the feeling of dissatisfaction about the Insurance Act), but has since much more than recovered. There was a feeling of disillusionment and resentment amongst that section of the profession which seemed to believe that the profession could be the final arbiter in a question which obviously was one of high politics and in which the final word must rest with Parliament. The Association was accused of weakness by those who could not realise that an organisation is only as strong as its members will allow it to be, and that even then there are limits beyond which no section of the community can be allowed to impose its will on the community as a whole. Parliament, the public and the Press were all greatly impressed with the fight the Association had put up, and proclaimed the result to be, on balance, a great victory for the Association. This feeling was epigrammatically stated by the *Westminster Gazette*, which said "We all admire .people who don't know when they are beaten. The trouble with the B.M.A. is that it doesn't know when it has won."

The Association took steps to consolidate its work in connection with the new Insurance system by calling a conference of representatives of the Local Medical Committees which had been set up by law to help in the administration of the Act. The first conference was called at Brighton, during the Annual Meeting of the

330

Association in July, 1913. Since then there have been Annual Conferences, of which the executive body is the Insurance Acts Committee of the Association, a body representative of the Association and of the grouped Local Medical and Panel Committees throughout the country. Since 1913 these bodies have actively defended the interests of insurance practitioners, and through their connection with the Association have established a liaison with all the other sections of medical practice which is invaluable in view of the extent of the population served by the system, and its possible development from one which provides only a general practitioner service to one which will inevitably in the future include hospital and specialist services.

In a phase of the Association's history in which over a long period the profession was united as it never had been before, and in which so many men and women all over the country showed a devotion and a willingness to work which were above all praise, it is very difficult to single out names for special mention, but no reader of the multifarious documents connected with the struggle could fail to be struck with the outstanding work of certain men.

Dr. J. A. Macdonald, Taunton, Chairman of Council, 1910–20, Dr. (now Sir Ewen) Maclean, Cardiff, Chairman of the Representative Body, 1910–11, and the late Sir Jenner (then Mr.) Verrall, Chairman of Representative Body, 1912–15, carried on their shoulders a great burden of responsibility. Dr. (now Sir James) Smith Whitaker, Medical Secretary of the Association, 1902–11, exhibited a statesmanship for which the leading part that he took in the Constitution Committee had well prepared him. His hand can be traced infallibly in the Contract Practice Inquiry Report and the various documents which educated the profession for the part it was called upon to play in this great struggle. In December, 1911, Dr. Smith Whitaker accepted office under the Government as Deputy Chairman of the National Health Insurance Commission, and upon the present Medical Secretary, Dr. Alfred Cox, fell the onerous duties of that office during the later stages of the struggle and the difficult times which followed immediately after the passing of the Act.

Since the inauguration of the system the Association has devoted to its problems a great deal of time and energy, directed not only to watching the interests of the doctors concerned in it, but also in trying to improve the service. This has necessitated almost continuous negotiations with the Ministry of Health. The question of remuneration has been raised acutely on several occasions.

Of recent years the most outstanding action which the Association has had to take was that in the year 1923, when the Government threatened to reduce the capitation fee from 9s. 6d. to 8s. After repeated negotiations the Minister of Health refused to offer more than 8s. 6d. for a period of three years, or, alternatively, 8s. for a period of five years. The Insurance Acts Committee of the Association recommended refusal of both offers unless arbitration was agreed to. Resignations of insurance practitioners were called for—these resignations to be placed in the hands of the Insurance Acts Committee to be used in the event of arbitration being again refused by the Minister of Health. Resignations to the extent of 97 per cent. were collected, and, in the face of such overwhelming evidence of the strong feeling on the part of the insurance practitioners, the Minister of Health then offered 8s. 6d. for five years or a Court of Inquiry. The Court of Inquiry was accepted, the resignations withdrawn, and the award of the Court was a capitation fee of 9s. This fact is worthy of note, as it is the one and only occasion upon which the Association has had to go to the length of refusing service, not, let it be noted, so that its demands might be granted, but so that an independent body might determine the justice of its claim.

The Insurance Acts Committee, which consists of representatives of the Panel Committees throughout the country, together with representatives appointed by the Association, has at all times had a very difficult task. The work of Dr. H. B. Brackenbury, for eight years Chairman of the Committee (and afterwards Chairman of Council), and of Dr. H. G. Dain, of Birmingham, Chairman since 1924, has been recognised by the profession on many occasions as having been of an outstanding and most valuable nature.

HOSPITAL ADMINISTRATION

THE question of the abuse of charity, especially in the Out-Patient Departments of Hospitals, has often received the attention of the Association. These departments grew up in the nineteenth century and were at their worst in its latter half. A vivid impression of the conditions obtaining in the Medical Casualty Department of a great hospital may be got by readers of an article from the pen of no less a person than the late Poet Laureate, Dr. Robert Bridges, who was then a Casualty Physician at St. Bartholomew's Hospital. (" Reports," Vol. XIV, 1878, p. 167.) This article is well worth reading even now, for its literary merit and wit and humour, as well as for the wisdom of its conclusions. As Dr. Bridges pointed out, thirty years before the time at which he wrote there was no out-patient department at St. Bartholomew's. He, as Casualty Physician, had to examine, make diagnoses and prescribe for an average number of 148 patients in a morning. Most of these patients should have been treated by general practitioners in their (often distant) homes, to whom should have been left the duty of selecting and recommending those who were in need of special advice and hospital treatment. Dr. Bridges gave it as his deliberate opinion that the system was intolerable.

Many attempts were made by the Association to check abuse in the interests as much of the deserving poor as of the general practitioner. In 1904 the Hospitals Committee drew up a series of recommendations in which it was laid down *inter alia* :—

(*a*) That poverty and sickness should be the consideration for the admission of all patients for hospital treatment.

(*b*) That where possible subscribers' letters should be abolished.

(*c*) That there should be some means of investigation into the circumstances of the applicants for relief.

(*d*) That except in emergencies, before a patient is admitted into any hospital, sufficient evidence should be obtained on two points—(a) that the patient is not in a position to pay for treatment ; (b) that the case is, from a hospital point of view, suitable for treatment.

(e) That the number of new cases to be seen on any one day by an honorary medical officer should be limited.

The present policy of the Association as regards the voluntary hospitals is embodied in the decisions of the Representative Body as published in the *Handbook* of the Association and published in a special booklet.

The position of the voluntary, and indeed of the municipal, hospitals has changed very considerably during recent years, partly through the drying up of many of the large subscriptions from charitable donors, partly to the development of contributory schemes which encourage working-class people to subscribe regularly to their local hospitals, and partly to the passing of the Local Government Act of 1929, which clearly envisages the improvement and greater use of the old poor law hospitals (now municipal or council hospitals). Fortunately the Association had foreseen these developments, and began in 1920 to prepare the mind of the profession for the inevitable changes. When hospitals were institutions for the " relief of the sick poor " medical men were glad to give their services gratuitously. But when they became (as they are rapidly becoming) places supported largely by the collective contributions of workmen and employers, and by funds derived from contributory schemes which are of the nature of insurance against the risk of the need of hospital treatment—when hospitals found themselves obliged to demand payment from patients according to their means, and above all as hospitals become more and more the resort of people who could not be said to be " poor persons "—then it became obvious that the members of the medical staffs could no longer afford to give their services gratuitously. The number of patients from whom moderate private fees would well have been expected rapidly decreased as they resorted more and more to the hospitals. The hospital policy which the Association has developed during recent years is a considered attempt to rectify the position by securing the acceptance by the governing bodies of the voluntary hospitals of the principle that

334

the staff has a right to some pecuniary recognition in respect of persons who pay for their hospital service in whole or in part, or who are paid for by some organisation. The process of education both of the public and of the profession has been a long and arduous one, but the policy is now securing recognition, though still with reluctance on the part of those who do not yet understand the great changes which have come over voluntary hospital administration. In this educational work among many names which could be mentioned two stand out prominently, Mr. N. Bishop Harman, Chairman of the Hospitals Committee from 1920 to 1924, and Sir Robert Bolam, Chairman 1919–20. To their persistence and persuasive gifts must be ascribed a large share in the change of opinion which is now so manifest in the hospital world, on both the medical and the lay sides.

The question of abuse of the Out-Patient Department is still as pressing as ever. Hospitals still continue to publish with pride the growing number of their out-patients ; hospital physicians and surgeons still find a great deal of their time is taken up with cases which could quite well be dealt with elsewhere, to the great economy of the time both of those patients who ought to be there, and of the officers of the hospital. The Association, at its Annual Representative Meeting, 1931, approved a report on " The Problem of the Out-Patient " (Supplement to *B.M.J.*, Feb. 21st, 1931, and also published separately) in which a series of propositions is laid down which the Association believes would, if adopted, materially lessen the financial strain on the hospitals, with advantage to all concerned.

In *The British Medical Journal* at different times over many years there will be found complaints about this perennial subject. The present position is that there is probably much less abuse of the beds of hospitals than twenty years ago, owing to the much greater frequency of payment by in-patients according to their means ; but so far as the Out-Patient departments are concerned the position is pretty much what it was in Dr. Bridges' time.

Places of Annual Meetings ; Presidents of Association ; Chairmen of Representative Body ; Chairmen of Council ; Treasurers.

(Note.—The Representative Body came into being in 1902 and first met in 1903.)

Year.	Place of Meeting.	President.	Chairman of Representative Body.	Chairman of Council.	Treasurer.
1832–3	Worcester	Edward Johnstone, M.D.		Charles Hastings	
1833–4	Bristol	Andrew Carrick, M.D.	—	,,	
1834–5	Birmingham	John Johnstone, M.D., F.R.S.	—	,,	
1835–6	Oxford	John Kidd, M.D., F.R.S.	—	,,	
1836–7	Manchester	Edward Holme, M.D.	—	,,	
1837–8	Cheltenham	Henry C. Boisragon, M.D.	—	,,	
1838–9	Bath	Edward Barlow, M.D.	—	,,	
1839–40	Liverpool	Thomas Jeffreys, M.D.	—	,,	
1840–1	Southampton	George Steed, M.D.	—	,,	
1841–2	York	George Goldie, M.D.	—	,,	
1842–3	Exeter	John H. James, Esq.	—	,,	
1843–4	Leeds	William Hey, Esq.	—	,,	
1844–5	Northampton	Archibald Robertson, M.D., F.R.S.	—	,,	
1845–6	Sheffield	Charles Frederick Favell, M.D.	—	,,	
1846–7	Norwich	John G. Crosse, Esq.	—	,,	
1847–8	Derby	James Heygate, M.D., F.R.S.	—	,,	
1848–9	Bath	George Norman, Esq.	—	,,	
1849–50	Worcester	Sir Charles Hastings, M.D.	—	Sir Charles Hastings	
1850–1	Hull	Fewster R. Horner, M.D.	—	,,	
1851–2	Brighton	George S. Jenks, M.D.	—	,,	
1852–3	Oxford	John W. Ogle, M.D.	—	,,	
1853–4	Swansea	G. Gwynne Bird, M.D.	—	,,	
1854–5	Manchester	William J. Wilson, Esq.	—	,,	
1855–6	York	Thomas Simpson, M.D.	—	,,	
1856–7	Birmingham	James Johnstone, M.D.	—	,,	

Year.	Place of Meeting.	President.	Chairman of Representative Body.	Chairman of Council.	Treasurer.
1857-8	Nottingham	BOOTH EDDISON, Esq.	—	Sir CHARLES HASTINGS	
1858-9	Edinburgh	WILLIAM P. ALISON, M.D.	—	,,	
1859-60	Liverpool	JAMES R. W. VOSE, M.D.	—	,,	
1860-1	Torquay	C. RADCLYFFE HALL, M.D.	—	,,	
1861-2	Canterbury	ALFRED LOCHÉE, M.D.	—	,,	
1862-3	London	GEORGE BURROWS, M.D., F.R.S.	—	,,	
1863-4	Clifton	JOHN A. SYMONDS, M.D.	—	,,	
1864-5	Cambridge	GEORGE E. PAGET, M.D., F.R.S.	—		
1865-6	Leamington	SAMUEL J. JEAFFRESON, M.D.	—	FRANCIS SIBSON, M.D., F.R.S., London	
1866-7	Chester	EDWARD WATERS, M.D.	—	,,	
1867-8	Dublin	Sir WILLIAM STOKES, M.D.	—	,,	
1868-9	Oxford	Sir H. W. ACLAND, M.D., F.R.S.	—	W. D. HUSBAND, F.R.C.S., York	
1869-70	Leeds	CHARLES CHADWICK, M.D.	—	,,	R. W. FALCONER, M.D., Bath
1870-1	Newcastle-on-Tyne	EDWARD CHARLTON, M.D.	—	,,	,,
1871-2	Plymouth	JOHN WHIPPLE, F.R.C.S.	—	GEO. SOUTHAM, F.R.C.S., Manchester	,,
1872-3	Birmingham	ALFRED BAKER, F.R.C.S.	—	,,	,,
1873-4	London	Sir WILLIAM FERGUSON, Bt., F.R.S.	—	R. W. FALCONER, M.D., Bath	,,
1874-5	Norwich	EDWARD COPEMAN, M.D.	—		W. D. HUSBAND, F.R.C.S., York
1875-6	Edinburgh	Sir ROBERT CHRISTISON, Bart., M.D.	—	,,	,,
1876-7	Sheffield	M. MARTIN DE BARTOLOMÉ, M.D.	—	ALFRED CARPENTER, M.D., Croydon	,,
1877-8	Manchester	M. A. EASON WILKINSON, M.D.	—	,,	,,
1878-9	Bath	RANDLE W. FALCONER, M.D.	—	,,	,,
1879-80	Cork	DENNIS C. O'CONNOR, M.D.	—	,,	,,
1880-1	Cambridge	Sir GEO. M. HUMPHRY, M.D., F.R.S.	—	C. G. WHEELHOUSE, Leeds	,,

Year.	Place of Meeting.	President.	Chairman of Representative Body.	Chairman of Council.	Treasurer.
1881–2	Ryde	Benjamin Barrow, F.R.C.S.	—	C. G. Wheelhouse, Leeds	W. F. Wade, M.D., Birmingham.
1882–3	Worcester	William Strange, M.D.	—	"	"
1883–4	Liverpool	A. T. H. Waters, M.D.	—	Sir B. Walter Foster, M.D., M.P., Birmingham	"
1884–5	Belfast	James Cuming, M.D.	—	"	N. C. Macnamara, F.R.C.S., London
1885–6	Cardiff	William Thomas Edwards, M.D.	—	"	"
1886–7	Brighton	W. Withers Moore, M.D.	—	Thos. Bridgwater, M.D., Harrow-on-Hill	"
1887–8	Dublin	Sir J. T. Banks, M.D.	—	"	C. Holman, M.D., Reigate
1888–9	Glasgow	W. T. Gairdner, M.D.	—	W. Withers Moore, M.D., Brighton	"
1889–90	Leeds	C. G. Wheelhouse, F.R.C.S.	—	"	"
1890–1	Birmingham	Sir Willoughby F. Wade, M.D., F.R.C.P.	—	"	H. T. Butlin, F.R.C.S., London
1891–2	Bournemouth	John Roberts Thomson, M.D.	—	John Ward Cousins, M.D., Portsmouth	"
1892–3	Nottingham	Joseph White, F.R.C.S.Ed., D.C.L.	—	"	"
1893–4	Newcastle-on-Tyne	George Hare Philipson, M.D., D.C.L., F.R.C.P.	—	"	"
1894–5	Bristol	Edward Long Fox, M.D.	—	"	"
1895–6	London	Sir John Russell Reynolds, Bart., M.D., F.R.C.P, F.R.S.	—	Prof. Robert Saundby, M.D., Birmingham	C. Parsons, M.D., Dover
1896–7	Carlisle	Henry Barnes, M.D., F.R.S.E.	—	"	"
1897–8	Montreal	Thomas George Roddick, M.D.	—	"	"
1898–9	Edinburgh	Sir Thomas Grainger Stewart, M.D., F.R.S.E.	—	John Roberts Thomson, M.D., Bournemouth	Andrew Clark, F.R.C.S., London
1899–1900	Portsmouth	John Ward Cousins, M.D., F.R.C.S.	—	"	"

Year.	Place of Meeting.	President.	Chairman of Representative Body.	Chairman of Council.	Treasurer.
1900–1	Ipswich	WILLIAM ALFRED ELLISTON, M.D.	—	JOHN ROBERTS THOMSON, M.D., Bournemouth	ANDREW CLARK, F.R.C.S., London
1901–2	Cheltenham	GEORGE BAGOT FERGUSON, M.D.	—	ANDREW CLARK, F.R.C.S., London	E. MARKHAM SKERRITT, M.D., Bristol
1902–3	Manchester	WALTER WHITEHEAD, F.R.C.S.Ed.		„	„
1903–4	Swansea	THOMAS DRUSLYN GRIFFITHS, M.D., M.R.C.S.	Sir VICTOR ALEXANDER HADEN HORSLEY, M.D., F.R.S., B.S., F.R.C.S., London	„	„
1904–5	Oxford	WILLIAM COLLIER, M.D., F.R.C.P.	„	HENRY WM. LANGLEY BROWNE, M.D., Ch.B., F.R.C.S.E., West Bromwich	H. RADCLIFFE CROCKER, M.D., F.R.C.P., London
1905–6	Leicester	GEORGE COOPER FRANKLIN, F.R.C.S.	„	EDMUND OWEN, F.R.C.S., LL.D., London	EDWIN RAYNER, M.D., F.R.C.S., Stockport
1906–7	Toronto	RICHARD ANDREWS REEVE, B.A., M.D., LL.D.	JAMES ALEXANDER MACDONALD, M.D., M.Ch., LL.D., Taunton	„	„
1907–8	Exeter	HENRY DAVY, M.D., F.R.C.P.	„	„	„
1908–9	Sheffield	SIMEON SNELL, F.R.C.S.Ed.	„	„	„
1909–10	Belfast	Sir WILLIAM WHITLA, M.D., LL.D.	HAMILTON ASHLEY BALLANCE, C.B., M.S., F.R.C.S., Norwich		
1910–11	London	H. T. BUTLIN, D.C.L., LL.D.	EWEN JOHN MACLEAN, M.D., M.R.C.P., Cardiff	JAMES ALEXANDER MACDONALD, M.D., M.Ch., LL.D., Taunton	„
1911–12	Birmingham	Professor ROBERT SAUNDBY, M.D., LL.D., F.R.C.P.	„	„	„
1912–13	Liverpool	Sir JAMES BARR, M.D., LL.D., F.R.C.P.	Jenner Verrall, LL.D., M.R.C.S., L.R.C.P., Bath	„	„
1913–14	Brighton	WILLIAM AINSLIE HOLLIS, M.A., M.D., F.R.C.P.	„	„	„

Year.	Place of Meeting.	President.	Chairman of Representative Body.	Chairman of Council.	Treasurer.
1914–15	Aberdeen ..	Sir Alexander Ogston, K.C.V.O., M.D., LL.D.	Jenner Verrall, LL.D., M.R.C.S., L.R.C.P., Bath	James Alexander Mac-donald, M.D., M.Ch., LL.D., Taunton	Edwin Rayner, M.D., F.R.C.S., Stockport
1915–16	London, Annual Business Meeting	Sir T. Clifford Allbutt, K.C.B., M.D., LL.D., F.R.S.	Edward Beadon Turner, F.R.C.S., London	,,	G. E. Haslip, M.D., London
1916–17	,,	,,	,,	,,	,,
1917–18	,,	,,	Thomas Walter Har-ropp Garstang, M.A.Oxon., M.R.C.S., D.P.H., Altrincham	,,	,,
1918–19	,,	,,		,,	,,
1919–20	Cambridge ..	,,	,,	Robert Alfred Bolam, M.D., LL.D., F.R.C.P., Newcastle-on-Tyne	,,
1920–1		,,	,,	,,	,,
1921–2	Newcastle-on-Tyne	Prof. David Drummond, C.B.E., M.A., M.D., D.C.L., LL.D.	Robert Wallace Wes-ley Henry, M.D., B.Ch., B.A., Leicester	,,	,,
1922–3	Glasgow ..	Sir William Macewen, C.B., M.D., LL.D., F.R.C.S., F.R.S., D.Sc., D.C.L.	,,	,,	,,
1923–4	Portsmouth	Charles P. Childe, F.R.C.S	Henry Britten Brack-enbury, M.R.C.S., L.R.C.P., Hendon	,,	N. Bishop Harman,LL.D., F.R.C.S., London
1924–5	Bradford ..	J. Basil Hall, M.C.Cantab, F.R.C.S.		,,	
1925–6	Bath ..	F. G. Thomson, M.A., M.D., F.R.C.P.	,,	Sir Robert Bolam, M.D., LL.D., F.R.C.P., New-castle-on-Tyne	,,
1926–7	Nottingham	R. G. Hogarth, C.B.E., F.R.C.S. ..	,,	,,	,,

Year.	Place of Meeting.	President.	Chairman of Representative Body.	Chairman of Council.	Treasurer.
1927–8	Edinburgh	Sir Robert Philip, M.A., M.D., LL.D., F.R.C.P. Ed., Hon. F.R.C.S.Ed.	Charles Oliver Hawthorne, M.D., LL.D., F.R.C.P., D.Sc., F.R.F.P., & S.G., London	Sir Henry Britten Brackenbury, LL.D., M.R.C.S., L.R.C.P., Hendon	N. Bishop Harman, LL.D., F.R.C.S., London
1928–9	Cardiff	Sir Ewen Maclean, M.D., D.Sc., F.R.C.P., F.R.S.E.	,,	,,	,,
1929–30	Manchester	Arthur H. Burgess, D.L., M.Sc., F.R.C.S.	,,	,,	,,
1930–1	Winnipeg	W. Harvey Smith, M.A., M.D., M.C.	E. Kaye Le Fleming, M.A., M.B., B.C., Wimborne	,,	,,
1931–2	Eastbourne	W. G. Willoughby, M.D., D.P.H.	,,	,,	,,
1932–33	London	The Rt. Hon. Lord Dawson of Penn, P.C., G.C.V.O., K.C.B., K.C.M.G., LL.D., M.D., P.R.C.P.(Lond.)		,,	

EDITORS OF *The British Medical Journal.*

1841–44 {	HENNIS GREEN	
	R. J. N. STREETEN	
1844–49	R. J. N. STREETEN	
1849–53 {	W. H. RANKIN	
	J. H. WALSH	
1853–55	JOHN ROSE CORMACK	
1855–61	ANDREW WYNTER	

1861–67	W. O. MARKHAM
1867–69	ERNEST HART
1869–71	JONATHAN HUTCHINSON
1871–98	ERNEST HART
1898–1928	Sir DAWSON WILLIAMS
1928	NORMAN GERALD HORNER

GENERAL SECRETARIES.

1833–43 {	CHARLES HASTINGS	
	JAMES P. SHEPPARD	
1843–48	R. J. N. STREETEN	
1848–53	JAMES P. SHEPPARD	
1853–55	JOHN ROSE CORMACK	

1855–63	R. A. WILLIAMS
1863–72	WATKIN WILLIAMS
1872–1902	FRANCIS FOWKE
1902–09	GUY ELLISTON

MEDICAL SECRETARIES.

1902–12	JAMES SMITH WHITAKER
1912–32	ALFRED COX

1932–	GEORGE CRANSTON ANDERSON.

FINANCIAL SECRETARIES AND BUSINESS MANAGERS.

1909–18	GUY ELLISTON
1918–21	WILLIAM ELSWORTH WARNE

1921	LEYCESTER FERRIS-SCOTT

BENEFACTORS.

RICHARD MIDDLEMORE.
ALEXANDER PATRICK STEWART.
FRANCIS FOWKE.
HENRY ISAAC FOTHERBY.
Lieut.-Col. J. W. F. RAIT, I.M.S., and Mrs. RAIT.

The Rt. Hon. Sir T. CLIFFORD ALLBUTT.
JAMES DON.
KATHERINE BISHOP HARMAN.
JOHN STEVENS.
R. WALLACE HENRY.